Great Horse Stories

GREAT HORSE STORIES

Selected by **PAGE COOPER**

Drawings by **PAUL BROWN**

GARDEN CITY BOOKS, GARDEN CITY, N.Y.

GARDEN CITY BOOKS REPRINT EDITION 1954,
by special arrangement with Doubleday & Company, Inc.

PRINTED IN THE UNITED STATES
AT
THE COUNTRY LIFE PRESS, GARDEN CITY, N. Y.

ACKNOWLEDGMENTS

For permission to reprint the titles in this book, acknowledgments are due to the following authors, agents, and publishers:

Ruth & Maxwell Aley—for "Dark Child," by E. N. Robinson.

D. Appleton-Century Company, Inc.—for "The Look of Eagles," by John Taintor Foote; and "The Ride of His Life," from *Gallops*, by David Gray.

J. W. Arrowsmith, Ltd.—for "Royal Cream Horses and Ponies," from *Beasts and Circuses*, by Sir Hugh Garrard Tyrwhitt-Drake.

The Bobbs-Merrill Company—for "Florian," from *Florian*, by Felix Salten, copyright, 1934, with special permission of Sanford Jerome Greenburger, agent, and The Bobbs-Merrill Company.

Paul Brown—for his story "It Happened at Aintree."

George Agnew Chamberlain—for his story "Highboy Rings Down the Curtain."

Doubleday & Company, Inc.—for "The Red Terror" from *Gone Away with O'Malley*, by M. O'Malley Knott and Page Cooper, copyright, 1944, by Doubleday, Doran & Company, Inc.

E. P. Dutton & Co., Inc.—for "Cristiano: A Horse," from *The Book of a Naturalist*, by W. H. Hudson, with permission from J. M. Dent & Sons, Ltd.

Farrar & Rinehart, Incorporated—for "The Ghost Horse," from *Long Lance*, by Chief Buffalo Child Long Lance, copyright, 1928.

Esther Forbes—for her story "Break-Neck Hill."

Houghton Mifflin Company—for "Chiquita," by Bret Harte; and "Under the Joshua Tree," from *Saddle Songs and Other Verses*, by Henry Herbert Knibbs.

Charles Tenney Jackson—for his story "The Horse of Hurricane Reef."

Harold Matson—for "The Begats," from *Horses and Americans*, by Phil Stong.

Oxford University Press—for "Strider: The Story of a Horse," by Leo Tolstoi, from the Centenary Edition of *Nine Stories*, with special permission from the Executors of Aylmer Maude; and "The Famous Ballad of the Jubilee Cup," by Arthur T. Quiller-Couch.

Charles Scribner's Sons—for "Skipper," by Sewell Ford; and "The Seeing Eye," from *Horses I Have Known*, by Will James.

E. OE. Somerville—for the story "A Grand Filly," from *All on the Irish Shore*, by E. OE. Somerville and Martin Ross.

A. P. Watt & Son—for "The Maltese Cat," from *The Day's Work*, by Rudyard Kipling, copyright, 1894, 1895, 1896, 1897, 1898, 1905, with special permission from Mrs. Bambridge and The Macmillan Co. of Canada; and "Cinderella and Warrior" from *My Horse Warrior*, by Lord Mottistone, published in England by Hodder & Stoughton.

The Western Kansas Publishing Company—for "Black Kettle," by Frank M. Lockard.

H. F. & G. Witherby Ltd.—for "The Wrong 'Un," from *Hoof Marks*, by John Orr Ewing.

Clement Wood—for his story "Tzagan."

Contents

CONTENTS

Introduction

THESE tales, true and fiction, are collected not only for horse lovers but for all who enjoy a good story. The horses in these pages are individuals, as spirited or cantankerous, noble, sly, devoted, as the people who stand out in the pattern of our everyday lives.

Here they are for our pleasure, to be chosen as we choose our friends. If the spirit is blue, what more effective pick-me-up than the pranks of "A Grand Filly," by those Irish wits, Somerville and Ross, or David Gray's "The Ride of His Life," a hunting episode that will bring a quirk to the lips of everyone who has followed the hounds. If racing quickens your pulse, you will want to read E. N. Robinson's "Dark Child," John Taintor Foote's "Look of Eagles," and "Highboy Rings down the Curtain," by George Agnew Chamberlain. Here is horse flesh at its most magnificent. Or perhaps you have a liking for history. Black Kettle, who roamed the prairie flaunting his six-foot tail at the United States Cavalry, belongs to our national past, and so do the Morgan sires in Phil Stong's amusing essay, "The Begats." I wish we could have found a good account of the cavalry horse who was the only survivor of Custer's last stand, but if there is one, it has escaped us.

"Florian," Felix Salten's tale of Emperor Franz Joseph's magnificent white stallion, prince of the Austrian Riding School, has an elegance and a nostalgic charm reminiscent of the gilded days before World War I when the Emperor's white stallions and Victoria's royal cream horses that pulled the coach of state were famous throughout the world of horsemen. Lord Mottistone's account of his horse, Warrior, who helped win the battle of Amiens, is as moving a story of the relations between a horse and his master as one can find. Then there are the magnificent rebels, such as the ghost horse who haunted the tribe of Chief Buffalo Child Long Lance, the Red Terror, and the stallion of Hurricane Reef.

ix

INTRODUCTION

But it would be a wearisome chronicle to list the virtues of each of these titles. You will want to discover them for yourselves. Let me add only that we have begun and ended our book with two stories which to us bear the indubitable mark of greatness, Esther Forbes's "Break-Neck Hill," and Tolstoi's story of the piebald gelding who was a record-breaking trotting horse but lived and died an outcast.

PAGE COOPER

Great Horse Stories

Break-Neck Hill

By ESTHER FORBES

DOWN Holly Street the tide had set for church. It was a proper, dilatory tide. Every silk-hat glistened, every shoe was blacked, the flowers on the women's hats were as fresh as the daffodils against the house fronts. Few met face to face, now and then a fast walker would catch up with acquaintances and join them or, with a flash of raised hat, bow, and pass on down the stream.

Then the current met with an obstacle. A man, young and graceful and very much preoccupied, walked through the church-goers, faced in the opposite direction. His riding breeches and boots showed in spite of the loose overcoat worn to cover them. He bowed continually, like royalty from a landau, almost as mechanically, and answered the remarks that greeted him.

"Hello, Geth."

"Hello."

"Good morning, Mr. Gethling. Not going to church this morning." This from a friend of his mother.

"Good morning. No, not this morning." He met a chum.

"Good riding day, eh?"

"Great."

"Well, Geth, don't break your neck."

"You bet not."

"I'll put a P.S. on the prayer for you," said the wag.

"Thanks a lot." The wag was always late—even to church on Easter morning. So Gethling knew the tail of the deluge was reached and past. He had the street almost to himself. It was noticeable that the man had not once called an acquaintance by name or made the first remark. His answers had been as reflex as his walking. Geth was thinking, and in the sombre eyes was the dumb look of a pain that would not be told—perhaps he considered it too slight.

He left Holly Street and turned into Holly Park. Here from the grass that bristled freshly, ferociously green, the tree trunks rose black and damp. Brown pools of water reflected a radiant sky through blossoming branches. Gethling subsided on a bench well removed from the children and nursemaids. He glanced at the corner of Holly Street and the Boulevard where a man from his father's racing stable would meet him with his horse. His face, his figure, his alert bearing, even his clothes promised a horseman. The way his stirrups had worn his boots would class him as a rider. He rode with his foot "through" as the hunter, steeple chaser and polo-player do—not on the ball of his foot in park fashion.

Pulling off his hat he ran his hand over his close-cropped head. Evidently he was thinking. Across his face the look of pain ebbed and returned, then he grew impatient. His wrist-watch showed him his horse was late and he was in a hurry to be started, for what must be done had best be done quickly. Done quickly and forgotten, then he could give his attention to the other horses. There was Happiness—an hysterical child, and Goblin, who needed training over water jumps, and Sans Souci, whose lame leg should be cocained to locate the trouble—all of his father's

2

stable of great thoroughbreds needed something except Cuddy, who waited only for the bullet. Gethling's square brown hand went to his breeches pocket, settled on something that was cold and drew it out—the revolver. The horse he had raced so many times at Piping Rock, Brookline, Saratoga had earned the right to die by this hand that had guided him. Cuddy's high-bred face came vividly before his eyes and the white star would be the mark. A child had stopped to look at him, and he thrust the revolver hastily back in his pocket, slowly rose and fell to pacing the gravel walk. A jay screamed overhead, "Jay, jay, jay!"

"You fool," Geth called to him and then muttered to himself. "Fool, fool—oh, Geth—" From the boulevard a voice called him.

"Mr. Gethling—if you please, sir—!" It was Willet, the trainer.

"All right, Willet." The trainer was mounted, holding a lean greyhound of a horse. Gethling pulled down the stirrups.

"I meant to tell you to bring Cuddy for me to ride, last time, you know."

"Not that devil. I could never lead him in. Frenchman, here, is well-behaved in cities."

Gethling swung up. He sat very much relaxed upon a horse. There was a lifetime of practice behind that graceful seat and manner with the reins. The horse started a low shuffling gait that would take them rapidly out of the city to the Gethling country place and stables.

"You know," Geth broke silence, "Cuddy's got his—going to be shot."

"Not one of us, sir," said Willet, "but will sing Hallelujah! He kicked a hole in Muggins, yesterday. None of the boys dare touch him, so he hasn't been groomed proper since your father said he was to go. It's more dangerous wipin' him off than to steeplechase the others."

Geth agreed. "I know it isn't right to keep a brute like that."

"No, sir. When he was young and winning stakes it seemed different. I tell you what, we'll all pay a dollar a cake for soap made out 'er old Cuddy."

"There'll be no soap made out of old Cuddy," Gethling interrupted him. "I'll ride him out—up to the top of Break-Neck Hill and shoot him there. You'd better begin the trench by noon. When it's dug I'll take him to the top and—"

"But nobody's been on his back since your father said it was useless to try to make him over. Too old for steeple-chasing and too much the racer for anything else, and too much the devil to keep for a souvenir."

"Well, I'll ride him once again."

"But, Mr. Geth, he's just been standing in his box or the paddock for four weeks now. We've been waiting for you to say when he was to be shot. He's in a sweet temper and d'yer know, I think, I do—"

"What do you think?"

Willet blushed purple. "I think Cuddy's got something in his head, some plan if he gets out. I think he wants to kill someone before he dies. Yes, sir, *kill* him. And you know if he gets the start of you there's no stopping the dirty devil."

"Yes, he does tear a bit," Geth admitted. "But I never was on a surer jumper. Lord! How the old horse can lift you!" Gethling dropped into a disconsolate silence, interrupted before long by Willet.

"'Happiness' will get Cuddy's box—she's in a stall. Cuddy was always mean to her—used to go out of his way to kick her—and she—sweet as a kitten."

"So you'll give her his box in revenge?"

"Revenge? Oh, no, sir. Just common sense."

"How long will the trench take?"

"A good bit of time, sir. Cuddy isn't no kitten we're laying by. I'll put them gardeners on the job—and they know how to shovel. You'll want an old saddle on him?"

"No, no, the one I've raced him in, number twelve, and his old bridle with the chain bit."

Willet considered the horse unworthy of any distinction, but in his desire to please Geth, took pains to prepare Cuddy for his death and burial. "Handsome corpse, what?" he said to a stable boy. Cuddy was handsome built on the cleanest lines of speed and strength, lean as an anatomical study, perfect for his type. The depth of chest made his legs, neck and head look fragile. His face was unusually beautiful—the white-starred face which had been before Geth's eyes as he had sat in Holly Park.

4

"Look at him," complained the boy, "he pays no more attention to us than as if we weren't there." Cuddy usually kicked during grooming, but his present indifference was more insulting.

"Huh!" said Willet, "he knows them sextons went to Break-Neck to dig the grave for him. Don't yer, Devil? Say, Joey, look at him listening like he was counting the number of spadefuls it takes to make a horse's grave. He's scheming what he'd like to do, old Cuddy is. Give me that curry. You wash off his face a bit." Cuddy turned his aristocratic face away from the wet cloth and blew tremulously. Joey tapped the blazing star on his forehead.

"Right there," he said to Willet. "Anyhow, he's begun to show his age." He pointed to the muzzle which had the run forward look of an old horse and to the pits above the eyes. The grooming was finished but neither Gethling came to the stable from the big house, nor the trench diggers from Break-Neck to say their work was done.

"Say, Joey," suggested Willet, "I'll do up his mane in red and yellow worsteds, like he was going to be exhibited. Red and yellow look well on a bay. You get to the paddock and see Frenchman hasn't slipped his blanket, while I fetch the worsteds from the office."

Cuddy left alone, stopped his listening and began pulling at his halter. It held him firm. From the brown dusk of their box stalls two lines of expectant horses' faces watched him. The pretty chestnut, Happiness, had been transferred already to his old box. Further down, on the same side, Goblin stood staring stupidly, and beyond were the heads of the three brothers, Sans Pareil, Sans Peur and the famous Sans Souci who could clear seven foot of timber. Opposite stood Bohemia, cold blood in her veins as a certain thickness about her throat testified, and little Martini, the flat racer. On either side of him were Hotspur and Meteor and there were a dozen others as famous. Above each stall hung the brass plate giving the name and pedigree, and above that, up to the roof the hay was piled sweet and dusty-smelling. The barn swallows twittered by an open window in the loft. In front of Cuddy the great double doors were open to the fields and pastures, the gray hills and the radiant sky. The horse reared abruptly, striking out with his front legs, crouched and sprang

5

against his halter again, but it held him fast. Willet, on returning with the worsted, found him as he had left him, as motionless as a bronze horse on a black marble clock.

Willet stood on a stool the better to work on the horse's neck. His practised fingers twisted and knotted the mane and worsted, then cut the ends into hard tassels. The horse's withers were reached and the tassels bobbing rakishly gave a hilarious look to the condemned animal.

Four men, very sweaty, carrying spades, entered.

"It's done," said the first, nodding, "and it's a big grave. Glad pet horses don't die oftener."

"This ain't a pet," snapped Willet. "He's just that much property and being of no more use is thrown away—like an old tin can. No more sense in burying one than the other. If I had my way about it—" but Geth entered.

"Hole dug? Well, let's saddle up and start out."

When Cuddy stood saddled and bridled, Willet turned in last appeal to his master's son.

"Mr. Geth, I wouldn't ride him—not even if I rode him as well as you, which I don't. That horse has grown worse these last months. He wants to kill someone, that's what he wants."

Geth shook his head. "No use, Willet, trying to scare me. I know what I'm doing, eh Cuddy?" He went to the horse and rubbed the base of his ear.

The satin head dropped forward onto the man's chest, a rare response from Cuddy. Gethling led him out of the stable; Willet held his head as the man mounted. As he thrust his foot in the stirrup, Cuddy lunged at Willet, and his savage yellow teeth crushed into his shoulder. The rider pulled him off, striking him with his heavy hunting whip. The horse squealed, arched himself in the air and sidled down the driveway. He did not try to run or buck, but seemed intent on twisting himself into curves and figures. The two went past the big house with its gables and numberless chimneys and down to the end of the driveway.

There is a four-foot masonry wall around the Gethling country-place. The horse saw it and began jerking at his bit and dancing, for ever since colthood walls had had but one meaning for him.

"Well, at it, old man," laughed Gethling. At a signal Cuddy

flew at it, rose into the air with magnificent strength and landed like thistle-down.

"Cuddy," cried the man, "there never was a jumper like you. Break-Neck will keep, we'll find some more walls first."

He crossed the road and entered a rough pasture. It was a day of abounding life. Crows sauntered across the sky, care free as hoboes. Under foot the meadow turf oozed water, the shad-bush petals fell like confetti before the rough assault of horse and rider. Gethling liked this day of wind and sunshine. Suddenly he realized that Cuddy, too, was pleased and contented, for he was going quietly now. Occasionally he threw up his head and blew "Heh, heh!" through his nostrils. Strange that Willet had thought Cuddy wanted to kill someone—all he really wanted was a bit of a canter. A brook was reached. It was wide, marshy, edged with cowslips. It would take a long jump to clear it. Gethling felt the back gather beneath him, the tense body flung into the air, the flight through space, then the landing well upon the firm bank.

"Bravo, Cuddy!" The horse plunged and whipped his head between his forelegs, trying to get the reins from the rider's hands. Gethling let himself be jerked forward until his face almost rested on the veiny neck.

"Old tricks, Cuddy. I knew *that* one before you wore your first shoes." He still had easy control and began really to let him out. There was a succession of walls and fences and mad racing through fields when the horse plunged in his gait and frightened birds fluttered from the thickets and Gethling hissed between his teeth as he always did when he felt a horse going strong beneath him.

They came to a hill that rose out of green meadows. Except the top, which was bare like a tonsure, it was covered with pines. A trail ran through the woods; a trail singularly morose and unattractive. This was Break-Neck Hill. Perhaps Cuddy felt his rider stiffen in the saddle for he refused passionately to take the path. He set his will against Gethling's and fought, bucking and rearing. When a horse is capable of a six-foot jump into the air, his strength and agility make his bucking terrible. The broncho is a child compared to Cuddy's race of super-horse. Twice Geth went loose in his flat saddle and once Cuddy almost threw himself. The chain bit had torn the edges of his mouth and blood

7

coloured his froth. Suddenly he acquiesced and, quiet again, he took the sombre path. Geth thrust his right hand into his pocket, the revolver was still there. His hand left it and rested on the tasseled mane.

"Old man," he addressed the horse, "I know you don't know where you are going and I know you don't remember much, but you must remember Saratoga and how we beat them all. And, Cuddy, you'd understand—if you could—how it's all over now and why I want to do it for you myself."

The woods were cleared. It was good to leave their muffled dampness for the pure sunshine of the crest. On the very top of the hill, clean-cut against the sky, stood a great wind-misshaped pine. At the foot of this pine was a bank of fresh earth and Gethling knew that beyond the bank was the trench. He bent in his saddle and pressed his forehead against the warm neck. Before his eyes was the past they had shared, the sweep of the turf course, the Grand Stand a-flutter, grooms with blankets, jockeys and gentlemen in silk, owners' wives with cameras, then the race that always seemed so short—a rush of horses, the stretching over the jumps, and the purse or not, it did not matter.

With a grim set to his jaw he straightened, gathering the loose reins. Cuddy went into a canter and so approached the earth bank. Suddenly he refused to advance and again the two wills fought, but not so furiously. Cuddy was shaking with fear. The bank was a strange thing, a fearsome thing and the trench beyond, ghastly. His neck stretched forward. "Heh, heh!" he blew through his nostrils.

"Six steps nearer, Cuddy." Geth struck him lightly with his spurs. The horse paused by the bank and began rocking slightly.

"Sist! Be quiet," for they were on the spot Gethling wished. The horse gathered himself, started to rear, then sprang into the air, cleared earth-mound and trench and bounded down the hill. The tremendous buck-jump he had so uexpectedly taken, combined with his frantic descent, gave Gethling no chance to get control until the level was reached. Then, with the first pull on the bridle, he realized it was too late. For a while at least Cuddy was in command. Gethling tried all his tricks with the reins, the horse dashed on like a furious gust of wind, he whirled through the valley, across a ploughed field, over a fence and into more pastures. Gethling, never cooler, fought for the control. The froth

Paul Brown
'45

blown back against his white shirt was rosy with blood. Cuddy was beyond realizing his bit. Then Gethling relaxed a little and let him go. He could guide him to a certain extent. Stop him he could not.

The horse was now running flatly and rapidly. He made no attempt to throw his rider. What jumps were in his way he took precisely. Unlike the crazed runaway of the city streets, Cuddy never took better care of himself. It seemed that he was running for some purpose and Gethling thought of Willet's repeated remark, "Look at him—old Cuddy, he's thinking." Two miles had been covered and the gait had become business-like. Gethling, guiding always to the left, was turning him in a huge circle. The horse reeked with sweat. "Now," thought Gethling, "he's had enough," but at the first pressure on the bit Cuddy increased his speed. His breath caught in his throat. There was another mile and the wonderful run grew slower. The man felt the great horse trip and recover himself. He was tired out. Again the fight between master and man began. Cuddy resisted weakly, then threw up his beautiful white-starred face as if in entreaty.

"Oh, I'm—" muttered Gethling and let the reins lie loose on his neck. "Your own way, Cuddy. Your way is better than mine. Old friend, I'll not try to stop you again." He knew if he tried he could now gain control.

Again Gethling turned, still keeping towards the left. A hill began to rise before them and up it the horse sped, his breath whirring and rattling in his throat, but his strength still unspent. To the very top he made his way and paused dazed.

"Oh, Cuddy," cried Gethling, "this is Break-Neck." Before them was the wind-warped pine, the bank of earth, the trench. The horse came to a shivering standstill. The bank looked strange to him. He stood sobbing, his body rocking slightly, rocking gently, then with a sigh, came slowly down onto the turf. Gethling was on his feet, his hand on the dripping neck.

"You always were a bad horse and I always loved you," he whispered, "and that was a great ride, and now—" He rose abruptly and turned away as he realized himself alone in the soft twilight. The horse was dead. Then he returned to the tense body, so strangely thin and wet, and removed saddle and bridle. With these hung on his arm he took the sombre path through the pines for home.

The Begats[1]

By PHIL STONG

BEFORE American movement and history carry too far from the period of East Mississippian development and communication it is necessary to go into some horse personalities, because the blood of such animals as Messenger, English Eclipse, Hambletonian, Denmark, Copperbottom, Mambrino King, even of the famous seafaring pacer, Ranger, and of many other horses of equal or only slightly lesser distinction must persist in the blood of many a good eighty-dollar Minnesota farm-horse today. Their blood, as shown in the traits of groups, can never be resurrected to the point of

[1]From *Horses and Americans,* by Phil Stong.

identification of the exact sire, of course, but when a nag of ordinary use steps out and runs or trots 3:00 minutes or so at some backwoods County Fair after dragging a cultivator or a mowing machine all year there is pretty certainly some fine ancestor in his family tree.

A top-flight harness mare, for use on Long Island and at horse shows will sell now for a thousand dollars and far up, and still be inferior to the buggy-horse that pulled some Dakota or Nebraska children to school this morning, some mare with persisting traits of old Rob Roy in her heart and legs. Justin Morgan, dead more than a hundred years, helped to win the World War and will help to win the next, if it is won.

The means by which obscure modern horses come into noble blood is one of mere mathematical diffusion. It is not possible to get dependable records on the very first "thoroughbreds" in this country. We do know that one of the sons of Hambletonian, George Wilkes, had ninety-four sons. The twenty-three most distinguished sons produced 304 grandsons of distinction, and how many the whole tribe produced can remain, as far as I am concerned, a matter of nothing more statistical than awed contemplation. Now, in the fourth and later generations from Hambletonian, taking daughters into account also (the twenty-three best sons also produced 205 distinguished granddaughters) there should, barring such disasters as war exports and the encroachment of the automobile, be a few hundred thousand horses with Hambletonian blood in the country. But this horse was foaled as recently as 1849. What about Messenger, whose first American generation must have appeared sixty years before, the horse having been imported in 1788? There could be millions of Messengers in the country. If one considered fifteen or twenty of the Foundation Sires and "thoroughbreds," some preceding and some succeeding George Wilkes, it is quite apparent that every horse, mule, burro, man, woman, child and cocker spaniel in this country has a touch of pedigreed horse in his veins.

For evident biological reasons it appears that some variable factors must have been neglected in these mathematics—exportation and the automobile having been mentioned previously. In the case of horses, frequent and regular incest (what an extraordinary word in connection with horses!) spoils the arithmetical progression which in the human race is usually more remotely foiled by cousins and second cousins and fiftieth cousins.

The substantial point in these whimsical calculations is that most of the good general-use horses in this country are likely to have the sparks of great ancestorship behind them. This does not count the modern types of heavy draft-horses, Belgians, Percherons and Clydesdales principally, who almost unexceptionally are required to have certificates of pure blood breeding to perpetuate themselves, with the new and strict laws on registration which preceded the later breeds in America.

One of the most famous practical jokers of the past century, whose name I have forgotten, was a champagne salesman who took a blue ribbon at an important Eastern society show with an animal called something like "Ipulla Hoscar." After the award he let it be known that "I Pull a Horse-Car" had been purchased by him from the New York street railways, groomed to a finish and decorated by experts, to see what the judges would think of him. Perhaps this was no joke. "I Pull a Horse-Car" may have had some of the genes of Messenger in his blood.

Heredity of the champagne salesman, unknown, sire or dam.

The horse which the American Saddle Horse Breeders Association selected in one of their earliest conclaves as the "technical head of the American Saddle Horse breed" is Denmark, son of imported Hedgeford (or Hedgford) and a "thoroughbred" dam. He is dignified with the title "F. S." for registry, rather than a number—"Foundation Sire." His great contribution to America was three fine sons, Gaines' Denmark 61, Rob Roy, and Muir's Denmark. The first of these was the greatest and, in the opinion of Mr. Wallace, was greater than his father as a sire. On his father's side his pedigree traces back easily to six generations, with seven cases of father fixation, a very famous ancestor with the cunning name of Pot-8-oes, and a seventh-generation grandma with the beguiling name of Bay Bloody Buttocks.

So much for the paternal side. His mother was a mare—and the painful subject should never have been brought up. Her father was Cockspur but her mother was just a woman of the streets, apparently; she is referred to vaguely as "a Stevenson mare."

The Salic Law seems to have applied quite regularly among

the Foundation Sires (Denmark being *the* Foundation Sire); the grandmother of Vanmeter's Waxy was "full sister to the dam of Denmark," but nothing is vouched about the mother's sire; Cabell's Lexington had a grandfather but no grandmother; so, too, with Stump the Dealer, Texas, Prince Albert, Peter's Halcorn, Copperbottom (the younger), Dave Akin, and Bald Stockings. The titular orphans among the Foundation Sires are Tom Hal, Varnon's Roebuck, and Davy Crockett. Out of twenty-three Foundation Sires this makes twelve who were in doubt about their mothers or grandmothers, or about both parents. These are the crème de la crème of the "thoroughbred" saddlers of America.

The younger Denmark was black, and is described in a silly horse phrase as "two ended," that is, he arched his head and tail high. Now there are two occasions on which horses arch their tails naturally and neither of them is polite. It is so common to repair this deficiency in nature by trifling surgically and painfully with the joint of the horse's tail that there is what one hopes will be an increasing movement to bar horses so mutilated from show rings. Indeed, the custom has already been almost abandoned—most of the good show breeders in this country prefer horses that are not hunchbacked—a horse with a dislocated tail is just that.

Nothing conspicuous ever came from Denmark's line except a steady succession of fine horses. There were no Dan Patch's or Flora Temple's or Man o' War's. There were merely lovely ladies and finished gentlemen. Gaines' Denmark sired Washington Denmark who never consented to "leap" at any mare except a blue blood. Denmark's son, Gaines' Denmark, sired Washington Denmark, who begat King William, who begat Black Eagle, who begat Black Squirrel. As to Black Squirrel, I quote from the reference at hand:

> It is said that no real horseman could come into the presence (yes, "presence") of Black Squirrel (58) without uncovering before him.

This note comes from a very respectable writer in one of the best horse magazines in the world. Still, it seems enthusiastic. In general, it is probably better to let the horse tip its hat first.

Such a statement by an otherwise sane and competent writer is sufficiently indicative of what happens when people who are very fond of horses write about them.

As a sire of beautiful horses many think his (Black Squirrel's) equal is not known.

This was written in 1931. There were at least two hundred fine sires in this country for every one that could authentically claim

Denmark blood. There were, for instance, about fourteen hundred registered sires of "beautiful horses" in Iowa in the Belgian and Percheron breeds. Black Squirrel had nothing to do with those. What the writer means, of course, is that Black Squirrel was a notable progenitor of handsome saddle-horses. Enthusiasm and unveracity are the curses of horse history.

The reader is entitled to believe as much as he pleases about that notable Foundation Sire, Tom Hal. He was foaled in 1802 —parents not known—and died in 1843. He spent his whole life on his feet; he slept standing, as many horses do, but except to roll occasionally he never had a shoulder on the ground. He walked when he ate, picking up a mouthful of fodder and then strolling with it until it was swallowed. He died at the age of forty-one, which would be nearly 125 for a man.

No horse ever lived forty-one years on his four legs, and horses are as much gourmand as pigs, cats and dogs. No horse strolls away from a plenished stall—eating is one of their natural and inexorable functions; nothing but a tempting mare could ever have drawn Tom Hal away from a peck of corn.

Of Stump the Dealer (3240) there is little to note except that he had only one eye. He lost the other fighting with another horse across a fence. The other horse apparently carried a knife.

Chester Dare—not included on the modern list of Foundation Sires—lost his eye plausibly, when he was hit across the nose with a rope. He was a son of Black Squirrel and his children were numerous and distinguished; he was on the original list of Foundation Sires but his name was extinguished in revision, and Black Squirrel's is not included, because of the blaze of glory about Denmark, to whom no poor mortal would dare to give a registration number. He is F. S., and the babies have to derive their eminence from the old Tsar. Chester Dare is merely No. 10 (The Foundation Sires' numbers are not chronological in the Registry. The horses were chosen from time to time.) He is not a Foundation Sire now. Tom Hal is the oldest of the present list of Foundation Sires. His number is 3237, though he was foaled 136 years ago, long before any registries or records had ever been seduced into any symptom of accuracy. In examining the subject of great progenitors one is most impressed by the number of "bests," "greatests," and "mosts." In one brief article at hand, Denmark, Gaines' Denmark and Black Squirrel are each mentioned within five hundred words as the greatest American sire of saddle-horses. Forrester's fine work of the 1850's has two on the same page—one "greatest" and one "immeasurably superior" and on the next page one "unexcelled." It must have been dimly in the writer's mind that these terms were conflicting because he has not repeated the superlatives as applied successively to Messenger, Baronet and Bashaw.

The whole Foundation Sire business is confusing in the respect that of "the earliest of our importations which laid a foundation," according to Forrester, all arrived in the country before the oldest Foundation Sire was foaled. Wildair and "the Cub mare"—no mother again—came in 1763; Sloven in 1765; Figure in 1766; Lath in 1768; Whirligig in 1773; Slender in 1785; Messenger, who by frequency of mention and depth of adulation must have been about the best of the crop, in 1788, and dozens of others

later. Tom Hal, the oldest of the recognized list, was foaled in
1802—as has been mentioned, of an unnamed "imported Canadian pacer" and an unknown mother.

Messenger was not particularly distinguished on the track either
in England or after his importation to this country, when he was
apparently eight years old. He first ran in England in 1783 when
he was supposed to be three. He arrived in Philadelphia in 1788.
The sanest commentator on early horses is John H. Wallace, who
comments sadly as follows:

The different representations that have been made about Messenger's importation would fill a much larger space than would be
profitable. About no horse has there been so much written and
about no horse has there been so little really known. . . . Every
writer was a eulogist of the most enthusiastic type whether he knew
anything of his hero or not.

Messenger was remarkable for much more than a splendid get
of colts. He stood at stud in the United States in 1788, by un-
contestable evidence, four years before he is supposed, by some
reports, to have landed here. His breeder testified to his lineage
at the time and his testimony cannot be questioned or doubted
since the breeder had been an angel in Heaven for two or three
years at the time he uttered his certificate. But the newspaper
copy in which Mr. Wallace found the announcement of the
horse's first stand at stud can hardly have been prophetic because
the notice was run in the advertising and not the editorial columns.

When Messenger was properly escorted from the boat by two
grooms clinging to his head, "a distinguished New Yorker" present remarked, "There, in that horse, a million dollars strikes American soil."[2] The prophecy proved out, but the debarkation was
in Philadelphia and the New Yorker could better have stayed in
New York to watch debarkations of horses, instead of taking the
arduous trip to Philadelphia to see an apparently mediocre race-
horse unloaded.

The date of importation has been variously fixed from 1785 to
1800; the latter date would have made the million-dollar sire
twenty years old when he reached America. Messenger died,

[2]Later observation of one Hiram Woodruff: "When Messenger charged
down the gangplank onto the dock at Philadelphia not less than one hundred
million dollars struck our soil."

authentically, in 1808; there seems to be little doubt that he must have been foaled in England about three years before he appeared on the track there in 1783. This would have made him twenty-eight when he died, which is not improbable, because there is direct testimony that in his later years he was growing gray and "flea-bitten," i.e., he had a senile baldness.

He was a gray horse and smaller than a big modern mule; an inch or so under sixteen hands. He was supposed to have killed one or more handlers and to have had a thoroughly bad disposition; the killings sound like the silliest kind of fantasy because no breeder with any sense deliberately perpetuates a murderously vicious strain. He would probably not have survived his first murder, and, in general, people would not have trusted valuable mares with a psychopathic stallion. It sounds very much like a contemporary publicity rumor. An excited stallion is not a very safe animal to meddle with but I have never heard of a sane horse turning on any well-known and friendly creature. Race-horses are nearly all neuropaths, of course, but Messenger was not a highly bred, trigger-finger animal. He was a slightly coarse, heavy-boned animal, with a head that was too big and a stubby neck. There is no doubt that he was ill-tempered, but everything about distinguished horses is tremendously magnified in the telling. For years a great many people believed that Childers once ran a mile in one minute, and the "Mile-a-Minute" horse became a racing phrase. Another record credits him with one minute and forty-five seconds for a mile. It was remarkable how the breed of horses declined with the appearance of good stop-watches and responsible officials. Great modern runners have gone as low as $1:35$ in three or four instances; Roamer did $1:34\frac{4}{5}$ against time in 1918, and Equipoise bettered this by $\frac{2}{5}$ of a second in 1932, with the difficulties of competition. Perhaps Equipoise could have done better than $1:30$ under the most ideal and favoring circumstances and on a straight track, but if he had done that in the time of Childers the "Mile-a-Minute" horse would have most probably been swept out of memory by the "Mile-a-Half-Minute" horse. The only charitable explanation of the "Mile-a-Minute" foolishness, devoutly believed and reported occasionally over a century and a half or more, is that it was a typographical error.

We have always the suspicion, too, that in great events even the stop-watches grow hysterical. When the time of a race is very fast and a record seems in the making even the finest horological constructions are likely to contract their stomachs and blow off the stop before some great horse has actually concluded a contest by crossing the line.

Today, electric timing probably does catch horses within a fifth of a second in a fair majority of cases; I doubt that manual timing often does, and when it does it is simply by a fortunate accident. When three judges can stand together and all agree with an electric timer as much as half the time, one can regard fifth-of-a-second times taken manually much more seriously. There are some remarkably keen eyes and steady thumbs in track timing— not to speak of pure consciences—but our pity should go out to the unfortunates who timed such great races as that of Boston and Fashion in 1823 or Eclipse and Sir Henry in the same year. The watches on both races were timed to the half-second, and the timers were, according to the accounts of experienced observers, which I shall presently retail, remarkably accurate—but a half-second is two and one-half fifths. Stop-watches were about a hundred years old on the track by this year and it may be presumed that they were fairly accurate and the timers were naturally the best procurable. Still, in the one split-second timing of the Eclipse race (Henry was not able to run a creditable fourth heat and was withdrawn; the distance of the heats was four miles) and the one split-second timing of the Fashion race (this one went only two of the intended four-mile heats) both split seconds were questioned by amateur, but expert, timers in the audience; both as being on the fast side by the other half-second or more.

It is almost beyond flesh and blood not to tug with the horses in the excitement of a great race, and timers are flesh and blood. Anyone with any timing experience knows that the almost irrepressible feeling is to get them in fast; to lean forward with the straining horses and snap the stop whenever, or *just before,* an object intrudes on a perceptional barrier.

But this is the least part of it. Modern tracks are carefully surveyed. Surveying, of a sort, is as old by record as 1600 B.C., but there are surveyors and surveyors. In the middle of the sidewalk at Sheridan Square in New York City there is a triangle hardly large enough for a man to stand on, which the City somehow failed to acquire when it purchased its right of way. Modern practice in major collegiate track meets is to survey the track before the meet and survey it again if there is any possibility that a record has been set in any race. There is no way of knowing how punctiliously this was done in the case of early tracks but even today races are cautiously labeled *"about* seven furlongs," and a few yards may make a considerable difference in time, because, as any runner and any horse knows, the longest yards in the race are always at the finish.

It is hard to put down all the remarkable times of early horses to sheer mendacity; though that is, of course, the case with the mile-a-minute horse; that or sheer lunacy. To some considerable extent, however, it must be true that modern horses are handicapped in competition with their remote ancestors' times by the scientific controls that have been put on timing and distances.

To revert for a moment and finally to the matter of stopwatches, the first literary reference I can find on their use in races dates to 1737—"Provided he is truly try'd by a stop Watch." One hundred and thirty years later, 1867, a writer specifies, "Place a practical man with one of M'Cabe's stop-watches at the finishing point." The mention of a particular type of watch surely indicates that through a century or more the behavior of stop-watches had been eccentric; indeed, our observer on the Fashion race boasts that *his* instrument was a good one.

Unless a good deal of allowance is made for a number of such possible inaccuracies one would be at a loss to discover why any improvement of the horse breed should have been attempted.

With modern veterinary medicine, modern breeding, modern training, and modern riding, no horse has ever approached that supposed mile-a-minute performance of Childers and no horse ever will.

It is worth while to dwell a minute on Childers because he begat Blaze who begat Sampson who begat Engineer who begat Mambrino who begat Messenger who begat the finest trotting progeny in the world and a great deal of trouble for the Union troops in the Civil War. The whole line was marked by what was great size for the time and "a coarse appearance." In 1750 or so, Sampson was enormous for a race-horse—he was fifteen hands two inches, which would be small for a milkman's nag today.

At the same time it must be reckoned that the "hand" has been variously defined at three inches, four and a half inches, and four inches at various moments of the English language, and I believe that Sampson may have been measured at the four-and-a-half-inch standard, which would make him 16.9 plus hands as hands are now counted. This would be reasonable for a horse of "great size and coarse appearance," even in the Dark Ages of the eighteenth century. The "hand" is now four inches, of course, and why horsemen continue with a vague term that is historically confusing and at best a mere complication to be translated into feet and inches in everyday measurement, in which we judge normally, outside a stable, is beyond my understanding. At the moment, I am eighteen hands, one inch; if this were 1700 I would be about sixteen hands, two inches; if it were 1600 I would be twenty-four hands, one inch, or eight feet, one. I suppose it is an arcane impulse—"I know and you don't"—that leads doctors and lawyers and hostlers to indulge in lodge languages. The excuse of precision is utterly silly, "a hand" now means four inches as definitely as "encephalomyelitis" means blind staggers or "nolle contendere" means No Fight.

Sampson, the son of Blaze, the son of Childers, etc., to a dubious infinity, was subject to disrespect when he made his first track appearance. The grooms and jockeys at Malton are supposed to have said, "Has Mr. Robinson sent us a coach-horse to win the Plate?" Sampson won, of course, or the story would not appear in recent literature. When a fine horse falls and breaks its leg it has a .38 caliber epitaph; when a good one unexpectedly upsets the field, it runs in print forever.

Sampson had a child by a "dam" who was a daughter of reputable parents but whose mother's dam was unknown. She was merely a beguilement for a sire and an incubator for the father's colt. But long before Weismann and the "germ plasm," breeders of horses began to realize that the dam was something more than a nest for the embryonic replica of the father. When a running sire and a pacing mother bred and the result was a colt that trotted or paced they came to believe that some abstruse influence came from the mother. If the sporting men had ever shown any trace of scientific intelligence or capacity for biological research, Mendel's work on peas might have been anticipated by a century.

He bred peas, to find out why they were good or bad, big or small, and it is a sad fact that the men who bred horses have never learned as much about how to breed horses and men as he learned in his small garden about peas.

The peas were a simpler subject, of course. But their fecundities represented the influence of the male and the female in the arithmetical proportion. It seemed that the female had something to do with the progeny. The genetic explanation is now known to almost everyone. For fifty years horse breeders have selected the dam as well as the sire. Before that, the mother needed to be nothing but a blonde with pretty hips and an air of anxiety.

The whole story of the founding stock—for one can only consider the official list of "Foundation Sires" as arbitrary, abbreviated, and *nouvelle élite*—is necessarily incoherent, and tentative as to authority. The business is complicated by crossbreedings of gaited horses. Denmark was a great ancestor of runners, and Messenger was a great ancestor of trotters, and Denmark was a great ancestor of trotters, and Messenger was a great ancestor of runners. The subject would hardly be worth exploring for the small residue of verifiable fact and it would not be important if it were not a phenomenon of the most absolute democracy—if one can speak of an absolute democracy—in nature: the democracy of biogenesis.

For where are the nobles of the blood royal? Serving very notably on plows and mowing machines; filling out the stables of the Army Remount; pulling ice wagons; running races; filling soldiers' bellies during the World War; winning blue ribbons in Kansas City and Madison Square Garden at the great horse shows; trotting the gizzards out of vacationists in Vermont and Montana. More than one derivative of Godolphin's Arabian has pulled a plow, just as the gets of the Hanovers, Hohenzollerns and Bourbons may not all be at resplendent occupations. As far as that is concerned, very little was known about a tanner's daughter, the dam of William the Conqueror.

"Davy Crockett," parents unknown, died at the age of five. He is a Foundation Sire. Denmark's son, Rob Roy, was a Foundation Sire, and he also died at the age of five but left some excellent soldiers for the Civil War. The dates of the births or deaths, or both, of ten of the twenty-three are not known. What horses they may have bred before they were knighted is equally unknown; even what horses they may have bred through the long years.

While even in early times the finest studs might stand at fifty guineas or more, they had plenty of sons who would serve for a guinea and plenty of their descendants are certainly standing out in Iowa, Minnesota, Illinois and Missouri for twenty, ten or five dollars—on a dull day in the stable for whatever can be obtained. Selection and gelding save the country from an overflow of horse Bourbons but the occasional appearance of some obscure, unheralded and unpedigreed prodigy usually marks an atavism—a belated reference back to very gentle blood.

The horse who left the greatest name was a little bay stallion. He dragged logs for a farmer who was cutting off one of the spotty clearings in the difficult State of Vermont. He was Justin Morgan, named for one of his owners, who would have rested unknown for this century and a half, had he not attached his own name to a two-year-old stud colt which he acquired with a three-year-old gelding in West Springfield, Mass., in 1791 most probably.

It might have made a difference in American history if the colt had been the gelding. Forrester, in 1857, refers with the implied irony of italics to the attempt to set up the little bay not only as the head of a line but as the great ancestor of a whole family of horses, on a titular par with Arabs, Percherons, Thoroughbreds, Belgians, Suffolks, Shires, Hackneys and Saddle Horses today.

Eighty-odd years later we can see that the attempt was successful. The Morgan breed is the only one that derives its breed name from an individual horse. There are types and there are families, but Morgan started a family that was and still is a type—the Morgan horse. Rose Wilder Lane's novel of the 1880's, "Free Land," remarks the covetousness of Dakota settlers for a horse of old Morgan's blood; the United States Army and the United States Department of Agriculture still prize and maintain the offspring of the little bay who was born from God knows what about 1793. Today his breed has declined in usefulness and numbers, but every horseman knows his name.

He has plowed fields and pulled stumps and fought wars for the people of America for a great deal more than a century, through his descendants, by some unbelievable succession of genes

Paul Brown
'45

which evidently go back to the old patriarch. With no ancestry, harnessed continually at his daily work, a nameless, ordinary, smallish stallion who came from nowhere and died in 1821 of a kick that was not properly attended, made himself his own royal name, Tudor, Stuart, Hohenzollern, Romanov, or Son of the Sun, in the world of horses. Messenger and Denmark have left what seem to be immortal names in horse history, but there is no Messenger breed and no Denmark breed. There are twenty common breeds or so now but only one of them is named for a single horse—Morgan.

There is a magnificence in this circumstance that dazzles everyone who attempts to write on the history of horses.[3] Several men have spent years of their mature lives in working out biographies and histories of Justin Morgan; most particularly, his pedigree. A Mr. D. C. Linsley published a book about 1860 in which the dates of the correspondence prove that he spent at least six years and very probably much more principally in gathering data on Justin Morgan. Battell's history and registry fills four volumes. The amount of writing that has been done to show that Justin Morgan was the son of a "thoroughbred"—Beautiful Bay—would fill out forty-one detective novels and an application for membership in the Liars' Club. Quite possibly he came from Beautiful Bay and quite possibly he didn't. No one knows; on one has ever known; no one will ever know. If Beautiful Bay had been properly registered or even noted someone would have produced proper evidence, in nearly a century and a half, that he was the father of the great sire.

The whole point would be trivial except for the fact that Morgan and Messenger fought the Civil War, the Spanish War, and the World War. Morgan plowed Nebraska and Dakota, and Messenger saw that the mails got to San Francisco, just after the Gold Rush.

All of us can smile at hippophiles; but our particular civilization swept across the greatest country of the world on horsehoes in such an incredibly brief time that it could have bewildered Cæsar—and it did cheat Napoleon, bluff Europe, steal from Spain and Mexico, and settle everything its own way; in the saddle.

So one finds a sober clergyman like the Reverend William

[3] Possibly including this writer.

Henry Harrison Murray, writing under the amusing sponsorship of the even more Reverend Henry Ward Beecher, so engaged in his devotions—to Justin Morgan—that he contradicts himself within two or three pages. Two pages are given to proving that Justin Morgan had no pedigree and did not need one and another to flat assertions that:

It is said that Justin Morgan was a low-bred horse. But such a statement is a gross slander. There can be no doubt, in any candid man's mind who investigates the matter that Justin Morgan was sired by True Briton, or Beautiful Bay, owned by Sealy Norton of East Hartford, Conn.

The paragraph concludes with a pretty specimen of homiletics:

That his dam was a mare of good breeding is also beyond question. (Her initials would have been useful if Dr. Murray could have supplied them.) Whether the sire of Beautiful Bay was the important horse Traveller or not,—and this point I do not attempt to decide,—it cannot be denied that Beautiful Bay was a horse noted for his fine-blooded qualities.

This horse, which no "candid" man should deny a pedigree from Beautiful Bay, also called True Briton, or perhaps the great Alexander's Bucephalus or the nag that got Absalom's hair tangled in a tree, or some pure-blooded trotter from the Augean stables— needed no clerical apologies. Dr. Murray gave the correct explanation in preceding material—it comes to "Mother and father unknown, for sure." These quotes are my own condensation.

In simple language, he was a tough little animal. He could sprint, pull or endure. In addition he was amiable and intelligent —he trained easily and never lost his serenity. Morgan was about fourteen hands high and weighed a little less than a thousand pounds; about the size of a smallish cow-pony today. His color was dark bay, which is deep mahogany, with black hair on the mane, legs and tail. He was long-bodied and strikingly muscular in appearance.

He left no time records. There is some argument about whether he ran a mile in three minutes or in four minutes, but either speed is ice-wagon gait in these days. Morgan's legs were short and with the power of his shoulders he ordinarily won a country race over a short distance before the starter could brush off the hat he had dropped to start the contest. The four-minute time seems ridiculous and the three-minute time seems fast, though Morgan had thirty or forty children that could trot a mile under two minutes and a half, by contemporary record. He may have run in the latter time.

Morgan may have been wronged as a racer but he was represented as Hercules when it came to pulling; however he was traduced in the one respect he must have been consoled by the testimony of Nathan Nye "who was an eye-witness," according to the Reverend Mr. Murray, "and whose testimony was never questioned." It will be necessary to question it, somewhat later.

With a prelude that Morgan was able to out-draw, out-walk, out-trot, out-run every horse that was matched against him, the narrative proceeds:

At the time Evans had this horse, a small tavern, a grist-mill and saw-mill were in operation on the branch of White River, in Randolph; and at this place the strength of men and horses in that settlement was tested. On one occasion I went to one of these mills, where I spent most of a day; and, during the time, many trials were had, for a small wager, to draw a certain pine log which lay some rods from the saw-mill.

Some horses were hitched to it that would weigh twelve-hundred pounds; but not one of them could move it its length.

About dusk, Evans came down from his logging-field, which was near by; and I told him the particulars of the drawing match. Evans requested me to show him the log; which I did. He then ran back to the tavern, and challenged the company to bet a gallon of rum that he could not draw the log fairly on to the logway, at three pulls, with his colt. The challenge was promptly accepted; and, each having "taken a glass," the whole company went down to the spot.

Arrived on the spot, Evans says, "I am ashamed to hitch my horse to a little log like that; but, if three of you will get on and ride, and I don't draw it I will forfeit the rum." Accordingly, three of those least able to stand were placed upon the log. I was present with a lantern and cautioned those on the log to look out for their legs, as I had seen the horse draw before, and knew something had got to come. At the word of command the horse started log and men, and ʿvent more than half the distance before stopping. At the next pull he landed his load at the spot agreed upon, to the astonishment of all present.

With all respect to Nathan Nye, to the cloth of the Rev. Murray, and particularly to the quality of a great sire of great horses, this story is unqualified foolishness. The men of Vermont are reliably reported to be lean, light and tough but few of them weigh as little as an ounce. The exact drag of the log is not known by modern dynamometric standards but some 1200-pound horses, presumably of superior strength, could not move it its length. Accordingly, three Vermonters "least able to stand" are placed upon the object, increasing its weight 450 pounds, perhaps, and its drag weight perhaps more or perhaps less, according to the surface. Then a 950-pound stallion hauls off what must have been two or three times the drag against which 1200-pound horses failed.

The story has an excellent pedigree, from the Rev. Murray, from D. C. Linsley, from Solomon Steele, from Nathan Nye "who was an eye-witness." It is obviously incorrect. If this 950-pound horse could pull what may have been at least double the burden in dead drag of what a good 1200-pound horse failed to move more than its own strength he was even more than Justin Morgan —he was Pegasus.

There are some substantial facts about Justin Morgan. When Justin Morgan, the man, bought him, or took him for a debt he made a speculation, intending to apply the horse on a loan. Back in Vermont he was unable to get a good price so he rented him out for a year to Robert Evans, for fifteen dollars. Today his modern equivalent would earn hundreds of times that each year, —and not at hauling rocks or pulling stumps, or even at trotting on a racetrack. A strange, indelible genius was in the fecundating cells of his body to continue after every human or horse contemporary had spent out his identity in the dissolving of repeated generations.

The first proof of excellence is offered almost phrase for phrase now as it was offered nearly a century and a half ago; then for Morgan and now for his remote descendants: they are intelligent and they have the corollary qualities of gentleness and courage. There is nothing more that can be said for an American or a horse. Justin Morgan's transmission of characteristics ranks easily with the Habsburg chin and the hæmophilia of the Spanish rulers; probably it is as extraordinary as the famous "cussedness" of the Jukes family; but among horses it is more fitting to compare the Morgans with the Adamses or the Roosevelts. Still, neither of those notable lines of sires has yet proved its ability to project fine qualities through as many generations as the Morgan has seen.

According to Mr. Nye's evidence, Justin Morgan must have kept his lessee in a rather remarkable condition for his annual rent of fifteen dollars. He was always running for a gallon of rum and Nye saw him win four races in one evening at eighty rods. One can only assume that Mr. Evans had a large and thirsty family; otherwise he must have been something more of a phenomenon than his miraculous horse.[4]

The slow times mentioned, in round minutes, on Justin Morgan may have been due to a number of things. In the first place, he seems to have run chiefly in the evening after a hard day at pulling stumps and dragging logs and rocks, and probably his competitors did, too. The fine sporting spirit of the Vermonters would never supersede their fine, practical Yankee sense that the boulder crop flourishes there as well as in any state in the Union and has to be removed if there is to be any room left for abandoned cellars, the second ranking crop, or stumps for Republican speakers.

Some of the Vermont villages have survived superficially almost unchanged since Justin Morgan ran, so that it is not too difficult to reconstruct the circumstances of his races in the imagination— the not too elaborate tavern with a convenient stretch of the new post road in front of it; the Solomon Steeles and Evanses and Nyes foregathering with, perhaps, a few Coolidges and the like to discuss virtuously the irretrievable errors of those dern fools down in Philadelphia and to perform the solemn evening rite of the sturdy Vermont farmer, the wetting of the whistle.

Praiseworthy as this social duty is, it does not make good jockeys. We can assume from the fact that the pulling contest was held by lantern light that most of the notable races were held under the same conditions; that is, in dusk or dark, with tired horses

---

[4]Please observe that whether Battell or Justin Morgan, Jr., is correct on the birth date, the colt was rented at two years for improbably heavy work. The stories are told for general feeling about the horse in his time.

ridden by owners at no particular weight, and with well-moistened whistles.

This makes the three- and four-minute times more plausible. Justin Morgan left forty probable descendants within a few generations who could trot a mile in 2:30 or less and fifty-one who could do 2:36 or better. Naturally they were by many different mothers so it is quite evident where the 2:30 blood came from; that is, it is quite evident as far back as Justin Morgan, who was variously described by his owner's son as "a Dutch horse" and a "thoroughbred."

Even in speaking of the great horse's descendants it is necessary to say "probable." Even while Mr. Linsley was compiling his researches and deductions on the lineage of Morgan, and years after that had first been a subject of controversy, the battle was raging again over the paternity of his most famous ("probable") grandson and his greatest (almost indubitable) great-grandson.

The paternity of Black Hawk, the son of Sherman Morgan, the son of Justin Morgan, was the subject of a lawsuit, because the owner of Sherman, who was chestnut, had also a black stud named Paddy. The "services"—which it is delightful to find were also called "embraces" by some of the early writers—of Paddy cost seven dollars; those of Sherman, fourteen. The owners of Black Hawk's mother paid the fourteen for the use of the Morgan stallion; the mare scandalously gave birth to a black colt which did not look or act like a Morgan and probably did not talk like one either. The godparents sued for seven dollars—the difference in price between Paddy's embraces and Sherman's, but they lost their case. Bitterly enough, after they had paid the seven dollars, Black Hawk and his whole line failed to produce a foal with the distinctive characteristics which are so marked that they mean "Morgan" to this day.

Note how injustice not only triumphs but rubs salt in the wounds —also the complexity and uncertainty of horse affairs in general:

Black Hawk's mother, Old Narragansett, was black, and this probably decided the judge or the jury in the case. Before the colt was born she was sold by her owner to Mr. Shade Twombly, living about two miles from Durham, N. H., with the customary provision that he was to pay the stud fee if the colt stood and fed. When the colt did so Mr. Twombly looked at his color and his contours and decided that the black Paddy had somehow been mixed up in the presumed romance of Sherman Morgan and Old Narragansett. It was "proved" that the lady was spotless and Mr. Twombly's estate was mulcted for the seven additional dollars.

After two years the heirs sold the colt for seventy dollars and the buyers sold him again to one Benjamin Thurston for two hundred dollars. Thereafter, for twelve years, from 1844 to 1856, he stood as the most expensive lover (among quadrupeds) in the United States; the first stud ever to charge a $100 fee.

This story would seem incredible—the observers who brought in effective legal evidence that Sherman Morgan was the father must have been as leeringly numerous as they usually are at a stud stable, and certainly the love affairs of horses are not complicated or furtive—but the history of the great Ethan Allen, Black Hawk's son, shows some of the general whimsicality and unreliability of the records, if they can be flattered with such a term.

Ethan Allen came, of course, from Ticonderoga, where he was undoubtedly bred by Black Hawk—such an event could not have happened in a comparatively small town without awakening the interest of everyone in the place who had ever heard of a horse, and at that time, naturally, everyone had heard of a horse. It was about the same situation as if Man o' War were taken to Fargo, South Dakota, in our times. The mother was identifiable because she was "a little flea-bitten mare with a spavin on one leg and a hip knocked down." The Queen Mother of her time. She must have had exceptional blood, of course, or her owner never would have bred her to Black Hawk.

In the face of all of these infinite sources of information a practical-joker named Holcomb managed to start a controversy about Ethan's parentage by advertising widely that as a jolly prank he had turned one of his own studs in with the colt's mother before Black Hawk could come at her. The owner was helpless, of course. He could produce reputable and directly informed witnesses to the fact that there was nothing in the story; he could have sued for damages but the legend spread and clung widely enough without a lawsuit to speed it.

These were two of the most famous descendants of Justin Morgan; there were, of course, hundreds of them within three or four generations. The materials on Justin Morgan are embarrassingly

numerous for the purposes of a sketch like this. Perhaps his services to Americans and influence on American life can best be shown in a contemporary summary. There are a number of horse clubs devoted to his name, the principal one being the Morgan Horse Club, Inc., of New York. The United States Department of Agriculture maintains a Morgan Horse Farm and the Army a stud. The brief bibliography compiled for this book, containing only source and some topical matters, contains six or seven fundamental books and a dozen or so articles and papers—it could easily run into scores of items, without counting references and articles in more general books.

It is unfortunate that the very indelibility of the Morgan traits has operated against the fine animal in one way, in the matter of size and ranginess, for the Morgan is still comparatively small by modern standards and not at all the match of the Thoroughbreds, Hackney crosses, Saddle Horses, and taller saddle types for spectacular sports. He has been badly squeezed in agriculture and general-utility service by the giants that have been developed in this century; there are Percherons that will weigh twice as much as a Morgan and against such odds not even Justin himself could hope to compete, even if he were as big as his finest modern descendant.

To deal finally, for the moment, with the Morgan breed, it is necessary to slip out of his immediate cycle briefly and report the Second Annual Trail Ride to the Green Mountain Horse Association on July 22, 23, and 24 as it appears in *The Horse* for Sept.-Oct., 1937. It is a little unfair, because Vermont is still loyal to its Morgans and fifteen of the twenty-one entries were Morgans, including two Morgan-Arabs, but they had noble competition; two of E. Arthur Ball's Arabs from Indiana, a Thoroughbred mare with an Army man up (I hope that the Army observes that it finished second to a Morgan), an American Saddle Horse (or Saddle Bred, if one prefers), another Thoroughbred mare, and another American Saddle Horse.

The horses had to carry a minimum weight of 155 pounds and make forty miles in seven hours the first day, including a stop for feed and rest; the same on the second day, and twenty miles on the morning of the third day. The time of 17½ hours for the hundred miles does not seem extraordinary unless one has seen

Vermont bridle paths. The contest started with an unbroken up-hill climb of ten miles. The horses averaged a loss of thirty-four pounds each on the hundred miles.

The first seven places were: Morgan—Thoroughbred—Arab—Morgan—Morgan—Arab—Morgan—Arab, all but the third-place Arab, a stallion, being mares. All the horses were good for their breeds, of course, but even considering the superior number of Morgans they seem to have held up well in competition, particularly as horse contests are not won by the number of horses voting.

Probably no horse has maintained as much outside enthusiasm and kept as much continuing loyalty as the begats of old Justin; certainly none over almost a century and a half; the "Messenger" horse has been spoken of that long but not by as many plowmen, wagon-drivers, saddle-riders and buggy-drivers—and please note that it is not necessary to use quotation marks around the Morgan of the Morgan horse.

The date of Morgan's birth given above is almost certainly correct.

Such a quantity of stuff has been written about Justin Morgan that it did not occur to me that there was any question about his birthday until I noticed that the Vermont Legislature had voted to celebrate his 150th anniversary this year, 1939. I checked back on Wallace and Battell and noticed what I had not, by some prodigy of inattention, noticed before; that one writer gave the date as 1793 and the other as 1789. This was serious, because Wallace's 1793 agreed with the statement of Morgan's son that his father went to West Springfield in 1795 and brought back the two-year-old colt, later called Justin Morgan; also, Wallace himself is a careful scholar.

Battell, however, had written something over a thousand pages about Morgan and his descendants, and presumably knew what he was talking about.

Adopting the laziest course, I sent inquiries to the Vermont Department of Agriculture and to the Morgan Horse Club of New York, after discovering that Linsley, Forrester and the rest of them were in disagreement—some of them with themselves. The results were two pleasant notes which were not, however, at all conclusive.

Mr. Edward H. Jones, Commissioner of Agriculture in Vermont, sent an excerpt from The Report of The Vermont Board of Agriculture for the years 1889–90:

The past year was the centennial of Justin Morgan, founder of the great family that bears his name. Were he now living he would be just 100 years old. For although it has generally been supposed that he was foaled in 1793 and brought by his owner and breeder, from whom he took his name, from Springfield, Mass., to Randolph, Vt., two years later, in the fall of 1795, recent investigation shows that these dates are incorrect. He was foaled in 1789 and brought to Randolph in the fall of 1791. His owner, Justin Morgan, had moved from Springfield, Mass., to our neighboring town of Randolph in the spring of 1788, and three years from the next fall he returned on horseback to Springfield and brought back with him the little bay two-year-old colt that was to make the name of Morgan a household word throughout the land.

This was all the material available on the "later investigations." It may have been some of Battell's data, though his "Registry" was not printed till 1894.

The Morgan Horse Club referred me to Battell, who was my second reference on the subject sometime back in 1938, and sent me a particularly well-designed and produced brochure on the Morgan Horse, which reads, in part, as follows:

According to his son, Justin Morgan, Jr., the elder Morgan went down to Springfield in the fall of 1795 to collect some money due him. But, instead of getting the money, he got a three-year-old gelding and a two-year-old colt. The colt was Justin Morgan, as he was later named.

Morgan seems to have called him "Figure."

The reference gives 1789 and the brochure 1793.

Battell is singularly detailed and convincing, but the experience of some months with writers on horses had shown me that being positive about horses and being accurate about them are two different things; the one is universal and the other impossible. Opposed to his testimony is the direct evidence of the owner's son.

Well, the owner's son was almost certainly wrong. A brief correspondence with the very helpful Town Clerk of Randolph,

Miss Evelyn Bashau, furnished the substantial data for some fairly reasonable inferences.

The facts of Justin Morgan's (man) life are not impeachable as given by Battell. The son was born in 1786, so that he was either five or nine years old when his father made the famous trip to West Springfield—not Springfield as stated in the Agriculture Report and the brochure. One can imagine that the trip was something of an event; it must have taken two or three days on horseback each way, possibly more, for Mr. Morgan was semi-invalid from his twentieth year until his death at fifty-one in 1798.

An event to a five-year-old? My father and grandfather made a three months' tour over Grandfather's old gold-mining route of 1850 when I was quite young, six or eight or something. It must have been about 1908; all I remember of it is that I acquired a lifetime scar sharpening a pencil with a butcher knife the evening they left and that at some point in the journey my father sent me a pyrographed leather postcard of an Indian, from Denver.

If, after ninety days, they had brought back a dozen colts I would have remembered that they brought back some colts.

So we will assume that Mr. Justin Morgan, Jr.'s, statement, in spite of the fact that he was the owner's son, was unduly specific, because long after the event, when the Morgan horse was a great national institution, it would have been almost treasonable not to remember the small and as yet undistinguished colt his father brought back from West Springfield, whether he remembered it or not.

This is a very brief sketch of some sires whom I, quite arbitrarily, consider the most important of all American sires outside the great work-horse breeds. They must be mentioned later, in their time. Copperbottom and twenty others should probably have more attention, but the histories of the ones cited are exemplary. It is not within the function of this study to expatiate on the histories of individual horses at the expense of some of the characteristics of Americans who almost unexceptionally dealt with the species till the general arrival of the motor car. These few accounts certainly show the optimism of our race, particularly about horses' pedigrees and speeds, our inventiveness and ingenuity in making the phenomena fit the case—and perhaps more seriously our true capacity to breed up noble traits, out of our circumstances and unknown genes.

Nicolls and Lovelace had horse races for the improvement of the blood and the general welfare of the country, as we do now. Old Justin was in many contests of various kinds, but in moments of piety, with a sermon and a gallon of rum under his belt, Mr. Evans no doubt reflected that this was a mere encouragement for the Vermonters to pay stud fees and hasten the clearing of the Green Mountains by the use of superior stock. As recently, comparatively, as 1870, the use of horse-cars on the city streets of Connecticut towns on the Sabbath was questioned and the application of an old Blue Law was prevented when some legislator discovered that Sunday labor was prohibited "except for works of charity and mercy," so the horse-cars went on performing their usual deeds of charity and mercy.

These are Americans with horses.[5]

[5]It will be noted that many horses have been chosen by various authorities as the "greatest" horse or the greatest race-horse. The scope of this piece does not give room for even a scattering of the distinguished horses that have lived in America. Their mere cataloguing would take up many volumes. A few are dwelt upon more particularly in the text because they seemed *most* significant or *most* colorful in their relation to phases of American social life or history.

This is the standing answer to inevitable objections that this, that or the other "greatest" horse has not been mentioned or has been scantily treated.

A Grand Filly

By E. OE. SOMERVILLE AND MARTIN ROSS

I AM an Englishman. I say this without either truculence or vainglorying, rather with humility—a mere Englishman, who submits his Plain Tale from the Western Hills with the conviction that the Kelt who may read it will think him more mere than ever.

I was in Yorkshire last season when what is trivially called "the cold snap" came upon us. I had five horses eating themselves silly all the time, and I am not going to speak of it. I don't consider it a subject to be treated lightly. It was in about the thickest of it that I heard from a man I know in Ireland. He is a little old horse-coping sportsman with a red face and iron-grey whiskers, who has kept hounds all his life; or, rather, he has always had hounds about, on much the same conditions that other men have rats. The rats are indubitably there, and feed themselves variously, and so do old Robert Trinder's "Rioters," which is their *nom de guerre* in the County Corkerry (the few who know anything of the map of Ireland may possibly identify the two counties buried in this cryptogram).

I meet old Robert most years at the Dublin Horse Show, and every now and then he has sold me a pretty good horse, so when he wrote and renewed a standing invitation, assuring me that there was open weather, and that he had a grand four-year-old filly to sell, I took him at his word, and started at once. The journey lasted for twenty-eight hours, going hard all the time, and during the last three of them there were no foot-warmers and the cushions became like stones enveloped in mustard plasters. Old Trinder had not sent to the station for me, and it was pelting rain, so I had to drive seven miles in a thing that only exists south of the Limerick Junction, and is called a "jingle". A jingle is a square box of painted canvas with no back to it, because, as was luminously explained to me, you must have some way to get into it, and I had to sit sideways in it, with my portmanteau bucking like a three-year-old on the seat opposite to me. It fell out on the road twice going uphill. After the second fall my hair tonic slowly oozed forth from the seams, and added a fresh ingredient to the smells of the grimy cushions and the damp hay that furnished the machine. My hair tonic costs eight-and-sixpence a bottle.

There is probably not in the United Kingdom a worse-planned entrance gate than Robert Trinder's. You come at it obliquely on the side of a crooked hill, squeeze between its low pillars with an inch to spare each side, and immediately drop down a yet steeper hill, which lasts for the best part of a quarter of a mile. The jingle went swooping and jerking down into the unknown, till, through the portholes on either side of the driver's legs, I saw Lisangle House. It had looked decidedly better in large red letters at the top of old Robert's notepaper than it did at the top of his lawn, being no more than a square yellow box of a house, that had been made a fool of by being promiscuously trimmed with battlements. Just as my jingle tilted me in backwards against the flight of steps, I heard through the open door a loud and piercing yell; following on it came the thunder of many feet, and the next instant a hound bolted down the steps with a large plucked turkey in its mouth. Close in its wake fled a brace of puppies, and behind them, variously armed, pursued what appeared to be the staff of Lisangle House. They went past me in full cry, leaving a general impression of dirty aprons, flying hair, and onions, and I feel sure that there were bare feet somewhere in it. My carman leaped from his perch and joined in the chase, and the whole party swept from my astonished gaze round or into a clump of bushes. At this juncture I was not sorry to hear Robert Trinder's voice greeting me as if nothing unusual were occurring.

"Upon me honour, it's the Captain! You're welcome, sir, you're welcome! Come in, come in, don't mind the horse at all; he'll eat the grass there as he's done many a time before! When the gerr'ls have old Amazon cot they'll bring in your things."

(Perhaps I ought to mention at once that Mr. Trinder belongs to the class who are known in Ireland as "Half-sirs". You couldn't say he was a gentleman, and he himself wouldn't have tried to say so. But, as a matter of fact, I have seen worse imitations.)

Robert was delighted to see me, and I had had a whisky-and-soda and been shown two or three more hound puppies before it occurred to him to introduce me to his aunt. I had not expected an aunt, as Robert is well on the heavenward side of sixty; but there she was: she made me think of a badly preserved Egyptian mummy with a brogue. I am always a little afraid of my hostess, but there was something about Robert's aunt that made me know I was a worm. She came down to dinner in a bonnet and black kid gloves—a circumstance that alone was awe-inspiring. She sat entrenched at the head of the table behind an enormous dish of thickly jacketed potatoes, and, though she scorned to speak to Robert or me, she kept up a sort of whispered wrangle with the parlour-maid all the time. The latter's red hair hung down over her shoulders—and at intervals over mine also—in horrible luxuriance, and recalled the leading figure in the pursuit of Amazon; there was, moreover, something about the heavy boots in which she tramped round the table that suggested that Amazon had sought sanctuary in the cowhouse. I have done some roughing it in my time, and I am not over-particular, but I admit that it was rather a shock to meet the turkey itself again, more especially as it was the sole item of the *menu*. There was no doubt of its identity, as it was short of a leg, and half the breast had been shaved away. The aunt must have read my thoughts in my face. She fixed her small implacable eyes on mine for one quelling instant, then she looked at Robert. Her nephew was obviously afraid to meet her eye; he coughed uneasily, and handed a surreptitious potato to the puppy who was sitting under his chair.

"This place is rotten with dogs," said the aunt; with which announcement she retired from the conversation, and fell again to the slaughter of the parlour-maid. I timidly ate my portion of turkey and tried not to think about the cowhouse.

It rained all night. I could hear the water hammering into something that rang like a gong; and each time I rolled over in the musty trough of my feather-bed I fractiously asked myself why the mischief they had left the tap running all night. Next morning the matter was explained when, on demanding a bath, I was told that "there wasn't but one in the house, and 'twas undher the rain-down. But sure ye can have it," with which it was dragged in full of dirty water and flakes of whitewash, and when I got out of it I felt as if I had been through the Bankruptcy Court.

The day was windy and misty—a combination of weather possible only in Ireland—but there was no snow, and Robert Trinder, seated at breakfast in a purple-red hunting coat, dingy drab breeches, and woollen socks, assured me that it was turning out a grand morning.

I distinctly liked the looks of my mount when Jerry the Whip pulled her out of the stable for me. She was big and brown, with hindquarters that looked like jumping; she was also very dirty and obviously underfed. None the less she was lively enough, and justified Jerry's prediction that "she'd be apt to shake a couple or three bucks out of herself when she'd see the hounds". Old Robert was on an ugly brute of a yellow horse, rather like a big mule, who began the day by bucking out of the yard gate as if he had been trained by Buffalo Bill. It was at this juncture that I first really respected Robert Trinder; his retention of his seat was so unstudied, and his command of appropriate epithets so complete.

Jerry and the hounds awaited us on the road, the latter as mixed a party as I have ever come across. There were about fourteen couple in all, and they ranged in style from a short-legged black-and-tan harrier, who had undoubtedly had an uncle who was a dachshund, to a thing with a head like a greyhound, a snow-white body, and a feathered stern that would have been a credit to a setter. In between these extremes came several broken-haired Welshmen, some dilapidated 24-inch foxhounds, and a lot of pale-coloured hounds, whose general effect was that of the table-cloth on which we had eaten our breakfast that morning, being dirty white, covered with stains that looked like either tea or egg, or both.

"Them's the old Irish breed," said Robert, as the yellow horse voluntarily stopped short to avoid stepping on one of them; "there's no better. That Gaylass there would take a line up Patrick Street on a fair day, and you'd live and die seeing her kill rats."

I am bound to say I thought it more likely that I should live to see her and some of her relations killing sheep, judging by their manners along the road; but we got to Letter crossroads at last with no more than an old hen and a wandering cur dog on our collective consciences. The road and its adjacent fences were thronged with foot people, mostly strapping young men and boys, in the white flannel coats and slouched felt hats that strike a stranger with their unusualness and picturesqueness.

"Do you ever have a row with Land Leaguers?" I asked, noting their sticks, while the warnings of a sentimental Radical friend as to the danger of encountering an infuriated Irish peasantry suddenly assumed plausibility.

"Land League? The dear help ye! Who'd be bothered with the Land League here?" said Robert, shoving the yellow horse into the crowd; "let the hounds through, boys, can't ye? No, Captain, but 'tis Saint November's Day, as they call it, a great holiday, and there isn't a ruffian in the country but has come out with his blagyard dog to head the fox!"

A grin of guilt passed over the faces of the audience.

"There's plinty foxes in the hill, Mr. Thrinder," shouted one of them; "Dan Murphy says there isn't a morning but he'd see six or eight o' them hoppin' there."

"Faith, 'tis thrue for you," corroborated Dan Murphy. "If ye had thim gethered in a quarther of ground and dhropped a pin from th' elements, 'twould reach one o' thim!"

(As a matter of fact, I haven't a notion what Mr. Murphy meant, but that is what he said, so I faithfully record it.)

The riders were farmers and men of Robert's own undeter-mined class, and there was hardly a horse out who was more than four years old, saving two or three who were nineteen. Robert pushed through them and turned up a bohireen—*i.e.*, a narrow and incredibly badly made lane—and I presently heard him cheering the hounds into covert. As to that covert, imagine a hill that in any civilised country would be called a mountain: its nearer side a cliff, with just enough slope to give root-hold to giant furze bushes, its summit a series of rocky and boggy ter-races, trending down at one end into a ravine, and at the other becoming merged in the depths of an aboriginal wood of low scrubby oak trees. It seemed as feasible to ride a horse over it as over the roof of York Minster. I hadn't the vaguest idea what to do or where to go, and I clave to Jerry the Whip.

The hounds were scrambling like monkeys along the side of the hill; so were the country boys with their curs; old Trinder moved parallel with them along its base. Jerry galloped away to the ravine, and there dismounting, struggled up by zigzag cattle paths to the comparative levels of the summit. I did the same, and was pretty well blown by the time I got to the top, as the filly scorned the zigzags, and hauled me up as straight as she could go over the rocks and furze bushes. A few other fellows had followed us, and we all pursued on along the top of the hill.

Suddenly Jerry stopped short and held up his hand. A hound spoke below us, then another, and then came a halloa from Jerry that made the filly quiver all over. The fox had come up over the low fence that edged the cliff, and was running along the terrace in front of us. Old Robert below us—I could almost have chucked a stone on to him—gave an answering screech, and one by one the hounds fought their way up over the fence and went away on the line, throwing their tongues in a style that did one good to hear. Our only way ahead lay along a species of trench between the hill, on whose steep side we were standing, and the cliff fence. Jerry kicked the spurs into his good ugly little horse, and making him jump down into the trench, squeezed along it after the hounds. But the delay of waiting for them had got the filly's temper up. When I faced her at the trench she reared, and whirled round, and pranced backwards in, considering the circumstances, a highly discomposing way. The rest of the field crowded through the furze past me and down into the trench, and twice I thought the mare would land herself and me on top of one of them. I don't wonder she was frightened. I know I was. There was nothing between us and a hundred-foot drop but this narrow trench and a low, rotten fence, and the fool behaved as though she wanted to jump it all. I hope no one will ever erect an equestrian statue in my honour; now that I have experienced the sensation of ramping over nothing, I find I dislike it. I believe I might have been there now, but just then a couple of hounds came up, and before I knew what she was at, the filly had jumped down after them into the trench as if she had been doing it all her life. I was not long about picking the others up; the filly could gallop anyhow, and we thundered on over ground where, had I been on foot, I should have liked a guide and an alpenstock. At intervals we jumped things made of sharp stones, and slates, and mud; I don't know whether they were banks or walls. Sometimes the horses changed feet on them, sometimes they flew the whole affair, according to their individual judgment. Sometimes we were splashing over sedgy patches that looked and felt like buttered toast, sometimes floundering through stuff resembling an ill-made chocolate soufflé, whether intended for a ploughed field or a partially drained bog-hole I could not determine, and all was fenced as carefully as cricket-pitches. Presently the hounds took a swing to the left and over the edge of the hill again, and our leader Jerry turned sharp off after them, down a track that seemed to have been dug out of the face of the hill. I should have liked to get off and lead, but they did not give me time, and we suddenly found ourselves joined to Robert Trinder and his company of infantry, all going hard for the oak wood that I mentioned before.

It was pretty to see the yellow horse jump. Nothing came amiss to him, and he didn't seem able to make a mistake. There was a stone stile out of a bohireen that stopped every one, and he changed feet on the flag on top and went down by the steps on the other side. No one need believe this unless they like, but I saw him do it. The country boys were most exhilarating. How they got there I don't know, but they seemed to spring up before us wherever we went. They cheered every jump, they pulled away the astounding obstacles that served as gates (such as the end of an iron bedstead, a broken harrow, or a couple of cartwheels), and their power of seeing the fox through a stone wall or a hill could only be equalled by the Röntgen rays. We fought our way through the oak wood, and out over a boggy bounds ditch into open country at last. The Rioters had come out of the wood on a screaming scent, and big and little were running together in a compact body, followed, like the tail of a kite, by a string of yapping country curs. The country was all grass, enchantingly green and springy; the jumps were big, yet not too big, and there were no two alike; the filly pulled hard, but not too hard, and she was jumping like a deer; I felt that all I had heard of Irish hunting had not been overstated.

We had been running for half an hour when we checked at a farmhouse; the yellow horse had been leading the hunt all the time, making a noise like a steam-engine, but perfectly undefeated, and our numbers were reduced to five. An old woman and a girl rushed out of the yard to meet us, screaming like sea-gulls.

"He's gone south this five minutes! I was out spreadin' clothes, and I seen him circling round the Kerry cow, and he as big as a man!" screamed the girl.

"He was, the thief!" yelled the old woman. "I seen him firsht on the hill, cringeing behind a rock, and he hardly able to thrail the tail afther him!"

"Run now, like a good girl, and show me where did he cross the fence," said old Robert, puffing and blowing, as with a purple face he hurried into the yard to collect the hounds, who, like practised foragers, had already overrun the farmhouse, as was evidenced by an indignant and shrieking flight of fowls through the open door.

The girl ran, snatching off her red plaid shawl as she went.

"Here's the shpot now!" she called out, flinging the shawl down on the fence; "here's the very way just that he wint! Go south to the gap; I'll pull the pole out for ye—this is a cross place."

The hunt gratefully accepted her good offices. She tore the monstrous shaft of a cart out of a place that with it was impossible, and without it was a boggy scramble, and as we began to gallop again, I began to think there was a good deal to be said in favour of the New Woman.

I suppose we had had another quarter of an hour, when the mist, that had been hanging about all day, came down on us, and it was difficult to see more than a field ahead. We had got down on to lower ground, and we were in a sort of marshy hollow when we were confronted by the most serious obstacle of the day: a tall and obviously rotten bank clothed in briars, with sharp stones along its top, a wide ditch in front of it, and a disgustingly squashy take-off. Robert Trinder and the yellow horse held their course undaunted: the rest of the field turned as one man, and went for another way round—I, in my arrogance, followed the Master. The yellow horse rose out of the soft ground with quiet, indescribable ease, got a foothold on the side of the bank for his hind legs, and was away into the next field without pause or mistake.

"Go round, Captain!" shouted Trinder; "it's a bad place!"

I hardly heard him; I was already putting the filly at it for the second time. It took about three minutes for her to convince me that she and Robert were right, and I was wrong, and by that time everybody was out of sight, swallowed up in the mist. I tried round after the others, and found their footmarks up a lane and across a field; a loose stone wall confronted me, and I rode at it confidently; but the filly, soured by our recent encounter, reared and would have none of it. I tried yet another way round, and put her at a moderate and seemingly innocuous bank, at which, with the contrariety of her sex, she rushed at a thousand miles an hour. It looked somehow as if there might be a bit of a drop, but the filly had got her beastly blood up, and I have been in a better temper myself.

She rose to the jump when she was a good six feet from it. I knew she would not put an iron on it, and I sat down for the drop. It came with a vengeance. I had a glimpse of a thatched roof below me, and the next instant we were on it or in it—I don't know which. It gave way with a crash of rafters, the mare's forelegs went in, and I was shot over her head, rolled over the edge of the roof, and fell on my face into a manure heap. A yell and a pig burst simultaneously from the door, a calf followed, and while I struggled up out of my oozy resting-place, I was aware of the filly's wild face staring from the door of the shed in which she so unexpectedly found herself. The broken reins trailed round her legs, she was panting and shivering, and blood was trickling down the white blaze on her nose. I got her out through the low doorway with a little coaxing, and for a moment hardly dared to examine as to the amount of damage done. She was covered with cobwebs and dirt out of the roof, and, as I led her forward, she went lame on one foreleg; but beyond this, and a good many scratches, there was nothing wrong. My own appearance need not here be dilated upon. I was cleaning off what they call in Ireland "the biggest of the filth" with a bunch of heather, when from a cottage a little bit down the lane in which I was standing a small barelegged child emerged. It saw me, uttered one desperate howl, and fled back into the house. I abandoned my toilet and led the mare to the cottage door.

"Is any one in?" I said to the house at large.

A fresh outburst of yells was the sole response; there was a pattering of bare feet, and somewhere in the smoky gloom a door slammed. It was clearly a case of "Not at Home" in its conventional sense. I scribbled Robert Trinder's name on one of my visiting cards, laid it and half a sovereign on a table by the door, and started to make my way home.

The south of Ireland is singularly full of people. I do not believe you can go a quarter of a mile on any given road without meeting some one, and that some one is sure to be conversationally disposed and glad of the chance of answering questions. By dint of asking a good many, I eventually found myself on the high road, with five miles between me and Lisangle. The mare's lameness had nearly worn off, and she walked beside me like a dog. After all, I thought, I had had the best of the day, had come safely out of what might have been a nasty business, and was supplied with a story on which to dine out for the rest of my life. My only anxiety was as to whether I could hope for a bath when I got in—a luxury that had been hideously converted by the *locale* of my fall into a necessity. I led the filly in the twilight down the dark Lisangle drive, feeling all the complacency of a man who knows he has gone well in a strange country, and was

just at the turn to the yard when I came upon an extraordinary group. All the women of the household were there, gathered in a tight circle round some absorbing central fact; all were shrieking at the tops of their voices, and the turkey cock in the yard gobbled in response to each shriek.

"Ma'am, ma'am!" I heard, "ye'll pull the tail off him!"

"Twisht the tink-an now, Bridgie! Twisht it!"

"Holy Biddy! the masther'll kill us!"

What the deuce were they at? and what was a "tink-an"? I dragged the filly nearer, and discovered that a hound puppy was the central point of the tumult, and was being contended for, like the body of Moses, by Miss Trinder and Bridgie the parlour-maid. Both were seated on the ground pulling at the puppy for all they were worth; Miss Trinder had him by the back of his neck and his tail, while Bridgie was dragging—what *was* she dragging at? Then I saw that the puppy's head was jammed in a narrow-necked tin milk-can, and that, as things were going, he would wear it, like the Man in the Iron Mask, for the rest of his life.

The small, grim face of Robert's aunt was scarlet with exertion; her black bonnet had slipped off her head, and the thin grey hair that was ordinarily wound round her little skull as tightly as cotton on a reel, was hanging in scanty wisps from its central knot; nevertheless, she was, metaphorically speaking, pulling Bridgie across the line every time. I gave the filly to one of the audience, and took Bridgie's place at the "tink-an". Miss Trinder and I put our backs into it, and suddenly I found myself flat on mine, with the "tink-an" grasped in both hands above my head.

A composite whoop of triumph rose from the spectators, and the filly rose with it. She went straight up on her hind legs, and the next instant she was away cross the drive and into the adjoining field, and, considering all things, I don't blame her. We all ran after her. I led, and the various female retainers strung out after me like a flight of wild-duck, uttering cries of various encouragement and consternation. Miss Trinder followed, silent and indomitable, at the heel of the hunt, and the released puppy, who had also harked in, could be heard throwing his tongue in the dusky shrubbery ahead of us. It was all exasperatingly absurd, as things seem to have a habit of being in Ireland. I never felt more like a fool in my life, and the bitterest part of it was that it was all I could do to keep ahead of Bridgie. As for the filly, she waited till we got near her, and then she jumped a five-foot coped wall into the road, fell, picked herself up, and clattered away into darkness. At this point I heard Robert's horn, and sundry confused shouts and sounds informed me that the filly had run into the hounds.

She was found next day on the farm where she was bred, fifteen miles away. The farmer brought her back to Lisangle. She had injured three hounds, upset two old women and a donkey-cart, broken a gate, and finally, on arriving at the place of her birth, had, according to the farmer, "fired the divil's pelt of a kick into her own mother's stomach". Moreover, she "hadn't as much sound skin on her as would bait a rat-trap"—I here quote Mr. Trinder—and she had fever in all her feet.

Of course I bought her. I could hardly do less. I told Robert he might give her to the hounds, but he sent her over to me in a couple of months as good as new, and I won the regimental steeplechase cup with her last April.

The Famous Ballad of the Jubilee Cup

By ARTHUR T. QUILLER–COUCH

YOU may lift me up in your arms, lad, and turn my face to the sun,
For a last look back at the dear old track where the Jubilee cup was won;
And draw your chair to my side, lad—no, thank ye, I feel no pain—
For I'm going out with the tide, lad; but I'll tell you the tale again.

I'm seventy-nine or nearly, and my head it has long turned gray,
But it all comes back as clearly as though it was yesterday—

The dust, and the bookies shouting around the clerk of the scales,
And the clerk of the course, and the nobs in force, and 'Is 'Igh-
  ness the Prince o' Wales.

'Twas a nine-hole thresh to wind'ard (but none of us cared for
    that),
With a straight run home to the service tee, and a finish along the
    flat,
"Stiff?" ah, well you may say it! Spot barred, and at five stone
    ten!
But at two and a bisque I'd ha' run the risk; for I was a green-
    horn then.

So we stripped to the B. race signal, the old red swallowtail—
There was young Ben Bolt and the Portland Colt, and Aston
    Villa, and Yale;
And W. G., and Steinitz, Leander and The Saint,
And the German Emperor's Meteor, a-looking as fresh as paint;

John Roberts (scratch), and Safety Match, The Lascar, and
    Lorna Doone,
Oom Paul (a bye), and Romany Rye, and me upon Wooden
    Spoon;
And some of us cut for partners, and some of us strung for baulk,
And some of us tossed for stations— But there, what use to talk!

Three-quarter-back on the Kingsclere crack was station enough
    for me,
With a fresh jackyarder blowing and the Vicarage goal a-lee!
And I leaned and patted her centre-bit and eased the quid in her
    cheek
With a "Soh, my lass!" and a "Whoa, you brute!"—for she could
    do all but speak.

She was geared a thought too high, perhaps; she was trained a
    trifle fine;
But she had the grand reach forward! I never saw such a line!

53

Smooth-bored, clean run, from her fiddle head with its dainty ear
    half-cock,
Hard-bit, *pur sang,* from her overhang to the heel of her off hind
    sock.

Sir Robert he walked beside me as I worked her down to the
    mark;
"There's money on this, my lad," said he, "and most of 'em's
    running dark;
But ease the sheet if you're bunkered, and pack the scrimmages
    tight,
And use your slide at the distance, and we'll drink to your health
    to-night!"

But I bent and tightened my stretcher. Said I to myself, said I—
"John Jones, this here is the Jubilee cup, and you have to do or
    die."
And the words weren't hardly spoken when the umpire shouted
    "Play!"
And we all kicked off from the Gasworks End with a "Yoicks!"
    and a "Gone Away!"

And at first I thought of nothing, as the clay flew by in lumps,
But stuck to the old Ruy Lopez, and wondered who'd call for
    trumps,
And luffed her close to the cushion, and watched each one as it
    broke,
And in triple file up the Rowley Mile we went like a trail of
    smoke.

The Lascar made the running, but he didn't amount to much,
For old Oom Paul was quick on the ball, and headed it back to
    touch;
And the whole first flight led off with the right as The Saint took
    up the pace,
And drove it clean to the putting green and trumped it there
    with an ace.

John Roberts had given a miss in baulk, but Villa cleared with a
    punt;
And keeping her service hard and low the Meteor forged to the
    front;
With Romany Rye to windward at dormy and two to play,
And Yale close up—but a Jubilee cup isn't run for every day.

We laid our course for the Warner—I tell you the pace was hot!
And again off Tattenham Corner a blanket covered the lot.
Check side! Check side! now steer her wide! and barely an inch
    of room,
With The Lascar's tail over our lee rail and brushing Leander's
    boom.

We were running as strong as ever—eight knots—but it couldn't
    last;
For the spray and the bails were flying, the whole field tailing
    fast;
And the Portland Colt had shot his bolt, and Yale was bumped
    at Doves,
And The Lascar resigned to Steinitz, stalemated in fifteen moves.

It was "bellows to mend" with Roberts—starred three for a
    penalty kick:
But he chalked his cue and gave 'em the butt, and Oom Paul
    marked the trick—
"Offside—No Ball—and at fourteen all! Mark Cock! and two
    for his nob!"
When W. G. ran clean through his lee and beat him twice with
    a lob.

He yorked him twice on a crumbling pitch and wiped his eye
    with a brace,
But his guy-rope split with the strain of it and he dropped back
    out of the race;
And I drew a bead on the Meteor's lead, and challenging none
    too soon,
Bent over and patted her garboard strake, and called upon
    Wooden Spoon.

She was all of a shiver forward, the spoondrift thick on her
flanks,
But I'd brought her an easy gambit, and nursed her over the
banks;
She answered her helm—the darling! and woke up now with a
rush,
While the Meteor's jock, he sat like a rock—he knew we rode for
his brush.

There was no one else left in it. The Saint was using his whip,
And Safety Match, with a lofting catch, was pocketed deep at
slip;
And young Ben Bolt with his niblick took miss at Leander's
lunge,
But topped the net with the ricochet, and Steinitz threw up the
sponge.

But none of the lot could stop the rot—nay, don't ask me to stop!
The Villa had called for lemons, Oom Paul had taken his drop,
And both were kicking the referee. Poor fellow! he done his best;
But, being in doubt, he'd ruled them out—which he always did
when pressed.

So inch by inch, I tightened the winch, and chucked the sand
bags out—
I heard the nursery cannons pop, I heard the bookies shout:
"The Meteor wins!" "No, Wooden Spoon!" "Check!" "Vantage!" "Leg Before!"
"Last Lap!" "Pass Nap!" At his saddle-flap, I put up the helm
and wore.

You may overlap at the saddle-flap and yet be loo'd on the tape,
And it all depends upon changing ends, how a seven-year-old will
shape;
It was tack and tack to the Lepe and back,—a fair ding-dong to
the Ridge,
And he led by his forward canvas yet as we shot 'neath Hammer-
smith Bridge.

He led by his forward canvas—he led from his strongest suit—
But along we went on a roaring scent, and at Fawley I gained a
    foot.
He fisted off with his jigger, and gave me his wash—too late!
Deuce—Vantage—Check! By neck and neck we rounded into the
    straight.

I could hear the "Conquering 'Ero" a-crashing on Godfrey's
    band,
And my hopes fell sudden to zero, just there, with the race in
    hand—
In sight of the Turf's Blue Ribbon, in sight of the umpire's tape,
And I felt the tack of her spinnaker c-r-rack! as I heard the
    steam escape!

Had I lost at that awful juncture my presence of mind? . . .
    but no!
I leaned and felt for the puncture, and plugged it there with my
    toe . . .
Hand over hand by the Members' Stand I lifted and eased her up,
Shot—clean and fair—to the crossbar there, and landed the
    Jubilee cup!

"The odd by a head, and leg before," so the Judge he gave the
    word:
And the umpire shouted "Over!" but I neither spoke nor stirred.
They crowded 'round: for there on the ground I lay in a dead-
    cold swoon
Pitched neck and crop on the turf atop of my beautiful Wooden
    Spoon.

Her dewlap tire was punctured, her bearings all red hot;
She'd a lolling tongue, and her bowsprit sprung, and her running
    gear in a knot;
And amid the sobs of her backers, Sir Robert loosened her girth
And led her away to the knacker's. She had raced her last on
    earth!

But I mind me well of the tear that fell from the eye of our
  noble Prince,
And the things he said as he tucked me in bed—and I've lain
  there ever since;
Tho' it all gets mixed up queerly that happened before my
  spill,—
But I drew a thousand yearly: it'll pay for the doctor's bill.

I'm going out with the tide, lad—you'll dig me a humble grave,
And whiles you will bring your bride, lad, and your sons, if sons
  you have,
And there when the dews are weeping, and the echoes murmur
  "Peace!"
And the salt, salt tide comes creeping and covers the popping-
  crease;

In the hour when the ducks deposit their eggs with a boasted
  force,
They'll look and whisper, "How was it?" and you'll take them
  over the course,
And your voice will break as you try to speak of the glorious first
  of June,
When the Jubilee cup, with John Jones up, was won upon
  Wooden Spoon.

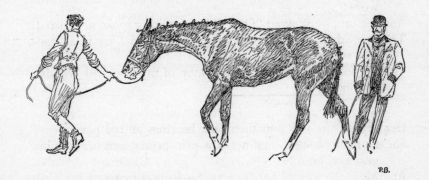

The Seeing Eye

By WILL JAMES

IT'S worse than tough for anybody to be blind but I don't think it's as tough for an indoor born and raised person as it is for one whose life is with the all out-of-doors the most of his life from childhood on. The outdoor man misses his freedom to roam over the hills and the sight of 'em ever changing. A canary would die outside his cage but a free-born eagle would dwindle away inside of one.

Dane Gruger was very much of an out-of-door man. He was born on a little ranch along a creek bottom, in the heart of the cow country, growed up with it to be a good cowboy, then, like with his dad, went on in the cow business. A railroad went thru the lower part of the ranch but stations and little towns was over twenty miles away either way.

He had a nice little spread when I went to work for him, was married and had two boys who done some of the riding. I'd been riding for Dane for quite a few days before I knew he was blind, not totally blind, but, as his boys told me, he couldn't see any further than his outstretched hand, and that was blurred. He couldn't read, not even big print, with any kind of glasses so he never wore any.

That's what fooled me, and he could look you "right square in the eye" while talking to you. What was more he'd go straight down to the corral, catch his horse, saddle him and ride away like any man with full sight. The thing I first noticed and wondered at was that he never rode with us, and after the boys told me, I could understand. It was that he'd be of no use out on the range and away from the ranch.

Dane had been blind a few years when I come there and he'd of course got to know every foot of the ten miles which the ranch covered on the creek bottom before that happened. The ranch itself was one to two miles wide in some places and taking in some brakes. The whole of that was fenced and cross-fenced into pastures and hay lands, and Dane knew to within an inch when he came to every fence, gate or creek crossing. He knew how many head of cattle or horses might be in each pasture, how all was faring, when some broke out or some broke in, and where. He could find bogged cattle, cow with young calf needing help, and know everything that went well or wrong with what stock would be held on the ranch.

He of course seldom could do much towards helping whatever stock needed it or fix the holes he found in the fences, but when he'd get back to the ranch house he could easy tell the boys when there was anything wrong, and the exact spot where, in which field or pasture, how far from which side of the creek or what fence and what all the trouble might be. It would then be up to the boys to set things to rights, and after Dane's description of the spot it was easy found.

During the time I was with that little outfit I got to know Dane pretty well, well enough to see that I don't think he could of lived if he hadn't been able to do what he was doing. He was so full of life and gumption and so appreciating of all around him that he could feel, hear and breathe in. I'd sometimes see him hold his horse to a standstill while he only listened to birds

Paul Brown
'45

or the faraway bellering of cattle, even to the yapping of prairie dogs which most cowboys would rather not hear the sound of.

To take him away from all of that, the open air, the feel of his saddle and horse under him and set him on a chair to do nothing but sit and babble and think, would of brought a quick end to him.

With the riding he done he felt satisfied he was doing something worth doing instead of just plain riding. He wouldn't of cared for that, and fact was he well took the place of an average rider.

But he had mighty good help in the work he was doing, and that was the two horses he used, for they was both as well trained to his wants and care as the dogs that's used nowadays to lead the blind and which are called "The Seeing Eye."

Dane had the advantage of the man with the dog, for he didn't have to walk and use a cane at every step. He rode, and he had more confidence in his horses' every step than he had in his own, even if he could of seen well. As horses do, they naturally sensed every foot of the earth under 'em without ever looking down at it, during sunlight, darkness or under drifted snow.

Riding into clumps of willows or thickets which the creek bottoms had much of, either of the two horses was careful to pick out a wide enough trail thru so their rider wouldn't get scratched or brushed off. If they come to a place where the brush was too thick and Dane was wanting to go thru that certain thicket, the ponies, regardless of his wants, would turn back for a ways and look for a better opening. Dane never argued with 'em at such times. He would just sort of head 'em where he wanted to go and they'd do the rest to pick out the best way there.

Them horses was still young when I got to that outfit, seven and eight years of age, and would be fit for at least twenty years more with the little riding and good care they was getting. Dane's boys had broke 'em especially for their dad's use that way and they'd done a fine job of it.

One of the horses, a gray of about a thousand pounds, was called Little Eagle. That little horse never missed a thing in sight, or sound. With his training the rustling of the brush close by would make him investigate and learn the cause before leaving that spot. Dane would know by his actions whether it was a new-born calf that had been hid or some cow in distress. It was the same at the boggy places along the creek or alkali swamps. If Little Eagle rode right on around and without stopping, Dane knew that all was well. If he stopped at any certain spot, bowed his neck and snorted low, then Dane knew that some horse or cow was in trouble. Keeping his hand on Little Eagle's neck he'd have him go on, and by the bend of that horse's neck as he went, like pointing, Dane could tell the exact location of where that animal was that was in trouble, or whatever it was that was wrong.

Sometimes, Little Eagle would line out on a trot, of his own accord and as tho there was something needed looking into right away. At times he'd even break into a lope, and then Dane wouldn't know what to expect, whether it was stock breaking thru a fence, milling around an animal that was down, or what. But most always it would be when a bunch of stock, horses or cattle, would be stringing out in single file, maybe going to water or some other part of the pasture.

At such times, Little Eagle would get just close enough to the stock so Dane could count 'em by the sounds of the hoofs going by, a near impossible thing to do for a man that can see, but Dane got so he could do it and get a mighty close count on what stock was in each pasture that way. Close enough so he could tell if any had got out or others got in.

With the horses in the pastures, there was bells on the leaders of every bunch and some on one of every little bunch that sort of held together and separate from others. Dane knew by the sound of every bell which bunch it was and about how many there would be to each. The boys kept him posted on that every time they'd run a bunch in for some reason or other. Not many horses was ever kept under fence, but there was quite a few of the pure-bred cattle for the upbreeding of the outside herds.

At this work of keeping tab on stock, Little Eagle was a cow-boy by himself. With his natural intellect so developed as to what was wanted of him, he could near tell of what stock was wanted or not and where they belonged. The proof of that was when he turned a bunch of cattle out of a hayfield one time, and other times, and drove 'em to the gate of the field where they'd broke out of, circled around 'em when the gate was reached and went to it for Dane to open. He then drove the cattle thru, none got away, not from Little Eagle, and Dane would always prepare to ride at such times, for if any did try to break away Little Eagle would be right on their tail to bring 'em back, and for a blind man, not knowing when his horse is going to break into a sudden run, stop or turn, that's kind of hard riding, on a good cowhorse.

About all Dane would have to go by most of the time was the feel of the top muscles on Little Eagle's neck, and he got to know by them about the same as like language to him. With one hand most always on them muscles he felt what the horse seen. Tenseness, wonder, danger, fear, relaxation and about all that a human feels at the sight of different things. Places, dangerous or smooth, trouble or peace.

Them top muscles told him more, and more plainly than if another rider had been riding constantly alongside of him and telling him right along of what he seen. That was another reason why Dane liked to ride alone. He felt more at ease, no confusion, and wasn't putting anybody out of their way by talking and describing when they maybe wouldn't feel like it.

And them two horses of Dane's, they not only took him wherever he wanted to go but never overlooked any work that needed to be done. They took it onto themselves to look for work which, being they always felt so good, was like play to them. Dane knew it when such times come and he then would let 'em go as they chose.

Neither of the horses would of course go out by themselves without a rider and do that work. They wouldn't of been interested doing that without Dane's company. What's more they couldn't have opened the gates that had to be gone thru, and besides they wasn't wanted to do that. They was to be the company of Dane and with him in whatever he wanted to do.

Dane's other horse was a trim bay about the same size as Little Eagle, and even tho just as good he had different ways about him. He was called Ferret, and a ferret he was for digging up and finding out things, like a cow with new-born calf or mare with colt, and he was even better than Little Eagle for finding holes in fences or where some was down.

All that came under the special training the boys had given him and Little Eagle, and if it wasn't for automobiles these days, such as them would be mighty valuable companions in the city, even more useful in the streets than the dog is, for the horse would soon know where his rider would want to go after being ridden such places a few times.

Unlike most horses it wasn't these two's nature to keep wanting to turn back to the ranch (home) when Dane would ride 'em away, and they wouldn't turn back until they knew the ride was over and it was time to. Sometimes Dane wouldn't show up for the noon meal, and that was all right with the ponies too, for he'd often get off of 'em and let 'em graze with reins dragging. There was no danger of either of them ever leaving Dane, for they seemed as attached to him as any dog could be to his master.

It was the same way with Dane for them, and he had more confidence in their trueness and senses than most humans have in one another.

A mighty good test and surprising outcome of that came one day as a powerful big cloudburst hit above the ranch a ways and left Dane acrost the creek from home. The creek had turned into churning wild waters the size of a big river in a few minutes, half a mile wide in some places and licking up close to the higher land where the ranch buildings and corrals was.

It kept on a-raining hard after the cloudburst had fell and it didn't act like it was going to let up for some time, and the wide river wouldn't be down to creek size or safe to cross, at least not for a day or so.

The noise of the rushing water was a-plenty to let Dane know of the cloudburst. It had come with a sudden roar and without a drop of warning, and Dane's horse, he was riding Little Eagle that day, plainly let him know the danger of the wide stretch of swirling fast waters. It wasn't the danger of the water only but uprooted trees and all kinds of heavy timber speeding along would make the crossing more than dangerous, not only dangerous but it would about mean certain death.

Little Eagle would of tackled the swollen waters or anything Dane would of wanted him to, but Dane knew a whole lot better than to make that wise horse go where he didn't want to, any time.

Dane could tell by the noise, and riding to the edge of the water and the location where he was, how wide the body of wild waters was. He knew that the stock could keep out of reach of it on either side without being jammed against the fences, but he got worried about the ranch, wondering if the waters had got up to the buildings. He worried too about his family worrying about him, and maybe try to find and get to him.

That worrying got him to figuring on ways of getting back. He sure couldn't stay where he was until the waters went down, not if he could help it. It wouldn't be comfortable being out so long in the heavy rain either, even if he did have his slicker on, and it wouldn't do to try to go to the neighbor's ranch which was some fifteen miles away. He doubted if he could find it anyway, for it was acrost a bunch of rolling hills, nothing to go by, and Little Eagle wouldn't know that *there* would be where Dane would be wanting him to go. Besides there was the thought of his family worrying so about him and maybe risking their lives in trying to find him.

He'd just have to get home, somehow, and it was at the thought of his neighbor's ranch and picturing the distance and country to it in his mind, that he thought of the railroad, for he would of had to cross it to get there, and then, thinking of the railroad, the thought came of the trestle crossing along it and over the creek. Maybe he could make that. That would be sort of a dangerous crossing too, but the more he thought of it the more he figured it worth taking the chances of trying. That was the only way of his getting on the other side of the high waters and back to the ranch.

The railroad and trestle was only about half a mile from where he now was and that made it all the more tempting to try. So, after thinking it over in every way, including the fact that he'd be taking chances with losing his horse also, he finally decided to take the chance, at the risk of both himself and his horse, that is if his horse seen it might be safe enough. He felt it had to be done and it could be done, and there went to show his faith and confidence in that Little Eagle horse of his.

And that confidence sure wasn't misplaced, for, a cooler-headed, brainier horse never was.

There was two fences to cross to get to the railroad and trestle, and it wasn't at all necessary to go thru gates to get there, for the swollen waters with jamming timbers had laid the fence down for quite a ways on both sides of the wide river, some of the wire strands to break and snap and coil all directions.

A strand of barbed wire, even if flat to the ground, is a mighty dangerous thing to ride over, for a horse might pick it up with a hoof, and, as most horses will scare, draw their hind legs up under 'em and act up. The result might be a wicked sawing wire cut at the joint by the hock, cutting veins and tendons and often crippling a horse for life. In such cases the rider is also very apt to get tangled up in the wire, for that wicked stuff seems to have the ways of the tentacles of a devilfish at such times.

Loose wire laying around on the ground is the cowboys' worst fear, especially so with Dane, for, as he couldn't see it was many times more threatening as he rode most every day from one fenced-in field to the other. But the confidence he had in his two cool-headed ponies relieved him of most all his fear of the dangerous barbed wire, and either one of 'em would stop and snort a little at the sight of a broken strand coiled to the ground. Dane knew what that meant and it always brought a chill to his spine. He'd get down off his saddle, feel around carefully in front of his horse, and usually the threatening coil would be found to within a foot or so of his horse's nose. The coil would then be pulled and fastened to the fence, to stay until a ranch hand who, with team and buckboard, would make the rounds of all fences every few months, done a general fixing of 'em.

It's too bad barbed wire *has* to be used for fences. It has butchered and killed many good horses, and some riders. But barbed wire is about the only kind of fence that will hold cattle, most of the time, and when there has to be many long miles of it, even with the smaller ranches, that's about the only kind of fence that can be afforded or used. Cattle (even the wildest) seldom get a scratch by it, even in breaking thru a four-strand fence of it, or going over it while it's loose and coiled on the ground, for they don't get rattled when in wire as a horse does, and they hold their hind legs straight back when going thru, while with the horse he draws 'em under him instead and goes to tearing around.

Both Little Eagle and Ferret had been well trained against scaring and fighting wire if they ever got into it, also trained not to get into it, and stop whenever coming to some that was loose on the ground. That training had been done with a rope and a piece of smooth wire at one end, and being they was naturally cool-headed they soon learned all the tricks of the wire and how to behave when they come near any of that coiled on the ground.

There was many such coils as the flood waters rampaged along the creek bottom, and as Dane headed Little Eagle towards the railroad and trestle he then let him pick his own way thru and around the two fence entanglements on the way there, along the edge of the rushing water.

Little Eagle done considerable winding around and careful stepping as he come to the fences that had been snapped and washed to scattering, dangerous strands over the field. Dane gave him his time, let him go as he choose, and finally the roar of the waters against the high banks by the trestle came to his ears. It sounded as tho it was near up to the trestle, which he knew was plenty high, and that gave him a good idea of what a cloudburst it had been.

He then got mighty dubious about trying to cross the trestle, for it was a long one, there was no railing of any kind on the sides, and part of it might be under water or even washed away. There was some of the flood water in the ditch alongside the railroad grade and it wasn't so many feet up it to the track level.

Riding between the rails a short ways he come to where the trestle begin and there he stopped Little Eagle. The swirling waters made a mighty roar right there, and how he wished he could of been able to see then, more than any time since his blindness had overtook him.

Getting off Little Eagle there he felt his way along to the first ties to the trestle, of the space between each, which was about five inches, and just right for Little Eagle's small hoofs to slip in between, Dane thought. One such a slip would mean a broken leg, and the horse would have to be shot right there, to lay between the rails. The rider would be mighty likely to go over the side of the trestle, too.

Dane hardly had any fear for himself, but he did have for Little Eagle. Not that he feared he would put a foot between the ties, for that little horse was too wise, cool-headed and careful to do anything like that, Dane knew. What worried him most was if the trestle was still up and above water all the way acrost.

There would be no turning back, for in turning is when Little Eagle would be mighty liable to slip a hoof between the ties. The rain had let up but the wind was blowing hard and the tarred ties was slippery as soaped glass.

It all struck Dane as fool recklessness to try to cross on that long and narrow trestle at such a time, but he felt he should try, and to settle his dubiousness he now left it to Little Eagle and his good sense as to whether to tackle it or not.

If he went he would *ride* him across, not try to crawl, feel his way and lead him, for in leading the horse he wouldn't be apt to pay as much attention to his footing and to nosing every dangerous step he made. Besides, Dane kind of felt that if Little Eagle should go over the side he'd go with him.

So, getting into the saddle again, he let Little Eagle stand for a spell, at the same time letting him know that he wanted to cross the trestle, for him to size it up and see if it could be done. It was up to him, and the little gray well understood.

It might sound unbelievable, but a good sensible horse and rider have a sort of feel-language which is mighty plain between 'em, and when comes a particular dangerous spot the two can discuss the possibilities of getting over or acrost it as well as two humans can, and even better, for the horse has the instinct which the human lacks. He can tell danger where the human can't, and the same with the safety.

It was that way with Little Eagle and Dane, only even more so, because as Little Eagle, like Ferret, had been trained to realize Dane's affliction, cater and sort of take care of him, they was always watchful. Then with Dane's affection and care for them, talking to 'em and treating 'em like the true pardners they was, there was an understanding and trust between man and horse that's seldom seen between man and man.

Sitting in his saddle with his hand on Little Eagle's neck the two "discussed" the dangerous situation ahead in such a way that the loud roar of the water foaming by and under the trestle didn't interfere any with the decision that was to come.

There was a tenseness in the top muscles of Little Eagle's neck as he looked over the scary, narrow, steel-ribboned trail ahead, nervous at the so careful investigation, that all sure didn't look well. But he'd now left it all to Little Eagle's judgment, and as

Dane had about expected he'd be against trying, Little Eagle, still all tense and quivering some, planted one foot on the first tie, and crouching a bit, all nerves and muscles steady, started on the way of the dangerous crossing.

Every step by step from the first seemed like a long minute to Dane. The brave little horse, his nose close to the ties, at the same time looking ahead, was mighty careful how he placed each front foot, and sure that the hind one would come up to the exact same place afterwards, right where that front one had been. He didn't just plank his hoof and go on, but felt for a sure footing on the wet and slippery tarred ties before putting any weight on it and making another step. Something like a mountain climber feeling and making sure of his every hold while going on with his climbing.

The start wasn't the worst of the crossing. That begin to come as they went further along and nearer to the center. There, with the strong wind blowing broadside of 'em, the swift waters churning, sounding like to the level of the slippery ties would seem about scary enough to chill the marrow in any being. But there was more piled onto that, for as they neared the center it begin to tremble and sway as if by earth tremors. This was by the high rushing waters swirling around the tall and now submerged supporting timbers.

Little Eagle's step wasn't so sure then, and as careful as he was there come a few times when he slipped, and a time or two when a hoof went down between the ties, leaving him to stand on three shaking legs until he got his hoof up and on footing again.

With most any other horse it would of been the end of him and his rider right then. As it was, Little Eagle went on, like a tightrope walker, with every muscle at work. And Dane, riding mighty light on him, his heart up his throat at every slip or loss of footing, done his best not to get him off balance but help him that way when he thought he could.

If the shaking, trembling and swaying of the trestle had been steady it would of been less scary and some easier, but along with the strong vibrations of the trestle there'd sometimes come a big uprooted tree to smash into it at a forty-mile speed. There'd be a quiver all along the trestle at the impact. It would sway and bend dangerously, to ship back again as the tree would be washed under and on.

Such goings on would jar Little Eagle's footing to where he'd again slip a hoof between the ties, and Dane would pray, sometimes cuss a little. But the way Little Eagle handled his feet and every part of himself, sometimes on the tip of his toes, the sides of his hoofs and even to his knees, he somehow managed to keep right side up.

Good thing, Dane thought, that the horse wasn't shod, for shoes without sharp calks would have been much worse on than none on the slippery ties. As it was, and being his shoes had been pulled off only a couple of days before to ease his feet some between shoeings, his hoofs was sharp at the edges and toe, and that gave him more chance.

The scary and most dangerous part of the trestle was reached, the center, and it was a good thing maybe that Dane couldn't see while Little Eagle sort of juggled himself over that part, for the trestle had been under repair and some of the old ties had been taken away in a few places, to later be replaced by new ones; but where each tie had been taken away that left an opening of near two feet wide. Mighty scary for Little Eagle too, but he eased over them gaps without Dane knowing.

Dane felt as tho it was long weary miles and took about that much time to finally get past the center and most dangerous part of the five-hundred-yard trestle, for them five hundred yards put more wear on him during that time than five hundred miles would of.

And he was far from near safe going as yet, for he'd just passed center and the trestle was still doing some tall trembling and dangerous weaving, when, as bad and spooky as things already was, there come the sound of still worse fear and danger, and Dane's heart stood still. It was a train whistle he'd heard above the roar of the waters. It sounded like the train was coming his way, facing him, and there'd sure be no chance for him to turn and make it back, for he'd crossed over half of the trestle, the worst part, and going back would take a long time.

All the dangers and fears piling together now, instead of exciting Dane, seemed to cool and steady him, like having to face the worst and make the best of it. He rode right on towards the coming train.

He knew from memory that the railroad run a straight line

to the trestle, that there was no railroad crossing nor other reason for the engineer to blow his whistle, unless it was for him,
himself. Then it came to him that the engineer must of seen him
on the trestle and would sure stop his train, if he could.

Standing up in his stirrups he raised his big black hat high as
he could and waved it from side to side as a signal for the engineer to stop his train. Surely they could see that black hat of his
and realize the predicament he was in. That getting off the trestle
would mean almost certain death.

But the train sounded like it was coming right on, and at that
Dane wondered if maybe it was coming too fast to be able to
stop. He got a little panicky then, and for a second he was about
to turn Little Eagle off the trestle and swim for it. It would of
been a long and risky swim, maybe carried for miles down country before they could of reached either bank, and it would of
taken more than luck to've succeeded. But if they'd got bowled
over by some tree trunk and went down the churning waters that
would be better, Dane thought, than to have Little Eagle smashed
to smithereens by the locomotive. He had no thought for himself.

About the only thing that made him take a bigger chance and
ride on some more was that he knew that the whole train and its
crew would be doomed before it got halfways on the trestle, and
what if it was a passenger train?

At that thought he had no more fear of Little Eagle keeping
his footing on the trestle. His fear now went for the many lives
there might be on the train, and he sort of went wild and to waving his big black hat all the more in trying to warn of the danger.

But he didn't put on no such action as to unbalance the little
gray in any way. He still felt and helped with his every careful
step, and then there got to be a prayer with each one, like with
the beads of the Rosary.

He rubbed his moist eyes and also prayed he could see, now
of all times and if only just for this once, and then the train
whistle blew again, so close this time that it sounded like it was on
the trestle, like coming on, and being mighty near to him.—Dane
had done his best, and now was his last and only chance to save
Little Eagle and himself, by sliding off the trestle. He wiped his
eyes like as tho to better see, and went to reining Little Eagle off
the side of the trestle. But to his surprise, Little Eagle wouldn't

respond to the rein. It was the first time excepting amongst the thick brush or bad creek crossings that horse had ever went against his wishes that way. But this was now very different, and puzzled, he tried him again and again, with no effect, and then, all at once, *he could see.*

Myself and one of Dane's boys had been riding, looking for Dane soon after the cloudburst hit, and seeing the stopped passenger train with the many people gathered by the engine we high-loped towards it, there to get the surprise of seeing Dane on Little Eagle on the trestle and carefully making each and every dangerous step towards us and solid ground.

We seen we sure couldn't be of no use to the little gray nor Dane only maybe a hindrance, and being there was only a little ways more we held our horses and watched. Looking on the length of the trestle we noticed that only the rails and ties showed above the high water, there was quite a bend in it from the swift and powerful pressure and the rails and ties was leaning, like threatening to break loose at any time.

How the little horse and Dane ever made it, with the strong wind, slippery ties and all a-weaving, was beyond us. So was it with the passengers who stood with gaping mouths and tense watching. What if they'd known that the rider had been blind while he made the dangerous crossing?

And as the engineer went on to tell the spellbound passengers how that man and horse on the trestle had saved all their lives, they was more than thankful, for, as the heavy cloudburst had come so sudden and hit in one spot, there'd been no report of it, and, as the engineer said, he might of drove onto the trestle a ways before knowing. Then it would of been too late.

But Little Eagle was the one who played the biggest part in stopping what would have been a terrible happening. He was the one who decided to make the dangerous crossing, the one who had to use his head and hoofs with all his skill and power, also the one who at the last of the stretch would not heed Dane's pull of the reins to slide off the trestle. His first time not to do as he was wanted to. He'd disobeyed and had saved another life. He'd been "The Seeing Eye."

The fuss over with as Dane finally rode up on solid ground and near the engine, we then was the ones due for a big surprise. For Dane *spotted* us out from the crowd, and smiling, rode straight for us and looked us both "square in the eye."

The shock and years he lived crossing that trestle, then the puzzling over Little Eagle not wanting to turn at the touch of the rein had done the trick, had brought his sight back.

After that day, Little Eagle and Ferret was sort of neglected, neglected knee deep in clover, amongst good shade and where clear spring water run. The seeing eyes was partly closed in contentment.

The Ghost Horse[1]

By CHIEF BUFFALO CHILD LONG LANCE

WITH the first touch of spring we broke camp and headed southwest across the big bend of the upper Columbia, toward the plateau between the Rockies and the Cascades. It was on this lofty plateau that the world's largest herd of wild horses had roamed during the last hundred and fifty years. Several hundred head of them are still there, where every summer efforts are being made to exterminate them by the provincial government of

[1]From *Long Lance*, by Chief Buffalo Child Long Lance.

British Columbia. It was these horses that we were after, to re-place the herd which the storm had driven away from our camp.

We struck the herd in the season of the year when it was weakest: early spring, after the horses had got their first good feed of green grass and their speed had been slowed by dysen-tery. Since these wild creatures can run to death any horse raised in captivity, it is doubly a hard job to try to ensnare them on foot. But, like wolves, wild horses are very curious animals; they will follow a person for miles out of mere curiosity. And, when chased, they will invariably turn back on their trails to see what it is all about; what their pursuers look like; what they are up to.

The big timber wolves would do the same, when we were traveling in the North Country. They would trot along behind us all day. When we would stop, they would stop, and stand mo-tionless and look at us with one foot raised; and when we would start again, they would continue to follow us. If we made a noise at them, they would jump back and hide behind the nearest bush. From then on, they would keep out of sight, but whenever we looked back we would see them peeping at us from behind the farthest bush.

They used to scare us children, but our fathers told us not to be scared; the wolves would not hurt us; they were just curious about us—although, they said, if the wolves followed us all day, they might try to snatch off our dogs when we camped that night. So they told us boys who were traveling in the rear to keep try-ing to "shoo" them away before we should make camp for the night. Wolves like dog meat better than any other, though male wolves will never harm a female dog.

But with the wild horses it was different. They always traveled ahead of us, but they had a way of turning back on their own trails and coming upon us from the side or the rear, to keep watch on us. It was this never-satisfied curiosity of the wild horse that enabled our braves to capture them on foot.

The method of our warriors was to locate a herd and then fol-low it unconcernedly for hours, and maybe for days, before mak-ing any attempt to round it up. This was to get the horses used to us and to show them that we would not harm them.

We had been trailing fresh manure for five days before we finally located our first herd away up on the expansive Couteau

Plateau of central British Columbia. There they were: a herd of about five hundred animals grazing away over on the side of a craggy little mountain on top of the plateau. Their quick, alert movements, more like those of a deer than those of a horse, showed they were high-strung beings that would dash off into space like a flock of wild birds on the slightest cause for excitement. There was one big, steel-dust stallion who grazed away from the rest and made frequent trips along the edge of the herd. It was obvious to our braves that this iron-colored fellow with the silver mane was the stallion who ruled the herd, and our warriors directed all of their attention to him, knowing that the movements of the entire herd depended on what he did.

When we had approached to within about five hundred yards of the herd, our braves began to make little noises, so that the horses could see us in the distance and would not be taken by surprise and frightened into a stampede at seeing us suddenly at closer range.

"Hoh! Hoh!" our braves grunted softly. The steel-dust stallion uttered a low whinny, and all the herd raised their heads high into the air and, standing perfectly still as though charmed, looked intently over at us with their big, nervous nostrils wide open. They stood that way for moments, without moving a muscle, looking hard at us. Then, as we came too near, the burly stallion tried to put fear into us by dashing straight at us with a deep, rasping roar.

Others followed him, and on they came like a yelling war party, their heads swinging wildly, their racing legs wide apart, and their long tails lashing the ground like faggots of steel wire. But before they reached us, the speeding animals stiffened their legs and came to a sudden halt in a cloud of dust. While they were close they took one more good look at us, and then they turned and scampered away with the rest of the herd, which had already begun to retreat over the brow of the mountain.

But the big steel-dust stallion stood his ground alone for a moment and openly defied us. He dug his front feet into the dirt far out in front of him, wagged his head furiously, and then stopped long enough to look and see what effect his mad antics were having upon us. Around and around he jumped gracefully into the air, swapping ends like a dog chasing its tail. Then again he raised his head as high as his superb stature would carry him, and with his long silver tail lying over his back, he blazed fire at us through the whites of his turbulent flint-colored eyes. Having displayed to us his courage, his defiance, and his remarkable leadership, he now turned and pranced off, with heels flying so high and so lightly that one could almost imagine he was treading air.

Our braves laughed and said: "Ah, *ponokamita,* vain elkdog, you are a brave warrior. But trot along and have patience. We shall yet ride you against the Crows."

For five days we chased this huge herd of horses, traveling along leisurely behind them, knowing that they would not wander afar; that they would watch us like wolves as long as we were in the vicinity.

By the fifth day they had become so used to us that they merely moved along slowly when we approached them, nibbling grass as they walked. All during this time our braves had been taming them by their subtle method. At first they just grunted at them. But now they were dancing and shouting at them. This was to let the horses know that although man could make a lot of noise and act fiercely, he would not harm them; that no injury could come to them through closer contact with man.

Nothing scares a horse quicker than a quiet thing that moves toward him and makes no noise. He will jump and break his neck at a noisy movement of a rodent in the grass or a falling twig, while a roaring buffalo or a steaming train will pass him unnoticed. That is because he has the same kind of courage that man has: real courage; the courage to face any odds that he can see and hear and cope with, but a superstitious fear of anything ghostlike. The mountain-lion, and most other animals of prey, have courage of a different kind. A slight unexplained noise will bring them to a low, crouching, waiting position, while a loud noise will send them scurrying for cover. They have more discretion and less valor than man or the horse.

On the tenth night of our chase our warriors made their final preparations to capture the herd. They had maneuvered the horses into the vicinity of a huge half-natural, half-artificial corral which they had built of logs against the two sides of a rock-bound gulch. From the entrance of this corral they had built two long fences, forming a runway, which gradually widened as it left the gate of the corral. This funnel-shaped entrance fanned out onto the plateau for more than a half mile, and it was covered over with evergreens to disguise its artificiality. It was a replica of the old buffalo corral which we used to build to round up the buffaloes when they were plentiful on the plains.

The mouth at the outer end of this runway was about one hundred yards wide. From this point on, the runway was further extended and opened up by placing big tree tops, stones and logs along the ground for several hundred yards. This was to direct the herd slowly into the mouth of the fenced part of the runway, where, once wedged inside, they could neither get out nor turn around and retrace their steps. They would be trapped; and the only thing left for them to do would be to keep on going toward the corral gate.

Subdued excitement reigned in our hidden camp on this tenth night of our chase; for it was the big night, the night that we were going to "blow in" the great, stubborn herd of wild horses. No one went to bed that night. Shortly before nightfall more than half of our braves, comprising all of our fastest-traveling scouts and young men, quietly slipped out of our camp and disappeared. According to prearranged directions, they fanned out to the right and left in a northerly route and crept noiselessly toward the place where the herd had disappeared that afternoon. All during the early night we heard wolves calling to one another; arctic owls, night hawks, and panthers crying out mournfully in the mystic darkness of the rugged plateau. They were the signals of our men, informing one another of their movements.

Then, about midnight, everything became deathly quiet. We knew that they had located the herd and surrounded it; and that they were now lying on their bellies, awaiting the first streaks of dawn and the signal to start the drive.

One of our subchiefs, Chief Mountain Elk, now went through our camp, quietly giving instructions for all hands to line themselves along the great runway to "beat in" the herd. Every woman, old person, and child in the camp was called up to take part in this particular phase of the drive. We children and the women crept over to the runway and sprawled ourselves along the outside of the fence, while the men went beyond the fenced part of the runway and concealed themselves behind the brush and logs—where it was a little more dangerous.

Thus we crouched on the ground and shivered quietly for an hour or more before we heard a distant "Ho-h! . . . Ho-h!" It was the muffled driving cry of our warriors, the cry which for ten days they had been uttering to the horses to let them know that no harm could come to them from this sound. Thus, the horses did not stampede, as they would have done had they not recognized this noise in the darkness.

We youngsters lay breathless in expectancy. We had all picked out our favorite mounts in this beautiful herd of wild animals, and to us as we lay there it was like the white boy lying in bed waiting for Santa Claus. Our fathers had all promised us that we could have the ponies that we had picked, and we could hardly wait to get our hands on them. My favorite was a beautiful calico pony, a roan, white and red pinto—three different colors all splashed on his shoulders and flanks like a crazy-quilt of exquisite design. He had a red star on his forehead between his eyes, and I had already named him *Naytukskie-Kukatos,* which in Blackfoot means One Star.

Presently we heard the distinct rumble of horses' hoofs—a dull booming which shook the ground on which we lay. Then "Yip-yip-yip, he-heeh-h-h," came the night call of the wolf from many different directions. It was our braves signaling to one another to keep the herd on the right path. From out of this medley of odd sounds we could hear the mares going, *"Wheeeeeh-hagh-hagh-hagh"*—calling their little long-legged sons to their sides that they might not become lost in the darkness and confusion.

Our boyish hearts began to beat fast when we heard the first loud "Yah! Yah! Yah!" We knew that the herd had now entered the brush portion of the runway and that our warriors were jumping up from their hiding-places and showing themselves with fierce noises, in order to stampede the horses and send them racing headlong into our trap.

Immediately there was a loud thunder of pattering hoofs— horses crying and yelling everywhere, like convulsive human beings in monster confusion. Above this din of bellowing throats and hammering feet we heard one loud, full, deep-chested roar which we all recognized, and it gave us boys a slight thrill of fear. It sounded like a cross between the roar of a lion and the bellow of an infuriated bull. It was the massive steel-dust stallion, furious king of the herd. In our imagination we could see his long silver tail thrown over his back, his legs lashing wide apart, and stark murder glistening from the whites of those terrible eyes. We wondered what he would do to us if he should call our bluff and crash through that fence into our midst.

But, now, here he came, leading his raging herd, and we had no further time to contemplate danger. Our job was to do as the others had done all along the line: to lie still and wait until the lead stallion had passed us, and then to jump to the top of the fence and yell and wave with all the ferocity that we could command. This was to keep the maddened herd from crashing the fence or trying to turn around, and to hasten their speed into our trap.

"Therump, therump, therump." On came the storming herd. As we youngsters peeped through the brush-covered fence, we could see their sleek backs bobbing up and down in the star-lit darkness like great billows of raging water. The turbulent steel-dust stallion was leading them with front feet wide apart and his forehead sweeping the ground like a pendulum. His death-dealing heels were swinging alternatingly to the right and left with each savage leap of his mighty frame.

Once he stopped and tried to breast the oncoming herd, but these erstwhile slaves of his whims struck and knocked him forward with terrific force. He rose from his knees, and like something that had gone insane, he shot his nostrils into the air and uttered a fearful bellow of defiance at any and everything. He seemed to curse the very stars themselves. Never before had he tasted defeat, utter helplessness. The loyal herd that had watched his very ears for their commands was now running wildly over him.

I believe that, if at that moment there had been a solid iron wall in front of that stallion, he would have dashed his brains out against it. I remember looking backward into the darkness for a convenient place to hop, if he should suddenly choose to rush headlong into the noise that was driving him wild with helpless rage. But, even as I looked back, I heard a whistling noise, and my eyes were jerked back to the runway just in time to see the steel-dust king stretching himself past us like a huge greyhound. With each incredible leap he panted a breath that shrieked like a whistle.

No one will ever know what was in his brain; why he had so suddenly broken himself away from his herd. But on he went, leaving the other horses behind like a deer leaving a bunch of coyotes. A few seconds later the rest of the herd came booming past us. As we went over the fence, shouting and gesticulating, we looked into a blinding fog of sweat and breath, which fairly stung our nostrils with its pungency.

I thought that herd would never stop passing us. I had never seen so many horses before, it seemed. We stuck to our posts until it was nearly daylight, and still they came straggling along; now mostly colts limping and whinnying for their mothers.

When we climbed down the fence and went down to the corral at daylight, the first thing we saw was four of our warriors lying on pallets, bleeding and unconscious. They were four of the best horsemen in our tribe: Circling Ghost, High Hunting Eagle, Wild Man, and Wolf Ribs. When our mothers asked what was the matter, someone pointed to the corral and said: *"Ponoko-mita—akai-mahkah-pay!"* ("That very bad horse!")

We looked and saw a dozen men trying to put leather on that wild steel-dust stallion, who, with his heavy moon-colored mane bristling belligerently over his bluish head and shoulders, looked now more like a lion than a horse. He was splotched here and there with his own blood, and his teeth were bared like a wolf's. Four men had tried to get down into the corral and throw raw-hide around his neck. While the other wild horses had scurried away to the nethermost corners of the corral, this ferocious beast of a horse had plunged headlong into them and all but killed them before they could be dragged away.

He had proved to be one of the rarest specimens of horse known to man—a killer—a creature that kicked and bit and tore and crushed his victims until they were dead. One might live a hundred years among horses without ever seeing one of these hideous freaks of the horse world, so seldom are they produced. He had already killed two of his own herd, young stallions, right there in our corral. Little did we wonder, now, that he was the leader.

Our braves were taking no more chances with him. They were high up on top of the seven-foot corral fence, throwing their rawhide lariats in vain attempts to neck the murderous monstrosity. But this devil disguised as a horse had the reasoning of a human being. He would stand and watch the rawhide come twirling through the air, and then just as it was about to swirl over his head, he would duck his shaggy neck and remain standing on the spot with his front feet spread apart, in devilish defiance of man and matter. None of our oldest men had ever seen anything like him.

It was finally decided to corner him with firebrands and throw a partition between him and the rest of the herd, so that our braves could get busy cutting out the best of the animals, before turning the rest loose. This was done, and by nightfall we had captured and hobbled two hundred of the best bottoms anywhere in the Northwest.

The next day our braves began the arduous task of breaking the wild horses to the halter. They used the Indian method, which is very simple and methodical. While four men held on to a stout rawhide rope which was noosed around the animal's neck, another man would approach the horse's head gradually, "talking horse" to him and making many queer motions and sounds as he went nearer.

"Horse talk" is a low grunt which seems to charm a horse and make him stand perfectly still for a moment or so at a time. It sounds like *"Hoh-hoh,"* uttered deep down in one's chest. The horse will stop his rough antics and strain motionless on the rope for a few seconds; while he is doing this and looking straight at the approaching figure, the man will wave a blanket at him and hiss at him—*"Shuh! Shuh!"* It takes about fifteen minutes of this to make the horse realize that the man is harmless; that no motion which he makes, no sound that he utters, will harm him in any way.

It is a strange fact that a wild horse, of either the ranch or the open ranges, will not react to quiet kindliness at first. He must first be treated gruffly—but not harshly—and then when he is on a touching acquaintance with man, kindness is the quickest way to win his affections.

When the man has reached the head of the horse, his hardest

Paul Brown
'45

job is to give him the first touch of man's hand, of which the horse seems to have a deathly fear. He maneuvers for several minutes before he gets a finger on the struggling nose, and rubs it and allows the horse to get his smell or scent. When this has been done, the brave loops a long, narrow string of rawhide around the horse's nose and then carries it up behind his ears and brings it down on the other side and slips it under the other side of the nose loop, making something like a loose-knotted halter, which will tighten up on the slightest pull from the horse.

This string is no stronger than a shoe-lace, yet, once the warrior has put it on the horse's head, he tells the other men to let go the strong rawhide thong, and from then on he alone handles the horse with the small piece of string held lightly in one hand. The secret of this is that whenever the horse makes a sudden pull on the string, it grips certain nerves around the nose and back of the ears, and this either stuns him or hurts him so badly that he doesn't try to pull again.

With the horse held thus, the warrior now stands in front of him and strokes the front of his face and hisses at him at close range. It is the same noise that a person makes to drive away chickens—*"shuh, shuh"*—and perhaps the last sound an untrained person would venture to use in taming a wild, ferocious horse; yet it is the quickest way of gaining a horse's confidence and teaching him not to be afraid.

When the warrior has run his fingers over every inch of the horse's head and neck, he now starts to approach his shoulders and flanks with his fingers. The horse will start to jump about again at this, but a couple of sharp jerks on the string stop him, and as he stands trembling with fear, the warrior slowly runs his hand over his left side. When this is finished he stands back and takes a blanket and strikes all of the portions of his body that he has touched, and shouts, *"Shuh!"* with each stiff stroke of the blanket.

When he has repeated these two operations on the other side of the horse, he now starts to do his legs. Each leg, beginning with his left front leg, must be gone over by his hand, with not an inch of its surface escaping his touch. This is the most ticklish part of the work; for his feet are the horse's deadliest weapons. But two more jerks on the string quiet the horse's resentment.

and within another fifteen minutes every square inch of the horse's body has been touched and rubbed, even down to his tail and the ticklish portions of his belly and between his legs.

Now the job of breaking the horse is all but finished. There is just one other thing to do, and that is to accustom the horse to a man hopping on his back and riding him. This is done very simply, and within about five minutes.

The warrior takes the blanket and strikes the horse's back a number of blows. Then he lays the blanket on his back very gently. The horse will be first to buck it off, but another jerk on the string, and he is quieted. The warrior picks the blanket up and lays it across his back again. The horse will jump out from under it perhaps twice before he will stand still. When he has been brought to this point, the man throws the blanket down and walks slowly to the side of the horse and presses down lightly. He keeps pressing a little harder and harder, until finally he places his elbows across his back and draws his body an inch off the ground, putting his full weight on the back of the animal. A horse might jump a little at the first experience of this weight, but he will stand still the next time it is tried.

After the warrior has hung on his back by his elbows for several periods of about thirty seconds each, he will now very gradually pull himself up, up, up until he is ready to throw his right foot over to the other side. It is a strange fact that few horses broken in this manner ever try to buck. He will stand perfectly still, and the man will sit there and stroke him for a moment and then gently urge him to go; and the horse will awkwardly trot off in a mild aimless amble, first this way and that—so bewildered and uncertain in his gait that one would think it was the first time he had ever tried to walk on his own feet.

The reason a horse can be broken in the above manner is that he is a remarkably intelligent being with rationality. A chicken has no reason; therefore it goes through its life running away from *"shuhs"* that will never harm it. This keeps it from getting many extra crumbs that it could leisurely eat if it only had the reason to learn from experience as the horse does.

Four months later we were again back on our beloved plains in upper Montana. Our horses were the envy of every tribe who saw us that summer. They all wanted to know where we got them. Our chief told the story of this wild-horse hunt so many times that it has since become legend among the Indians of these prairies.

But at the end of the story our venerable leader would always look downcast, and in sadly measured words he would tell of the steel-dust stallion with the flowing moon-colored mane and tail, which he had picked out for himself. He would spend many minutes describing this superb horse; yet he would never finish the story, unless someone should ask him what became of the spectacular animal.

Then he would slowly tell how our band had worked all day trying to rope this beast, and how that night they had decided to leave him in the little fenced-off part of the corral, thinking that two or three days contact with them might take some of the devil out of him. But the next morning when they visited the corral he had vanished. The horse had literally climbed over more than seven feet of corral fence, which separated him from the main corral, and there, with room for a running start, he had attacked the heavy log fence and rammed his body clear through it. Nothing was left to tell the tale but a few patches of blood and hair and a wrecked fence.

That should have ended the story of the steel-dust beast, but it did not. On our way out of the camp on the wild-horse plateau we had come across the bodies of seven wild stallions and a mare, which this fiend of the plateau had mutilated in his wake. He had turned killer through and through, even unto the destruction of his own kind. Our old people said that he had been crazed by the fact that he had lost control of his herd in that terrible dash down the runway. This blow to his prowess and pride of leadership had been too much for him; it had turned him into a destructive demon, a roaming maniac of the wilds.

This horse became famous throughout the Northwest as a lone traveler of the night. He went down on to the plains of Montana and Alberta, and in the darkest hours of the night he would turn up at the most unexpected points in the wilderness of the prairies. Never a sound from him; he had lost his mighty bellow. He haunted the plains by night, and was never seen by day. His sinister purpose in life was to destroy every horse he came across.

This silent, lone traveler of the night was often seen silhouetted against the moon on a butte, with his head erect, his tail thrown over his back like a statue, his long moon-colored mane and tail flowing like silver beneath the light of the stars. Owing to his peculiar nocturnal habits and to the fact that his remarkable tail and mane gave off in the moonlight something like a phosphorescent glow, he became known throughout the Northwest as the *Shunka-tonka-Wakan*—the Ghost Horse. The steel-blue color of his body melted so completely into the inky blueness of the night that his tail and mane stood out in the moonlight like shimmering threads of lighted silver, giving him a halo which had a truly ghostly aspect.

The Maltese Cat

By RUDYARD KIPLING

THEY had good reason to be proud, and better reason to be afraid, all twelve of them; for, though they had fought their way, game by game, up the teams entered for the polo tournament, they were meeting the Archangels that afternoon in the final match; and the Archangels' men were playing with half-a-dozen ponies apiece. As the game was divided into six quarters of eight minutes each, that meant a fresh pony after every halt. The Skidars' team, even supposing there were no accidents, could only supply one pony for every other change; and two to one is heavy odds. Again, as Shiraz, the gray Syrian, pointed out, they were meeting the pink and pick of the polo-ponies of Upper India; ponies that had cost from a thousand rupees each, while they themselves were a cheap lot gathered, often from country carts, by their masters who belonged to a poor but honest native infantry regiment.

'Money means pace and weight,' said Shiraz, rubbing his black silk nose dolefully along his neat-fitting boot, 'and by the maxims of the game as I know it—'

'Ah, but we aren't playing the maxims,' said the Maltese Cat. 'We're playing the game, and we've the great advantage of knowing the game. Just think a stride, Shiraz. We've pulled up from bottom to second place in two weeks against all those fellows on the ground here; and that's because we play with our heads as well as with our feet.'

'It makes me feel undersized and unhappy all the same,' said Kittiwynk, a mouse-coloured mare with a red browband and the cleanest pair of legs that ever an aged pony owned. 'They've twice our size, these others.'

Kittiwynk looked at the gathering and sighed. The hard, dusty Umballa polo-ground was lined with thousands of soldiers, black and white, not counting hundreds and hundreds of carriages, and drags, and dog-carts, and ladies with brilliant-coloured parasols, and officers in uniform and out of it, and crowds of natives behind them; and orderlies on camels who had halted to watch the game, instead of carrying letters up and down the station, and native horse-dealers running about on thin-eared Biluchi mares, looking for a chance to sell a few first-class polo-ponies. Then there were the ponies of thirty teams that had entered for the Upper India Free-for-All Cup—nearly every pony of worth and dignity from Mhow to Peshawar, from Allahabad to Multan; prize ponies, Arabs, Syrian, Barb, country bred, Deccanee, Waziri, and Kabul ponies of every colour and shape and temper that you could im-agine. Some of them were in mat-roofed stables close to the polo-ground, but most were under saddle while their masters, who had been defeated in the earlier games, trotted in and out and told each other exactly how the game should be played.

It was a glorious sight, and the come-and-go of the little quick hoofs, and the incessant salutations of ponies that had met before on other polo-grounds or race-courses, were enough to drive a four-footed thing wild.

But the Skidars' team were careful not to know their neigh-bours, though half the ponies on the ground were anxious to scrape acquaintance with the little fellows that had come from the North, and, so far, had swept the board.

'Let's see,' said a soft, golden-coloured Arab, who had been playing very badly the day before, to the Maltese Cat, 'didn't we meet in Abdul Rahman's stable in Bombay four seasons ago? I won the Paikpattan Cup next season, you may remember.'

'Not me,' said the Maltese Cat politely. 'I was at Malta then, pulling a vegetable cart. I don't race. I play the game.'

'O-oh!' said the Arab, cocking his tail and swaggering off.

'Keep yourselves to yourselves,' said the Maltese Cat to his companions. 'We don't want to rub noses with all those goose-rumped half-breeds of Upper India. When we've won this cup they'll give their shoes to know us.'

'We shan't win the cup,' said Shiraz. 'How do you feel?'

'Stale as last night's feed when a musk-rat has run over it,' said Polaris, a rather heavy-shouldered gray, and the rest of the team agreed with him.

'The sooner you forget that the better,' said the Maltese Cat cheerfully. 'They've finished tiffin in the big tent. We shall be wanted now. If your saddles are not comfy, kick. If your bits aren't easy, rear, and let the saises know whether your boots are tight.'

Each pony had his sais, his groom, who lived and ate and slept with the pony, and had betted a great deal more than he could afford on the result of the game. There was no chance of anything going wrong, and, to make sure, each sais was shampooing the legs of his pony to the last minute. Behind the saises sat as many of the Skidars' regiment as had leave to attend that match—about half the native officers, and a hundred or two dark, black-bearded men with the regimental pipers nervously fingering the big be-ribboned bagpipes. The Skidars were what they call a Pioneer regiment; and the bagpipes made the national music of half the men. The native officers held bundles of polo-sticks, long cane-handled mallets, and as the grand-stand filled after lunch they arranged themselves by ones and twos at different points round the ground, so that if a stick were broken the player would not have far to ride for a new one. An impatient British cavalry band struck up 'If you want to know the time, ask a p'leeceman!' and the two umpires in light dust-coats danced out on two little excited ponies. The four players of the Archangels' team followed, and the sight of their beautiful mounts made Shiraz groan again.

'Wait till we know,' said the Maltese Cat. 'Two of 'em are playing in blinkers, and that means they can't see to get out of the way of their own side, or they may shy at the umpires' ponies. They've all got white web reins that are sure to stretch or slip!'

'And,' said Kittiwynk, dancing to take the stiffness out of her, 'they carry their whips in their hands instead of on their wrists. Hah!'

'True enough. No man can manage his stick and his reins, and his whip that way,' said the Maltese Cat. 'I've fallen over every square yard of the Malta ground, and I ought to know.' He quivered his little flea-bitten withers just to show how satisfied he felt; but his heart was not so light. Ever since he had drifted into India on a troopship, taken, with an old rifle, as part pay-ment for a racing debt, the Maltese Cat had played and preached polo to the Skidars' team on the Skidars' stony polo-ground. Now

a polo-pony is like a poet. If he is born with a love for the game he can be made. The Maltese Cat knew that bamboos grew solely in order that polo-balls might be turned from their roots, that grain was given to ponies to keep them in hard condition, and that ponies were shod to prevent them slipping on a turn. But, besides all these things, he knew every trick and device of the finest game of the world, and for two seasons he had been teaching the others all he knew or guessed.

'Remember,' he said for the hundredth time as the riders came up, 'we must play together, and you must play with your heads. Whatever happens, follow the ball. Who goes out first?'

Kittiwynk, Shiraz, Polaris, and a short high little bay fellow with tremendous hocks and no withers worth speaking of (he was called Corks) were being girthed up, and the soldiers in the background stared with all their eyes.

'I want you men to keep quiet,' said Lutyens, the captain of the team, 'and especially not to blow your pipes.'

'Not if we win, Captain Sahib?' asked a piper.

'If we win, you can do what you please,' said Lutyens, with a smile, as he slipped the loop of his stick over his wrist, and wheeled to canter to his place. The Archangels' ponies were a little bit above themselves on account of the many-coloured crowd so close to the ground. Their riders were excellent players, but they were a team of crack players instead of a crack team; and that made all the difference in the world. They honestly meant to play together, but it is very hard for four men, each the best of the team he is picked from, to remember that in polo no brilliancy of hitting or riding makes up for playing alone. Their captain shouted his orders to them by name, and it is a curious thing that if you call his name aloud in public after an Englishman you make him hot and fretty. Lutyens said nothing to his men because it had all been said before. He pulled up Shiraz, for he was playing 'back,' to guard the goal. Powell on Polaris was half-back, and Macnamara and Hughes on Corks and Kittiwynk were forwards. The tough bamboo-root ball was put into the middle of the ground one hundred and fifty yards from the ends, and Hughes crossed sticks, heads-up, with the captain of the Archangels, who saw fit to play forward, and that is a place from which you cannot easily control the team. The little click as the caneshafts met was heard all over the ground, and then Hughes made some sort of quick wrist-stroke that just dribbled the ball a few yards. Kittiwynk knew that stroke of old, and followed as a cat follows a mouse. While the captain of the Archangels was wrenching his pony round Hughes struck with all his strength, and next instant Kittiwynk was away, Corks following close behind her, their little feet pattering like rain-drops on glass.

'Pull out to the left,' said Kittiwynk between her teeth, 'it's coming our way, Corks!'

The back and half-back of the Archangels were tearing down on her just as she was within reach of the ball. Hughes leaned forward with a loose rein, and cut it away to the left almost under Kittiwynk's feet, and it hopped and skipped off to Corks, who saw that, if he were not quick, it would run beyond the boundaries. That long bouncing drive gave the Archangels time to wheel and send three men across the ground to head off Corks. Kittiwynk stayed where she was, for she knew the game. Corks was on the ball half a fraction of a second before the others came up, and Macnamara, with a back-handed stroke, sent it back across the ground to Hughes, who saw the way clear to the Archangels' goal, and smacked the ball in before any one quite knew what had happened.

'That's luck,' said Corks, as they changed ends. 'A goal in three minutes for three hits and no riding to speak of.'

'Don't know,' said Polaris. 'We've made 'em angry too soon. Shouldn't wonder if they try to rush us off our feet next time.'

'Keep the ball hanging then,' said Shiraz. 'That wears out every pony that isn't used to it.'

Next time there was no easy galloping across the ground. All the Archangels closed up as one man, but there they stayed, for Corks, Kittiwynk, and Polaris were somewhere on the top of the ball, marking time among the rattling sticks, while Shiraz circled about outside, waiting for a chance.

'We can do this all day,' said Polaris, ramming his quarters into the side of another pony. 'Where do you think you're shoving to?'

'I'll—I'll be driven in an ekka if I know,' was the gasping reply, 'and I'd give a week's feed to get my blinkers off. I can't see anything.'

'The dust is rather bad. Whew! That was one for my off hock. Where's the ball, Corks?'

'Under my tail. At least a man's looking for it there. This is beautiful. They can't use their sticks, and it's driving 'em wild. Give old blinkers a push and he'll go over!'

'Here, don't touch me! I can't see. I'll—I'll back out, I think,' said the pony in blinkers, who knew that if you can't see all round your head you cannot prop yourself against a shock.

Corks was watching the ball where it lay in the dust close to his near fore, with Macnamara's shortened stick tap-tapping it from time to time. Kittiwynk was edging her way out of the scrimmage, whisking her stump of a tail with nervous excitement.

'Ho! They've got it,' she snorted. 'Let me out!' and she galloped like a rifle-bullet just behind a tall lanky pony of the Archangels, whose rider was swinging up his stick for a stroke.

'Not to-day, thank you,' said Hughes, as the blow slid off his raised stick, and Kittiwynk laid her shoulder to the tall pony's quarters, and shoved him aside just as Lutyens on Shiraz sent the ball where it had come from, and the tall pony went skating and slipping away to the left. Kittiwynk, seeing that Polaris had joined Corks in the chase for the ball up the ground, dropped into Polaris's place, and then time was called.

The Skidars' ponies wasted no time in kicking or fuming. They knew each minute's rest meant so much gain, and trotted off to the rails and their saises, who began to scrape and blanket and rub them at once.

'Whew!' said Corks, stiffening up to get all the tickle out of the big vulcanite scraper. 'If we were playing pony for pony we'd bend those Archangels double in half an hour. But they'll bring out fresh ones and fresh ones, and fresh ones after that—you see.'

'Who cares?' said Polaris. 'We've drawn first blood. Is my hock swelling?'

'Looks puffy,' said Corks. 'You must have had rather a wipe. Don't let it stiffen. You'll be wanted again in half an hour.'

'What's the game like?' said the Maltese Cat.

'Ground's like your shoe, except where they've put too much water on it,' said Kittiwynk. 'Then it's slippery. Don't play in the centre. There's a bog there. I don't know how their next four are going to behave, but we kept the ball hanging and made 'em

lather for nothing. Who goes out? Two Arabs and a couple of countrybreds! That's bad. What a comfort it is to wash your mouth out!'

Kitty was talking with the neck of a leather-covered soda-water bottle between her teeth and trying to look over her withers at the same time. This gave her a very coquettish air.

'What's bad?' said Gray Dawn, giving to the girth and admiring his well-set shoulders.

'You Arabs can't gallop fast enough to keep yourselves warm —that's what Kitty means,' said Polaris, limping to show that his hock needed attention. 'Are you playing "back," Gray Dawn?'

'Looks like it,' said Gray Dawn, as Lutyens swung himself up. Powell mounted the Rabbit, a plain bay countrybred much like Corks, but with mulish ears. Macnamara took Faiz Ullah, a handy short-backed little red Arab with a long tail, and Hughes mounted Benami, an old and sullen brown beast, who stood over in front more than a polo-pony should.

'Benami looks like business,' said Shiraz. 'How's your temper, Ben?' The old campaigner hobbled off without answering, and the Maltese Cat looked at the new Archangel ponies prancing about on the ground. They were four beautiful blacks, and they saddled big enough and strong enough to eat the Skidars' team and gallop away with the meal inside them.

'Blinkers again,' said the Maltese Cat. 'Good enough!'

'They're chargers—cavalry chargers!' said Kittiwynk indignantly. 'They'll never see thirteen three again.'

'They've all been fairly measured and they've all got their certificates,' said the Maltese Cat, 'or they wouldn't be here. We must take things as they come along, and keep our eyes on the ball.'

The game began, but this time the Skidars were penned to their own end of the ground, and the watching ponies did not approve of that.

'Faiz Ullah is shirking as usual,' said Polaris, with a scornful grunt.

'Faiz Ullah is eating whip,' said Corks. They could hear the leather-thonged polo-quirt lacing the little fellow's well-rounded barrel. Then the Rabbit's shrill neigh came across the ground. 'I can't do all the work,' he cried.

'Play the game, don't talk,' the Maltese Cat whickered; and all the ponies wriggled with excitement, and the soldiers and the grooms gripped the railings and shouted. A black pony with blinkers had singled out old Benami, and was interfering with him in every possible way. They could see Benami shaking his head up and down and flapping his underlip.

'There'll be a fall in a minute,' said Polaris. 'Benami is getting stuffy.'

The game flickered up and down between goal-post and goal-post, and the black ponies were getting more confident as they felt they had the legs of the others. The ball was hit out of a little scrimmage, and Benami and the Rabbit followed it; Faiz Ullah only too glad to be quiet for an instant.

The blinkered black pony came up like a hawk, with two of his own side behind him, and Benami's eye glittered as he raced. The question was which pony should make way for the other; each rider was perfectly willing to risk a fall in a good cause. The black who had been driven nearly crazy by his blinkers trusted to his weight and his temper; but Benami knew how to apply his weight and how to keep his temper. They met, and there was a cloud of dust. The black was lying on his side with all the breath knocked out of his body. The Rabbit was a hundred yards up the ground with the ball, and Benami was sitting down. He had slid nearly ten yards, but he had had his revenge, and sat cracking his nostrils till the black pony rose.

'That's what you get for interfering. Do you want any more?' said Benami, and he plunged into the game. Nothing was done because Faiz Ullah would not gallop, though Macnamara beat him whenever he could spare a second. The fall of the black pony had impressed his companions tremendously, and so the Arch-angels could not profit by Faiz Ullah's bad behaviour.

But as the Maltese Cat said, when time was called and the four came back blowing and dripping, Faiz Ulla ought to have been kicked all round Umballa. If he did not behave better next time, the Maltese Cat promised to pull out his Arab tail by the root and eat it.

There was no time to talk, for the third four were ordered out.

The third quarter of a game is generally the hottest, for each side thinks that the others must be pumped; and most of the winning play in a game is made about that time.

Lutyens took over the Maltese Cat with a pat and a hug, for Lutyens valued him more than anything else in the world. Powell had Shikast, a little gray rat with no pedigree and no manners outside polo; Macnamara mounted Bamboo, the largest of the team, and Hughes took Who's Who, alias The Animal. He was supposed to have Australian blood in his veins, but he looked like a clothes-horse, and you could whack him on the legs with an iron crowbar without hurting him.

They went out to meet the very flower of the Archangels' team, and when Who's Who saw their elegantly booted legs and their beautiful satiny skins he grinned a grin through his light, well-worn bridle.

'My word!' said Who's Who. 'We must give 'em a little foot-ball. Those gentlemen need a rubbing down.'

'No biting,' said the Maltese Cat warningly, for once or twice in his career Who's Who had been known to forget himself in that way.

'Who said anything about biting? I'm not playing tiddly-winks. I'm playing the game.'

The Archangels came down like a wolf on the fold, for they were tired of football and they wanted polo. They got it more and more. Just after the game began, Lutyens hit a ball that was coming towards him rapidly, and it rose in the air, as a ball sometimes will, with the whirr of a frightened partridge. Shikast heard, but could not see it for the minute, though he looked everywhere and up into the air as the Maltese Cat had taught him. When he saw it ahead and overhead he went forward with Powell as fast as he could put foot to ground. It was then that Powell, a quiet and level-headed man as a rule, became inspired and played a stroke that sometimes comes off successfully on a quiet afternoon of long practice. He took his stick in both hands, and standing up in his stirrups, swiped at the ball in the air, Munipore fashion. There was one second of paralysed astonishment, and then all four sides of the ground went up in a yell of applause and delight as the ball flew true (you could see the amazed Archangels ducking in their saddles to get out of the line of flight, and looking at it with open mouths), and the regimental pipes of the Skidars squealed from the railings as long as the piper had breath.

Shikast heard the stroke; but he heard the head of the stick fly off at the same time. Nine hundred and ninety-nine ponies out of a thousand would have gone tearing on after the ball with a useless player pulling at their heads, but Powell knew him, and he knew Powell; and the instant he felt Powell's right leg shift a trifle on the saddle-flap he headed to the boundary, where a native officer was frantically waving a new stick. Before the shouts had ended Powell was armed again.

Once before in his life the Maltese Cat had heard that very same stroke played off his own back, and had profited by the confusion it made. This time he acted on experience, and leaving Bamboo to guard the goal in case of accidents, came through the others like a flash, head and tail low, Lutyens standing up to ease him—swept on and on before the other side knew what was the matter, and nearly pitched on his head between the Archangels' goal-posts as Lutyens tipped the ball in after a straight scurry of a hundred and fifty yards. If there was one thing more than another upon which the Maltese Cat prided himself it was on this quick, streaking kind of run half across the ground. He did not believe in taking balls round the field unless you were clearly overmatched. After this they gave the Archangels five minutes' football, and an expensive fast pony hates football because it rumples his temper.

Who's Who showed himself even better than Polaris in this game. He did not permit any wriggling away, but bored joyfully into the scrimmage as if he had his nose in a feed-box, and were looking for something nice. Little Shikast jumped on the ball the minute it got clear, and every time an Archangel pony followed it he found Shikast standing over it asking what was the matter.

'If we can live through this quarter,' said the Maltese Cat, 'I shan't care. Don't take it out of yourselves. Let them do the lathering.'

So the ponies, as their riders explained afterwards, 'shut up.' The Archangels kept them tied fast in front of their goal, but it cost the Archangels' ponies all that was left of their tempers; and ponies began to kick, and men began to repeat compliments, and they chopped at the legs of Who's Who, and he set his teeth and stayed where he was, and the dust stood up like a tree over the scrimmage till that hot quarter ended.

They found the ponies very excited and confident when they went to their saises; and the Maltese Cat had to warn them that the worst of the game was coming.

'Now we are all going in for the second time,' said he, 'and they are trotting out fresh ponies. You'll think you can gallop, but you'll find you can't; and then you'll be sorry.'

'But two goals to nothing is a halter-long lead,' said Kittiwynk prancing.

'How long does it take to get a goal?' the Maltese Cat answered. 'For pity sake, don't run away with the notion that the game is half-won just because we happen to be in luck now. They'll ride you into the grand-stand if they can; you must not give 'em a chance. Follow the ball.'

'Football as usual?' said Polaris. 'My hock's half as big as a nose-bag.'

'Don't let them have a look at the ball if you can help it. Now leave me alone. I must get all the rest I can before the last quarter.'

He hung down his head and let all his muscles go slack; Shikast, Bamboo, and Who's Who copying his example.

'Better not watch the game,' he said. 'We aren't playing, and we shall only take it out of ourselves if we grow anxious. Look at the ground and pretend it's fly-time.'

They did their best, but it was hard advice to follow. The hoofs were drumming and the sticks were rattling all up and down the ground, and yells of applause from the English troops told that the Archangels were pressing the Skidars hard. The native soldiers behind the ponies groaned and grunted, and said things in undertones, and presently they heard a long-drawn shout and a clatter of hurrahs!

'One to the Archangels,' said Shikast, without raising his head. 'Time's nearly up. Oh, my sire and—dam!'

'Faiz Ullah,' said the Maltese Cat, 'if you don't play to the last nail in your shoes this time, I'll kick you on the ground before all the other ponies.'

'I'll do my best when my time comes,' said the little Arab sturdily.

The saises looked at each other gravely as they rubbed their ponies' legs. This was the first time when long purses began to tell, and everybody knew it. Kittiwynk and the others came back with the sweat dripping over their hoofs and their tails telling sad stories.

'They're better than we are,' said Shiraz. 'I knew how it would be.'

'Shut your big head,' said the Maltese Cat; 'we've one goal to the good yet.'

'Yes, but it's two Arabs and two countrybreds to play now,' said Corks. 'Faiz Ullah, remember!' He spoke in a biting voice.

As Lutyens mounted Gray Dawn he looked at his men, and they did not look pretty. They were covered with dust and sweat in streaks. Their yellow boots were almost black, their wrists were red and lumpy, and their eyes seemed two inches deep in their heads, but the expression in the eyes was satisfactory.

'Did you take anything at tiffin?' said Lutyens, and the team shook their heads. They were two dry to talk.

'All right. The Archangels did. They are worse pumped than we are.'

'They've got the better ponies,' said Powell. 'I shan't be sorry when this business is over.'

That fifth quarter was a sad one in every way. Faiz Ullah played like a little red demon; and the Rabbit seemed to be everywhere at once, and Benami rode straight at anything and everything that came in his way, while the umpires on their ponies wheeled like gulls outside the shifting game. But the Archangels had the better mounts—they had kept their racers till late in the game—and never allowed the Skidars to play football. They hit the ball up and down the width of the ground till Benami and the rest were outpaced. Then they went forward, and time and again Lutyens and Gray Dawn were just, and only just, able to send the ball away with a long splitting backhander. Gray Dawn forgot that he was an Arab; and turned from gray to blue as he galloped. Indeed, he forgot too well, for he did not keep his eyes on the ground as an Arab should, but stuck out his nose and scuttled for the dear honour of the game. They had watered the ground once or twice between the quarters, and a careless waterman had emptied the last of his skinful all in one place near the Skidars' goal. It was close to the end of play, and for the tenth time Gray Dawn was bolting after a ball when his near hind foot slipped on the greasy mud and he rolled over and over, pitching Lutyens just clear of the goal-post; and the triumphant Archangels made their goal. Then time was called—two goals all; but Lutyens had to be helped up, and Gray Dawn rose with his near hind leg strained somewhere.

'What's the damage?' said Powell, his arm round Lutyens.

'Collar-bone, of course,' said Lutyens between his teeth. It was the third time he had broken it in two years, and it hurt him.

Powell and the others whistled. 'Game's up,' said Hughes.

'Hold on. We've five good minutes yet, and it isn't my right hand,' said Lutyens. 'We'll stick it out.'

'I say,' said the captain of the Archangels, trotting up. 'Are you hurt, Lutyens? We'll wait if you care to put in a substitute. I wish—I mean—the fact is, you fellows deserve this game if any team does. Wish we could give you a man or some of our ponies —or something.'

'You're awfully good, but we'll play to a finish, I think.'

The captain of the Archangels stared for a little. 'That's not half bad,' he said, and went back to his own side, while Lutyens borrowed a scarf from one of his native officers and made a sling of it. Then an Archangel galloped up with a big bath-sponge and advised Lutyens to put it under his arm-pit to ease his shoulder, and between them they tied up his left arm scientifically, and one of the native officers leaped forward with four long glasses that fizzed and bubbled.

The team looked at Lutyens piteously, and he nodded. It was the last quarter, and nothing would matter after that. They drank out the dark golden drink, and wiped their moustaches, and things looked more hopeful.

The Maltese Cat had put his nose into the front of Lutyens' shirt, and was trying to say how sorry he was.

'He knows,' said Lutyens, proudly. 'The beggar knows. I've played him without a bridle before now—for fun.'

'It's no fun now,' said Powell. 'But we haven't a decent substitute.'

'No,' said Lutyens. 'It's the last quarter, and we've got to make our goal and win. I'll trust the Cat.'

'If you fall this time you'll suffer a little,' said Macnamara.

'I'll trust the Cat,' said Lutyens.

'You hear that?' said the Maltese Cat proudly to the others. 'It's worth while playing polo for ten years to have that said of you. Now then, my sons, come along. We'll kick up a little bit, just to show the Archangels this team haven't suffered.'

And, sure enough, as they went on to the ground the Maltese Cat, after satisfying himself that Lutyens was home in the saddle, kicked out three or four times, and Lutyens laughed. The reins were caught up anyhow in the tips of his strapped hand, and he never pretended to rely on them. He knew the Cat would answer to the least pressure of the leg, and by way of showing off—for his shoulder hurt him very much—he bent the little fellow in a close figure-of-eight in and out between the goal-posts. There was a roar from the native officers and men, who dearly loved a piece of dugabashi (horse-trick work), as they called it, and the pipes very quietly and scornfully droned out the first bars of a common bazaar-tune called 'Freshly Fresh and Newly New,' just as a warning to the other regiments that the Skidars were fit. All the natives laughed.

'And now,' said the Cat, as they took their place, 'remember that this is the last quarter, and follow the ball!'

'Don't need to be told,' said Who's Who.

'Let me go on. All those people on all four sides will begin to crowd in—just as they did at Malta. You'll hear people calling out, and moving forward and being pushed back, and that is going to make the Archangel ponies very unhappy. But if a ball is struck to the boundary, you go after it, and let the people get out of your way. I went over the pole of a four-in-hand once, and picked a game out of the dust by it. Back me up when I run, and follow the ball.'

There was a sort of an all-round sound of sympathy and wonder as the last quarter opened, and then there began exactly what the Maltese Cat had foreseen. People crowded in close to the boundaries, and the Archangels' ponies kept looking sideways at the narrowing space. If you know how a man feels to be cramped at tennis—not because he wants to run out of the court, but because he likes to know that he can at a pinch—you will guess how ponies must feel when they are playing in a box of human beings.

'I'll bend some of those men if I can get away,' said Who's Who, as he rocketed behind the ball; and Bamboo nodded without speaking. They were playing the last ounce in them, and the Maltese Cat had left the goal undefended to join them. Lutyens gave him every order that he could to bring him back, but this was the first time in his career that the little wise gray had ever played polo on his own responsibility, and he was going to make the most of it.

'What are you doing here?' said Hughes, as the Cat crossed in front of him and rode off an Archangel.

'The Cat's in charge—mind the goal!' shouted Lutyens, and bowing forward hit the ball full, and followed on, forcing the Archangels towards their own goal.

'No football,' said the Cat. 'Keep the ball by the boundaries and cramp 'em. Play open order and drive 'em to the boundaries.'

Across and across the ground in big diagonals flew the ball, and whenever it came to a flying rush and a stroke close to the boundaries the Archangel ponies moved stiffly. They did not care to go headlong at a wall of men and carriages, though if the ground had been open they could have turned on a sixpence.

'Wriggle her up the sides,' said the Cat. 'Keep her close to the crowd. They hate the carriages. Shikast, keep her up this side.'

Shikast with Powell lay left and right behind the uneasy scuffle of an open scrimmage, and every time the ball was hit away Shikast galloped on it at such an angle that Powell was forced to hit it towards the boundary; and when the crowd had been driven away from that side, Lutyens would send the ball over to the other, and Shikast would slide desperately after it till his friends came down to help. It was billiards, and no football, this time— billiards in a corner pocket; and the cues were not well chalked.

'If they get us out in the middle of the ground they'll walk away from us. Dribble her along the sides,' cried the Cat.

So they dribbled all along the boundary, where a pony could not come on their right-hand side; and the Archangels were furious, and the umpires had to neglect the game to shout at the people to get back, and several blundering mounted policemen tried to restore order, all close to the scrimmage, and the nerves of the Archangels' ponies stretched and broke like cobwebs.

Five or six times an Archangel hit the ball up into the middle of the ground, and each time the watchful Shikast gave Powell his chance to send it back, and after each return, when the dust had settled, men could see that the Skidars had gained a few yards.

Every now and again there were shouts of ' 'Side! Off side!' from the spectators; but the teams were too busy to care, and the umpires had all they could do to keep their maddened ponies clear of the scuffle.

At last Lutyens missed a short easy stroke, and the Skidars had to fly back helter-skelter to protect their own goal, Shikast leading. Powell stopped the ball with a backhander when it was not fifty yards from the goal-posts, and Shikast spun around with a wrench that nearly hoisted Powell out of his saddle.

'Now's our last chance,' said the Cat, wheeling like a cock-chafer on a pin. 'We've got to ride it out. Come along.'

Lutyens felt the little chap take a deep breath, and, as it were, crouch under his rider. The ball was hopping towards the right-hand boundary, an Archangel riding for it with both spurs and

a whip; but neither spur nor whip would make his pony stretch himself as he neared the crowd. The Maltese Cat glided under his very nose, picking up his hind legs sharp, for there was not a foot to spare between his quarters and the other pony's bit. It was as neat an exhibition as fancy figure-skating. Lutyens hit with all the strength he had left, but the stick slipped a little in his hand, and the ball flew off to the left instead of keeping close to the boundary. Who's Who was far across the ground, thinking hard as he galloped. He repeated, stride for stride, the Cat's manœuvres with another Archangel pony, nipping the ball away from under his bridle, and clearing his opponent by half a fraction of an inch, for Who's Who was clumsy behind. Then he drove away towards the right as the Maltese Cat came up from the left; and Bamboo held a middle course exactly between them. The three were making a sort of Government-broad-arrow-shaped attack; and there was only the Archangels' back to guard the goal; but immediately behind them were three Archangels racing all they knew, and mixed up with them was Powell, sending Shikast along on what he felt was their last hope. It takes a very good man to stand up to the rush of seven crazy ponies in the last quarters of a cup game, when men are riding with their necks for sale, and the ponies are delirious. The Archangels' back missed his stroke, and pulled aside just in time to let the rush go by. Bamboo and Who's Who shortened stride to give the Maltese Cat room, and Lutyens got the goal with a clean, smooth, smacking stroke that was heard all over the field. But there was no stopping the ponies. They poured through the goal-posts in one mixed mob, winners and losers together, for the pace had been terrific. The Maltese Cat knew by experience what would happen, and, to save Lutyens, turned to the right with one last effort that strained a back-sinew beyond hope of repair. As he did so he heard the right-hand goal-post crack as a pony cannoned into it—crack, splinter, and fall like a mast. It had been sawed three parts through in case of accidents, but it upset the pony nevertheless, and he blundered into another, who blundered into the left-hand post, and then there was confusion and dust and wood. Bamboo was lying on the ground, seeing stars; an Archangel pony rolled beside him, breathless and angry; Shikast had sat down dog-fashion to avoid falling over the others, and was sliding along on his little bobtail in a cloud of dust; and Powell was sitting on the ground, hammering with his stick and trying to cheer. All the others were shouting at the top of what was left of their voices, and the men who had been spilt were shouting too. As soon as the people saw no one was hurt, ten thousand native and English shouted and clapped and yelled, and before any one could stop them the pipers of the Skidars broke on to the ground, with all the native officers and men behind them, and marched up and down, playing a wild northern tune called 'Zakhme Bagan,' and through the insolent blaring of the pipes and the high-pitched native yells you could hear the Archangels' band hammering, 'For they are all jolly good fellows,' and then reproachfully to the losing team, 'Ooh, Kafoozalum! Kafoozalum! Kafoozalum!'

Besides all these things and many more, there was a Commander-in-Chief, and an Inspector-General of Cavalry, and the principal veterinary officer in all India, standing on the top of a regimental coach, yelling like schoolboys; and brigadiers and colonels and commissioners, and hundreds of pretty ladies joined the chorus. But the Maltese Cat stood with his head down, wondering how many legs were left to him; and Lutyens watched the men and ponies pick themselves out of the wreck of the two goal-posts, and he patted the Cat very tenderly.

'I say,' said the captain of the Archangels, spitting a pebble out of his mouth, 'will you take three thousand for that pony—as he stands?'

'No, thank you. I've an idea he's saved my life,' said Lutyens, getting off and lying down at full length. Both teams were on the ground too, waving their boots in the air, and coughing and drawing deep breaths, as the saises ran up to take away the ponies, and an officious water-carrier sprinkled the players with dirty water till they sat up.

'My Aunt!' said Powell, rubbing his back and looking at the stumps of the goal-posts, 'that was a game!'

They played it over again, every stroke of it, that night at the big dinner, when the Free-for-All Cup was filled and passed down the table, and emptied and filled again, and everybody made most eloquent speeches. About two in the morning, when there might have been some singing, a wise little, plain little, gray little head looked in through the open door.

'Hurrah! Bring him in,' said the Archangels; and his sais, who was very happy indeed, patted the Maltese Cat on the flank, and he limped into the blaze of light and the glittering uniforms, looking for Lutyens. He was used to messes, and men's bedrooms, and places where ponies are not usually encouraged, and in his youth had jumped on and off a mess-table for a bet. So he behaved himself very politely, and ate bread dipped in salt, and was petted all round the table, moving gingerly; and they drank his health, because he had done more to win the Cup than any man or horse on the ground.

That was glory and honour enough for the rest of his days, and the Maltese Cat did not complain much when his veterinary surgeon said that he would be no good for polo any more. When Lutyens married, his wife did not allow him to play, so he was forced to be an umpire; and his pony on these occasions was a flea-bitten gray with a neat polo-tail, lame all round, but desperately quick on his feet, and, as everybody knew, Past Pluperfect Prestissimo Player of the Game.

The Wrong'un

By JOHN ORR EWING

AMONG the smartest sons of Mars
Was Trooper Jones, the Nth Hussars.
We find him pretty nearly beat
One midnight in the Mons retreat.
And endless road the Nth had marched,
And Trooper Jones's throat was parched:
He dozed, and dreamt of quarts of Beer,
Then—"Halt! Dismount! And lead in here!"

"Here" proved to be a biggish farm,
That so far had not come to harm—
"File in that doorway on the right,
And nobody must show a light!
Off-saddle, get what sleep you can!"
Oh, blessed words for horse, and man!

A great black vault that smelt of hay,
And cows, brought back his boyhood's day;
He heard them chew the cud, and snort—
How many had his father bought?—
He groped, he found a ring, and tied
His mare up to the manger-side,
Off-saddled, staggered with his tack,
And soon was snoring on his back.

Five minutes later, so it seemed,
Poor Trooper Jones no longer dreamed—
The Sergeant's voice in raucous tones
Was shouting, "Where the hell is Jones?"

" 'Ere, Sergeant"! "Well then, saddle up!
And make it 'juldi'! Now, no gup!"

In darkness black as any hat
Our Jones still knew what he was at,
He felt for where his mare had been,
He knew her back, so long and lean.
The blankets first, with "channel fold,"
And there she stood, as good as gold.
'Twas odd the girths, though, would not meet
By what he judged a good two feet—
"Ah! Lizzie, would yer? Artful 'soor'!
Balloons ain't in it! That is sure."

Try later then. The bridle now—
He tripped against a squealing sow—

THE WRONG'UN

Returned, and felt for Lizzie's head,
Encountered something hard instead—
"Well! What will happen next, Gawd knows!
Her blinking ears have gone and froze!"

Ask Jones—he's a civilian now—
The way to saddle up a cow!

The Ride of His Life

By DAVID GRAY

CORDILLAS Y SANDOVAL was an attaché of the Spanish legation, whom Varick invited to Oakdale to please Mrs. Varick and, more especially, her widowed sister.

"I believe I met him once at the club in Washington," Varick remarked. "I thought he was rather an ass; but we've plenty of stable-room. Does he hunt?"

Mrs. Innis, the sister-in-law, was afraid he did (in a hunting-country men who do not ride are at a premium), but was uncertain about it; therefore upon his arrival the question was referred to Cordillas himself.

The Spaniard dashed Mrs. Innis's hopes. He asserted that he was "practised in equestrianism," and "worshipped horses."

"Yes, and I haf yoomp, too," he added. Then he branched off on the merits of his "fiery-eyed steed" in Madrid, which he was bound to believe would make an unparalleled "yoomper," although, as there was no fox-hunting in his country, its ability had never been called out.

"I can see," said Varick, pleasantly interrupting, "that you are the man for us. I shall put you up on that good horse Thomas Dooley." There was no duplicity in this, for Varick distrusted the horsemanship of all Latin foreigners; but the Spaniard suspected it not, and the sister-in-law discreetly held her peace.

Thomas Dooley, at the time when fate introduced him to Cordillas, was going on seventeen, and he knew more about getting across a hunting-country than men usually acquire in half a century. His ancestry was not discussed, but he had the best box-stall in Varick's stable, and would be gloriously pensioned when his time of service expired. Ten years back he had exchanged the plow for the saddle, as the result of a memorable humiliation which he put upon the entire Oakdale Hunt. One dismal, sloppy morning Dooley had appeared at a meet, ridden by a farmer's boy. Not long after the hounds had found, twenty angry men were sitting on as many sulky, discouraged horses in a deep plowed field waiting for some one to break the fence in front of them. They were not soothed when they saw Dooley playfully switch his flowing tail over five feet of new oak rails and disappear after the pack. Varick had been one of these men; and that same afternoon he possessed Thomas Dooley, who ever since had carried him with unerring judgment and ability.

As the years went by, Dooley came to be known as Varick's "morning-after" horse, and he never betrayed the confidence this title implied. Nevertheless, it must be said that, for a man whose nerves had not been outraged, Dooley could hardly be called an agreeable mount.

He was, by general admission, the plainest horse that ever followed hounds. His legs and feet were coarse, and he galloped with as much spring as if he were on stilts. The mighty quarters wherein dwelt his genius for getting over high timber were so much too big for him that he seemed to have got another horse's hind legs by mistake. He had a mouth no bit could conquer. He chose what he would jump, and how, regardless of his rider. Only the certainty that he would never fall made him venerated, and most persons who hunt resent the imputation that they need this kind of horse. If a man's heart is strong with sleep and November air, there is little satisfaction in being carried over the country by a machine.

When Cordillas made his first appearance on Thomas Dooley, it was noted that he rode with uncommonly long stirrup-leathers —too long for hunting—and sat stiff as a horse-guard, bouncing dismally with Thomas's hard trot. The tails of his pink coat were unsullied by the loin-sweat of the chase, and there was no mark of stirrup-iron across the instep of his freshly treed boots.

" 'E's quite noo," remarked the first whip, in an undertone.

"With Thomas," remarked the huntsman, " 'e won't be long noo."

The hounds found unexpectedly, and the advice Varick intended to give his guest was cut short.

"Don't try to steer him at his fences," he yelled; "it won't do any good." The next moment the rattle-headed four-year-old he was riding took off in a bit of marsh, and became mixed up with a panel of boards. Varick got up in time to see Dooley bucking over from good ground, his rider with him, although well on toward his ears.

"I guess he'll do; he's got to," said Varick, softly swearing at his muddied boots. He scrambled up into the saddle, saw his guest slide back into his, and together they swept on after the hounds.

For the most part Cordillas managed to remain inconspicuous, though he took a spectacular "voluntary" on the way back to the kennels. He tried to "lark" Dooley over a wayside fence, possibly for the benefit of Mrs. Innis who was driving by in her cart. Dooley, knowing that the jump was needless, stopped at the fence and the Spaniard went over alone; but his heart seemed to be in the right place, and he got up again, laughing.

The next time he went out, on a hint from Varick he shortened his leathers, thrust his feet home through the irons, and really did very creditably. He was good-looking, and had nice manners, and Mrs. Innis was so complimentary that by the end of the week he believed himself the keenest man in the field. But as he grew in confidence he also became aware of the reputation which his

Paul Brown
'45

mount enjoyed. He began to hint to Varick that Dooley was not a suitable horse for him.

"If I only had my prancer here," he observed one morning, "you would see yoomping." Finally he told his host point-blank that, however well meant it might be, to give him such a tame mount as Dooley was no kindness; it was a reflection upon his equestrianism.

"Then," said Varick, who was annoyed, "you may ride Emperor tomorrow, but I tell you plainly that he may kill you." For the moment, he almost hoped he would.

"Fear not," said Cordillas and thanked him much.

Varick says that he did *not* forget to tell William to have Emperor saddled for Cordillas. The head groom refuses to talk about it, but shakes his head. Those who know William hesitate to decide between him and his master, so the truth is likely to remain hid.

At the meeting next morning Cordillas flabbergasted the stable-boy who assisted him to mount by slipping a bill into his hand.

"An' 'im a haline," said the boy as he related the matter to William. "Then 'e pats 'is neck, an' sez 'e, 'Ain't 'e a good 'un! Gawd! look at 'is fiery heye! This *is* a 'oss!' 'W'y, yes,' sez I; 'an' clipped yesterday, sir, which improves 'is looks uncommon. I might almost say, sir, one 'u'd scaicely know 'im.' Then 'e sez, 'Git up, Hemperor!' an' moves awfter 'em."

That day there was vouchsafed one of those "historic" runs which come usually when a man's best horse is laid up, or when he judges that the day is too dry for scent and stops at home. In the first covert the pack blundered on a fox, and burst wildly out of the woods, every hound giving tongue, and Reynard in full view, barely half a field away.

The men sat listening to the foxhounds' "music," half-eager bark, half-agonized yelp, with a fluttering of the pulses and a stirring of primeval instincts. The horses quivered and pawed, mouthed the bits, and tossed white slaver into the air. But the hounds had to get their distance; so the field held back, each man intently studying the far-off fence, and playing with the mouth of his restless horse. The excited Spaniard tugged on the curb, and his mount reared indignantly.

Paul Brown
'45

"Demon!" he shouted. A snicker rippled from the grooms in the rear.

"Good Lord!" exclaimed Varick. "He hasn't done that for eight years. Give him his head, man!"

At that instant the M. F. H. waved his hand, and the field charged across the meadow for the boards, over which the tail-end hounds were scrambling.

It was seven miles without a check to Christian's Mills, and the fox most of the time in view; then across the river, horses and hounds swimming together, and on again at a heartbreaking pace to Paddock's Gully where they killed in the bottom. Three horses that went into the ravine were too pumped to get out again, and stayed there all night. In the memory of man such a run, without slow scent or check, had never been seen. It became the great after-dinner run of the Oakdale hunt; and when they brag of their horses, they tell how twice in the twelve miles eleven men jumped five feet of stiff timber without breaking a rail.

In the last mile Cordillas followed the insane Braybrooke over four strands of naked wire that turned the field aside, beat him into the ravine, and was first at the death. They came upon him half buried in the yelping, panting pack which fought for the mangled fox he held over his head.

"Beat 'em off!" yelled Braybrooke. The reply was a torrent of Spanish oaths. Then the huntsman rode up and rescued Cordillas, plastered with blood and filth but content. He patted his mount's dripping neck.

"How magnificent a horse!" he exclaimed.

"Carried you extremely well," said Braybrooke. "Never saw the old fellow do better or show so much speed. Great gallop, wasn't it? Let's have a pull at your flask; mine's dry."

"To the run," said the Spaniard as he received the flask back, "and your good health!" He clutched the mask in his other hand.

"You rode well," said Braybrooke. His respect for the Latin races had increased. "The blood's dripping on your coat," he added as Galloway came up, but Cordillas only held his trophy closer.

That night Varick had a man's dinner. There were toasts and healths, and bumpers to the five-foot fences, and perdition to the man who invented wire; bumpers to every good horse and man who was out that day; long life to hounds and good luck to all hound puppies. But the Spaniard was the lion of the evening, and toward midnight there were cries of "Speech!"

Cordillas rose cautiously and stood facing the party with a glass of champagne in his tremulous hand. He was touched and his voice showed it. He thanked the company as a gentleman, as a Spaniard and as a sportsman. He spoke in praise of his host's country, their women and their bath-tubs. Then he got around to his prancer in Madrid, and settled down to horses. To an equestrian like himself, he said, whose bosom throbbed in sympathy with every fiery impulse of creation's most noble animal, the fox-chase was the sport of kings. To a distinguished company of huntsmen he might well repeat the words of the English poet with which they might be familiar, "My kingdom for a horse!" Developing his theme, he asserted that, of the various kinds of horses, the hunter was the noblest. "And of all noble hunters," he shouted, "the noblest, the fieriest, the most intrepid, I haf rode today! I drink to Emperor!"

At that moment Thomas Dooley, the newly clipped, was sniffing a bran mash, stiff and sore with weariness born of his day's exertions under Cordillas y Sandoval. As every one at the table except the Spaniard knew, Emperor had not been out of his stall.

There was a moment's hush. The toast was drunk in silence. The men looked at one another and then a tumult of cheers burst forth which set the grooms waiting at the stables to speculating upon the probable condition of their masters. To Cordillas it was an ovation, and the climax of his triumph. The tears stood in his eyes. To the Oakdale Hunt it was the only way of saving appearances and their good breeding.

"Keep the racket going," said Forbes to Braybrooke. "Don't let him know any one's laughing."

"I shall die of this," gasped Willie Colfax; and he slipped under the table gurgling hysterically.

What else might have happened no one can say, because Charley Galloway started "For he's a jolly good fellow!" at the top of his lungs. Mrs. Galloway, who was sitting up for him in her own house half a mile down the road, says she recognized her husband's barytone. Every other man did the best nature permitted. The Spaniard was reduced to tears, and the party recovered its gravity.

"But what is going to be the end of this?" whispered Varick to Chalmers. "If he catches on he will have me out and kill me. And there's Mrs. Innis. Oh, Lord! Reggie, you know everybody and all about everything in Washington; if you love me, get him back there."

Then Chalmers sent for his groom and wrote some telegrams, and the following afternoon Cordillas came to Varick, sorely cast down, and announced that the minister had sent him imperative orders to return.

"I fear," he said, "those infamous Cubaños have caused complications which necessitate my presence at the capital."

Varick said he was awfully sorry—but saw to it personally that he caught the evening train. As it moved off, the Spaniard stood on the steps and wrung his hand.

"My friend, possessor of that great horse, Emperor," he said, "I thank you for the ride of my whole life."

"Please don't mention it," said Varick. "Don't speak of it!"

"But," he added to himself, "I am much afraid he will."

The Red Terror[1]

By M. O'MALLEY KNOTT AND PAGE COOPER

MOST thrilling of all the horses that came to our stables for handling and training were the outlaws, the like of which I had never seen in Ireland. California was full of them: man-eaters, runaways, kickers, balkers, fighters, buckers, and stupid horses. One of the worst and the most magnificent was a large well-developed chestnut, built to be a hunter but so wicked and unmanageable that we named him the Red Terror.

I saw the chestnut for the first time at the annual sale of the Haggin Ranch. Mr. J. P. Haggin, the father of the artist, Ben Ali, was one of the greatest breeders of thoroughbreds in California. He owned five or six hundred brood mares, and at his yearly sale of culls one could find the best blood in the country. That day when the big chestnut was led in he was so terrifying that he absolutely cleared the ring. The quivering muscles stood out under his skin, and his eyes blazed with defiance. No one wanted any part of him in spite of his beauty.

While the bidding lagged, creeping up dollar by dollar, I thought frantically of my possessions, but there was no way in the world that I could raise enough to own that gorgeous creature. I almost hated the man who bid him in for forty dollars.

As his new owner cautiously took over the Red Terror, I asked my boss, Dr. Egan, if he knew the man and learned that he was one of our customers who lived in the slaughterhouse district known as Butcher Town. No one ever went there on foot because long-horned cattle, driven in by cowboys from hundreds of miles around, filled the streets from curb to curb. The cowboys boasted that they could ride anything with hair on it and were always ready to demonstrate on a "bad" horse, but I prayed in my heart that they would never master the Red Terror.

[1]From *Gone Away with O'Malley*, by M. O'Malley Knott and Page Cooper.

Nor did they. The chestnut thoroughbred was springier and lighter on his feet than the ordinary common-bred bronco and more comfortable to ride—for the first few bucks; but to the outlaw tricks of a bronco he added tremendous power and staying qualities. There wasn't a man who could remain on his back for more than five minutes. He had no intention of submitting to any human, and I gloried in his defiance.

As the fame of the chestnut spread throughout San Francisco, the ambition of the man who owned him, and of everyone who had tried to ride or handle him, was to break his spirit. The owner hitched him to the wheel of a big six-horse wagon, but he plunged and reared so badly that he threw himself and his team-mate, broke most of the harness, and wrenched off the wagon tongue. He also injured himself, so one fine day he was brought to Dr. Egan's hospital.

Anxiously I hung around while Chick and three or four Negroes held the Red Terror for Dr. Egan to examine the wound, an injury on the top of the head, known as a poll evil. It would have been simple to cure if we had been able to turn the horse upside down to drain it. Since this was impossible, the wound worked deeper and deeper and was increasingly difficult to treat. We kept him in a stall small enough to prevent his turning around, and fastened two long shanks to his halter. One was used to tie him in front and the other was left lying along the floor of the stall. When he was taken out, we untied the first rope and pulled back on the second, and in this way no one ever went into the stall with him.

Every spare moment I hung around the stall admiring the beast, who twitched his nostrils and glared at me with malevolent fury. But that was the way I liked it; I should have been disappointed if he had shown the faintest trace of a conciliatory spirit.

When the Red Terror had been with us only a few weeks a rodeo came to town, advertising, as usual, that the showmen could and would ride any horse in the country. The chestnut's owner entered him at once. Tremendous sums of money were bet by people who knew him. Buck and I collected every penny we could scrape and expected to make a killing.

Both winners and losers, the Red Terror gave us our money's worth. When he was led into the ring he stood quietly while the saddle was put on, but this did not disturb us. We knew that he was absolutely unpredictable; half of the time he was quiet as a lamb when he was being saddled, the other half he was a maniac. But we did worry a little when, without making a move, he allowed the cowboy to mount. Perhaps, we thought, some new whim had entered his devilish head and he had decided not to buck at all when our fortunes depended on it.

But he was only momentarily bewildered by the lights and the crowd. The instant the rider's spurs touched his sides, he was off. He began to buck and he kept on bucking, stiff-legged, writhing and twisting as if he meant to tie a knot in his backbone. There was no bucking strap or cinch on him such as is used on professional buckers in order to annoy them and keep them pitching. The boy rode him marvelously, and it looked at first like a fair duel.

None of the spectators had seen such a show before. They held their breath; Gentleman Jim Corbett, who lived on our street, hung over the rail so far that we were afraid he was going to tumble into the ring. For a moment there was silence; then the crowd as one man leaped to its feet and began a steady roar of cheers.

Huge wagers had been placed on the Red Terror before the show started, but now everyone was making side bets on the number of minutes and seconds the rider could last. Most of the betters gave the boy too much margin, for they reckoned without the horse's blood. His bucks did not lessen in violence; they increased, and not for one second did he let up. The rider's nose began to bleed and the upper half of his body to sway leadenly, like a sack of meal. At last when he came off he was not hurt but lay where he landed as if dead—too exhausted to move. None of the other showmen cared to try the Red Terror, so we collected our bets and took him home, Buck, Chick, and I following him as if we were the captains of a Roman Caesar.

Finally an operation on the poll evil could not be postponed. Five of us managed to get the horse into the paddock back of the hospital, a good-sized yard enclosed by a high strong board fence. Dr. Egan's plan was to throw him down in the deep sand that covered the floor of the corral. The chestnut stood quietly enough while the hobbles were adjusted on his front feet. On each hobble was a ring through which passed a chain, and when the hobbles were all fastened, a jerk on the rope was supposed to bring the horse's four feet together and drop him on his side.

This was the theory of the contraption, but the Red Terror was far too clever for us. Chick and the Negroes got the hobbles on his forefeet and began very carefully to tackle the rear ones. I was at the horse's head and actually saw the swift, wild gleam of suspicion in his eyes. Even so, I had barely time to yell and jump away as he reared and plunged to the end of the corral. He wheeled when he reached the fence, stood up and came straight at us with his mouth open, making terrifying speed on two legs.

Paul Brown

Chick and one of the Negroes vanished through the stable door, but the three of us who were not near enough to reach it went over that five-foot fence as if it were not there. I don't remember touching it, and there had been no time to climb it.

This was the last victory of the great horse. When Dr. Egan told me that the owner had engaged "One-eye" to break him, I seethed with indignation. This was the only man in San Francisco or in the entire West who was capable of doing it. We never knew him by any other name than One-eye, so called because of the black patch over his useless eye. He was tough, stringy, rawboned, and middle-aged, and wherever he went he was preceded and followed by legends. In his early days he had drunk and run amok after each bout, killed more than one man in tavern brawls, and served countless terms in jail before he was converted by the Salvation Army lassies. Then he had gone "on the wagon" and settled down to an honest living breaking outlaws. Traveling from town to town, he advertised that he could gentle the meanest horse alive within two hours. When he came to the stable to break the chestnut, the whole street gathered to see the show.

Watching the man with a hateful fascination, I stayed with the Red Terror to the last minute. First One-eye put a leather surcingle on the horse. There were three rings riveted to this strap, one on each side and one underneath the belly. Two light hobbles were fastened to the front feet. One-eye then tied the end of the long rope to the ring on the right side of the surcingle, brought the rope down through the ring on the off hobble, up through the ring under the belly, down through the ring on the near hobble, and finally through the ring on the left side of the surcingle. He held the free end of this rope in one hand, and in the other a long rope attached to the noseband of the halter. The horse's hind legs were entirely free.

When everything was set, we all hastily withdrew and left One-eye in the middle of the corral alone with the Red Terror. At once the horse plunged viciously, but One-eye's jerk on the rope attached to the hobbles pulled his front feet up under him and threw him on his knees. He reared up on his hind legs and lunged halfway across the yard while One-eye kept out of his way and guided him to some extent with the halter rope. The great horse's eyes shone red with rage, and his fine nostrils were rigidly

distended. Grimly I watched with a stone in my heart, knowing
that he could not win. One-eye worked his ropes and jumped
backward and forward and from side to side, like a boxer, all the
time humming Salvation Army songs under his breath. As he
worked, the volume swelled until he sounded like an organ.

The battle raged for an hour and a half, and it was a cruel
thing to see. My stomach contracted in a hard knot, and I wanted
to cry out and beat that inhuman singer with my fists. Time and
again the Red Terror came down on his knees and put his head
on the sand to rest himself, and each time he renewed the fight to
free his front legs by rearing up on his hind legs and plunging at
his tormentor. At last he allowed himself to fall over on his side,
but was instantly on his knees again. His staying power was unbelievable. When he collapsed on his side for the fourth or fifth
time, we thought he was done, but the minute One-eye moved
toward him he was up in a flash, rearing and plunging as if he
could last forever.

Finally the Red Terror was so exhausted that the man was able
to reach his side before he attempted to get up. When the horse
raised his head, One-eye shortened his hold on the halter rope
and pulled the head back over the chestnut's shoulder. With his
forefeet doubled under him and without the use of his head, the
animal could not move. Several times One-eye let go the halter
and taunted the horse with shouts and his terrible singing, and
each time the horse found his head free he would try to get up,
only to have his head snatched back over his shoulder again.
This went on until the poor creature lay panting and lathered,
too dead to care what happened to him.

One-eye himself was as fresh and unperturbed as he had been
when he started the dreadful struggle, and if I could, I would
have choked his singing in his throat. He bounded nimbly around
the fallen chestnut, patting and caressing him, particularly around
the head and ears, but the horse might have been dead for the
notice he took of it.

We led the broken horse to the stall as if we were going to a
funeral. Now it was easy to drain and dress the poll evil, and Dr.
Egan thought it safe to break the horse to harness. I begged him
to let me do it, hoping that I could awaken some flash of spirit in
those dead eyes, but the Red Terror allowed me to touch him,

Paul Brown

stroke him, even push him around, with a desolate indifference that was more terrible than his defiance. His beautiful coat gleamed with my currying, his muscles rippled under the satin skin, but his fine proud carriage was gone. He might as well have been a wooden horse.

At last the owner sent for him. I harnessed the Red Terror to a gig and drove him to Butcher Town, thinking desperately of running away with him, taking him some place where I could look after him and gradually win back his spirit, but as we came nearer and nearer to Butcher Town and the stench of the slaughter yards, my spirits sank into a leaden despair.

As we pushed along the steep streets filled with cattle, the men of Butcher Town stopped their horses to watch us drive by, unable to believe that this was the Red Terror. I hung my head and tried to look the other way, but there was no other way; they were all around me.

Driving slowly, pretending that the road was blocked, I killed as much time as I dared, but finally, when I could put it off no longer, we turned into the owner's yard. The man came out of the stable with a buggy whip in his hand.

"So he's broken, eh? One-eye always does the trick." Raising the whip, he cut the Red Terror across the head. The horse didn't lift his bleak eyes or move by the quiver of a nostril. I ran out of that yard into the street, dodging in and out carelessly among the long-horned cattle, haunted by that last sight of the Red Terror, wishing he were dead.

Florian[1]

By FELIX SALTEN

AN EIGHTEENTH-CENTURY fanfare sounded through the wide hall as the Emperor stepped into the Court Box at the Riding School. Above the box was the escutcheon held aloft by genii and martial emblems. Behind it had been placed the bugle-sextet, musicians from the orchestra of the opera.

Purple velvet hangings covered the balcony and enlivened the hall with their luminous tints. Few people occupied the balcony; officers, ladies, chamberlains of the archdukes present, ladies-in-waiting, and the wives of various Court officials.

In the Court Box five archdukes sat waiting, the Heir Apparent, Franz Ferdinand, in their midst. He did not acknowledge the greeting of the equerry and showed the Imperial princes an unfriendly countenance. "Blessings, blessings, blessings!" he said in rapid succession while his right hand described the sign of the cross in the air. That precluded the necessity of shaking hands.

Then the fanfare.

Franz Joseph entered. After their obeisances the princes remained silent. The archduchesses rose from their deep curtsies.

A brief "Good morning" from the Emperor was accompanied by a circular movement of his hand. The moment he sat down, a door in the opposite wall was thrown wide, and four horsemen rode into the arena. In a straight line they swept toward the Court Box and stopped at an appropriate distance. Simultaneously they doffed their two-cornered hats and swung them until their arms were horizontal. Then they wheeled and to the strains of the *Gypsy Baron* began their quadrille.

The circle and capers cut by the four horses were precisely alike, and gave the effect of music in the flowing rhythm of their execution. The regularity of the horses' strides, and the horseman-

[1]From *Florian, The Emperor's Horse,* by Felix Salten.

ship of the four riders aroused the spectators to a gay pitch, no one could have said why; it was sheer rapture evoked by the beautiful, blooded animals and their artistry.

Every one in the hall could ride, knew horse-flesh, and enjoyed the spectacle with the relish of a connoisseur. Franz Joseph, too, was stimulated by it all, his brows contracted. His white-gloved right hand kept pushing up his thick white mustache.

Suddenly a voice close to him whispered: "How boring!"

The Emperor recognized the Heir Apparent. Turning his head, he said with some heat: "Whoever is bored ought to leave." His voice betrayed rising anger.

Franz Ferdinand mock-apologetically replied: "Forgive me, your Majesty. I didn't mean the quadrille."

With a negligent wave, his uncle commanded: "Be still."

Franz Ferdinand obeyed, remained sitting, and grinned covertly behind his thick black mustache. He had succeeded in ruffling the Emperor.

The quadrille was over, the horsemen had made their exit. The wooden door remained wide open.

Next seven mounted stallions entered and filed in front of the Court Box. Seven bicornes were removed from seven heads, swung to a horizontal position, and replaced.

Florian stood in the center. To his right stood three older stallions, thoroughly trained, and to his left three equally tested ones. He resembled a fiery youth among men. In a row of white steeds he stood out as the only *pure* white one. His snowy skin, unmarred by a single speck, called up memories of cloudless sunny days, of Nature's gracious gifts. His liquid dark eyes, from whose depths his very soul shone forth, sparkled with inner fire and energy and health. Ennsbauer sat in the saddle like a carved image. With his brown frock-coat, his chiseled, reddish brown features and his fixed mien, he seemed to have been poured in metal.

The Emperor had just remarked, "Ennsbauer uses no stirrups or spurs," when the sextet began to play.

The horses walked alongside the grayish-white wainscoting. Their tails were braided with gold, with gold also their waving manes. Pair by pair they were led through the steps of the High School; approached from the far side toward the middle, and went into their syncopated, cadenced stride.

Paul Brown
'45

The Emperor had no eyes for any but Florian. Him he watched, deeply engrossed. His connoisseur's eye tested the animal, tested the rider, and could find no flaw that might belie the unstinted praise he had heard showered on them. His right hand played with his mustache, slowly, not with the impatient flick that spelled disappointment over something.

Ennsbauer felt the Emperor's glance like a physical touch. He stiffened. He could hope for no advancement. Nor did he need to fear a fall. Now—in the saddle, under him this unexcelled stallion whose breathing he could feel between his legs and whose readiness and willingness to obey he could sense like some organic outpouring—now doubt and pessimism vanished. The calm, collected, resolute animal gave him calmness, collectedness, resolution.

At last he rode for the applause of the Emperor, of Franz Joseph himself, and by Imperial accolade for enduring fame. Now it was his turn. . . .

Away from the wall he guided Florian, into the center of the ring. An invisible sign, and Florian, as if waiting for it, fell into the Spanish step.

Gracefully and solemnly, he lifted his legs as though one with the rhythm of the music. He gave the impression of carrying his rider collectedly and slowly by his own free will and for his own enjoyment. Jealous of space, he placed one hoof directly in front of the other.

The old Archduke Rainer could not contain himself: "Never have I seen a horse *piaffe* like that!"

Ennsbauer wanted to lead Florian out of the Spanish step, to grant him a moment's respite before the next tour. But Florian insisted on prolonging it, and Ennsbauer submitted.

Florian strode as those horses strode who, centuries ago, triumphantly and conscious of the triumphant occasion, bore Cæsars and conquerors into vanquished cities or in homecoming processions. The rigid curved neck, such as ancient sculptors modeled; the heavy short body that seemed to rock on the springs of his legs, the interplay of muscle and joint, together constituted a stately performance, one that amazed the more as it gradually compelled the recognition of its rising out of the will to perfect performance. Every single movement of Florian's revealed nobility, grace, significance and distinction all in one; and in each one of his poses he was the ideal model for a sculptor, the composite of all the equestrian statues of history.

The music continued and Florian, chin pressed against chest, deliberately bowed his head to the left, to the right.

"Do you remember," Elizabeth whispered to her husband, "what our boy once said about Florian? He sings—only one does not hear it."

Ennsbauer also was thinking of the words of little Leopold von Neustift as he led Florian from the Spanish step directly into the *volte*. The delight with which Florian took the change, the effortless ease with which he glided into the short, sharply cadenced gallop, encouraged Ennsbauer to try the most precise and exacting form of the *volte,* the *redoppe,* and to follow that with the *pirouette*.

As though he intended to stamp a circle into the tanbark of the floor, Florian pivoted with his hindlegs fixed to the same place, giving the breath-taking impression of a horse in full gallop that could not bolt loose from the spot, nailed to the ground by a sorcerer or by inner compulsion.

And when, right afterward, with but a short gallop around, Florian rose into the *pesade,* his two forelegs high in the air and hindlegs bent low, and accomplished this difficult feat of balance twice, three times, as if it were child's play, he needed no more spurring on. Ennsbauer simply had to let him be, as he began to *courbette,* stiffly erect. His forelegs did not beat the air, now, but hung limply side by side, folded at the knee. Thus he carried his rider, hopped forward five times without stretching his hindlegs. In the eyes of the spectators Florian's execution of the *courbette* did not impress by its bravura, or by the conquest of body heaviness by careful dressure and rehearsal, but rather as an exuberant means of getting rid of a superabundance of controlled gigantic energy.

Another short canter around the ring was shortened by Florian's own impatience when he voluntarily fell into the Spanish step. He enjoyed the music, rocked with its rhythm. These men and women and their rank were nothing to him. Still, the presence of onlookers fired him from the very outset. He wanted to please, he had a sharp longing for applause, for admiration; his

ambition, goaded on by the music, threw him into a state of in-
toxication; youth and fettle raced through his veins like a stream
overflowing on a steep grade. Nothing was difficult any longer.
With his rider and with all these human being around him, he
celebrated a feast. He did not feel the ground under his feet,
the light burden on his back. Gliding, dancing with the melody,
he could have flown had the gay strains asked for it.

On Florian's back as he hopped on his hindlegs once, twice,
Ennsbauer sat stunned, amazed.

Following two successive *croupades,* a tremendous feat, Florian
went into the Spanish step still again. Tense and at the same time
visibly exuberant, proud and amused, his joyously shining eyes
made light of his exertions. From the *ballotade* he thrust himself
into the *capriole,* rose high in the air from the standing position,
forelegs and hindlegs horizontal. He soared above the ground, his
head high in jubilation. Conquering!

Frenetic applause burst out all over the hall, like many fans
opening and shutting, like the rustle of stiff paper being torn.

Surrounded by the six other stallions Florian stepped before
the Court Box, and while the riders swung their hats in unison,
he bowed his proud head just once, conscious, it seemed, of the
fact that the ovation was for him and giving gracious thanks in
return.

Franz Joseph himself had given the signal for the applause by
lightly clapping his hands together. Now he rose and turned to
Archduke Rainer, who, as the most distant claimant to the
Throne, sat farthest removed from him. Rainer was the oldest
among all the archdukes, older even than the seventy-six-year-old
Emperor himself. "Well, did you ever see anything like it?" Franz
Joseph asked.

"Never!" Rainer answered.

"Well, then," said the Emperor, enunciating each word sharply,
"I can not understand how any one could be bored by it."

Rainer tried to pacify him.

"Nobody could have said it bored him."

"Oh, yes," Franz Joseph shot back, the point in his words as
sharp as a knife's tip. "Oh, yes!"

Franz Ferdinand stifled a yawn.

What ensued, four young stallions between the pillars and on the longe, did not interest the Emperor. He became impatient and made ready to leave.

"I can't stand any more," he explained to Isabella and Friedrich. "After Florian—impossible."

To the equerry, who appeared in the box, he said: "I thank you, my dear Bertingen. It was really beautiful. An unusual performance."

He stopped. "This is something for the King of England when he visits us." And in accents as sharp as before, while his laughing eyes took on a steely glint: "He won't be bored with it. . . . Not he."

He walked out.

Franz Ferdinand made a face, shook his head and murmured: "How mad he is. Marvelous!"

Everybody heard it. Even the Emperor might have heard it.

Franz Joseph stood in front of the open door and talked with the equerry. "Tell Ennsbauer that I am very pleased."

Then he departed, and the rest did likewise, since Bertingen announced that the final number on the program, Florian on the longe, had been canceled.

Count Bertingen sent for the riding master who arrived full of dour forebodings. But the equerry had good news.

"Congratulations, Ennsbauer!" he began, obviously aping the Emperor in tone and attitude, a rather necessary and unsubtle cliché in Court circles. "Congratulations! His Majesty has condescended to have me express to you his very highest satisfaction."

Ennsbauer bowed. His face remained unchanged, his mien as inscrutable as that of a statue. His eyes, however, shone.

"A great success, Ennsbauer," Count Bertingen went on. "The performance will be repeated on the occasion of the visit of his Majesty the King of England. Then you may show Florian on the longe also."

Cristiano: A Horse

By W. H. HUDSON

A GAUCHO of my acquaintance, when I lived on the pampas and was a very young man, owned a favourite riding-horse which he had named Cristiano. To the gaucho "Christian" is simply another word for white man: he gave it that name because one of its eyes was a pale blue-grey almost white—a colour sometimes seen in the eyes of a white man, but never in an Indian. The other eye was normal, though of a much lighter brown than usual. Cristiano, however, could see equally well out of both eyes, nor was the blue eye on one side correlated with deafness, as in a white cat. His sense of hearing was quite remarkable. His colour was a fine deep fawn, with black mane and tail, and altogether he was a handsome and a good, strong, sound animal; his owner was so much attached to him that he would seldom ride any other horse, and as a rule he had him saddled every day.

Now if it had only been the blue eye I should probably have forgotten Cristiano, as I made no notes about him, but I remember him vividly to this day on account of something arresting in his psychology: he was an example of the powerful effect of the conditions he had been reared in and of the persistence of habits acquired at an early period after they have ceased to be of any significance in the creature's life. Every time I was in my gaucho friend's company, when his favourite Cristiano, along with other saddle horses, was standing at the *palenque,* or row of posts set up before the door of a native rancho for visitors to fasten their horses to, my attention would be attracted to his singular behaviour. His master always tied him to the *palenque* with a long cabresto, or lariat, to give him plenty of space to move his head and whole body about quite freely. And that was just what he was always doing. A more restless horse I had never seen. His head was always raised as high as he could raise it—like an ostrich, the gauchos would say—his gaze fixed excitedly on some far object; then presently he would wheel round and stare in another direction, pointing his ears forward to listen intently to some faint far sound, which had touched his sense. The sounds that excited him most were as a rule the alarm cries of lapwings, and the objects he gazed fixedly at with a great show of apprehension would usually turn out to be a horseman on the horizon; but the sounds and sights would for some time be inaudible and invisible to us on account of their distance. Occasionally, when the bird's alarm cries grew loud and the distant rider was found to be approaching, his excitement would increase until it would discharge itself in a resounding snort—the warning or alarm note of the wild horse.

One day I remarked to my gaucho friend that his blue-eyed Cristiano amused me more than any other horse I knew. He was just like a child, and when tired of the monotony of standing tethered to the *palenque* he would start playing sentinel. He would imagine it was war-time or that an invasion of Indians was expected, and every cry of a lapwing or other alarm-giving bird, or the sight of a horseman in the distance would cause him to give a warning. But the other horses would not join in the game; they let him keep watch and wheel about this way and that, spying or pretending to spy something, and blowing his loud trumpet, without taking any notice. They simply dozed with heads down, occasionally switching off the flies with their tails or stamping a hoof to get them off their legs, or rubbing their tongues over the bits to make a rattling sound with the little iron rollers on the bridle-bar.

He laughed and said I was mistaken, that Cristiano was not amusing himself with a game he had invented. He was born wild and belonged to a district not many leagues away but where there was an extensive marshy area impracticable for hunting on horse-back. Here a band of wild horses, a small remnant of an immense troop that had formerly existed in that part, had been able to keep their freedom down to recent years. As they were frequently hunted in dry seasons when the ground was not so bad, they had become exceedingly alert and cunning, and the sight of men on horseback would send them flying to the most inaccessible places in the marshes, where it was impossible to follow them. Eventually plans were laid and the troop driven from their stronghold out into the open country, where the ground was firm, and most of them were captured. Cristiano was one of them, a colt about four or five months old, and my friend took possession of him, attracted by his blue eye and fine fawn colour. In quite a short time the colt became perfectly tame, and when broken turned out an exceptionally good riding-horse. But though so young when captured the wild alert habit was never dropped. He could never be still: when out grazing with the other horses or when standing tied to the *palenque* he was perpetually on the watch, and the cry of a plover, the sound of galloping hoofs, the sight of a horseman, would startle him and cause him to trumpet his alarm.

It strikes me as rather curious that in spite of Cristiano's evident agitation at certain sounds and sights, it never went to the length of a panic; he never attempted to break loose and run away. He behaved just as if the plover's cry or the sound of hoofs or the sight of mounted men had produced an illusion—that he was once more a wild hunted horse—yet he never acted as though it was an illusion. It was apparently nothing more than a memory and a habit.

Highboy Rings Down the Curtain

By GEORGE AGNEW CHAMBERLAIN

HELEN OF TROY, out of Suydam Queen, was a high-stepping mare, one of the best tandem leaders that ever sidled out for a turn, and she was killed by an overdose of the joy of life. Bimbo, the stable trainer, was to blame; but only in part. Going back to the true source of cause and effect, it was her genial owner, familiarly known as Kindly Crewe, who was at fault, because he had been away for three weeks and because the last thing he had said to Bimbo was "Keep your hands off Helen; I like her full of oats."

She had grown so full of oats in that short space of time that in trying to race them out of her system in the Lower Paddock she took a header over the fence, breaking one slim ankle and her neck. It was small comfort to say that no horse had ever before done such a fool thing, and that if the mare had so little sense as to try to stop a twenty-mile pace in three yards rather than jump a four-barred barrier, she deserves her fate. No; there was no comfort whatever in putting the blame on Helen of Troy, darling of the stable and of her master's heart.

On the day that Kindly was to return Bimbo took a twenty-four-hour leave by assault. He told Mrs. Crewe that he would rather spend the rest of his life mucking out the stalls of the Grady Short Haul Trucking Corporation than be on the place when the master came back; and, as to performing the feat of actually breaking the news to him, why, he'd rather run at the fence the way Helen did and break his own bally neck.

Staring at Bimbo's corpulent figure, Mrs. Crewe did not smile; she trembled. She wished she, too, could run away, and then thought for one cowardly moment of sending a telegram which would catch Kindly as he came through town. Promptly she put the impulse behind her and fell back on love to help her through

Brown

the ordeal with such effect that Crewe was to remember the soft, firm feel of her straining arms for the rest of his days with a sort of adoring wonder. It was not Mrs. Crewe but Kindly himself who spoke first after the blow of the news was struck, and then only to comfort:

"Buck up, Nelly girl. Don't take it so much to heart, my dear."

That was all he ever said in regard to the death of Helen of Troy. He braced his shoulders and went calmly about his business, but not his pleasure. In person, he was one of those young-old men whose spines have been ramrod trained in the saddle and on the box seat, and who paint their cheeks with the brush of the keen morning breezes of autumn. Florid, you might have called him; tousled of hair, shot with gray, bulky, but with the kindliness which had nicknamed him radiating from his eyes and face in a benign and perpetual glow.

He and Nelly had no living children. He loved Nelly—and horses; she loved him.

Horses had been his sole pleasure, but with the tragic death of his adored mare the love of a lifetime seemed to shrivel within him, and let no man wonder. For a blue-ribbon tandem leader is a rare thing. Leaders can and have been made; but such are mediocre. Your true leader—a rhythm of lovely flesh, slender bone and taut nerves, that beats the signal of the slip of the rein and the caress of the tossed lash at a turn with an instinct sympathy which makes horse and master one heart, one pulse and one understanding love—is never made, but born.

Such had been Helen of Troy. Watch Kindly Crewe bringing his team along at a spanking trot, shoulders squared, arms out, whip at the salute and Helen in the lead. See the ripple and the spring of her glossy body, the red glow of her wide nostrils, the forward prick of her nervous ears and the wise flashing of her noble eyes.

"B-r-r-u! Ho, my pretty! Up with your knees! Swing wide! Swing wide! See the people stare! Out you go for the turn, girlie! Cluck! Cluck!"

Was that the song that was ringing in Kindly's ears, making him deaf to all other calls? No harsh word escaped him, and he uttered no breath of reproach against Fate or Bimbo, and least of all against Helen of Troy. He was still the kindliest of men;

but it was cruel to see the way he turned his back on the paddocks and the stables and crueler still to watch the withering of his youth. Golf! Bridge! How pitifully ineffectual were his mind and hands, so adept at a grander game!

And that was not the worst of it. His cheeks grew pouchy, his shoulders drooped and his big chest looked as if it were beginning to cave in. He would start to go somewhere and then stop, as though, after all, it were not worth while. Even in town, in the executive offices of F. S. & K. D. Crewe, his eyes would suddenly quit work, but stay wide open, so that they gave his secretary the creeps.

Mrs. Crewe was at her wits' ends to know what to do, for a mood is not like a single moment of sorrow. It is continuous, intangible, something that cannot be surrounded by two arms.

Bimbo had run away, leaving to her the whole burden of breaking the terrible news, and she had handled the crisis magnificently. Now he felt that it was his turn. He knew horses and he knew his master. He knew just what was the matter with Kindly and he knew the only cure. A man's love for a woman is one thing—an individual loyalty; his love for horses is quite another. Your true horseman may have a great affection for a special pet, but what he loves and reveres from deep down in his being is not a horse but horseflesh—horseflesh as a temple of noble qualities, of endearing foibles, of an astonishing capacity for understanding and coöperation, and alas, for going to the bad. Horses have all the great traits of man and a few of the mean ones; courage, strength, loyalty, fortitude, and a kick below the belt for an enemy. They are more knowable and scarcely less lovable than women. Comfort does not depend in any one of them, but in all. These things Bimbo knew thoroughly, however far short he might have fallen of expressing them in words.

He mooned about the stables, sat on the top rails of the Upper and Lower Paddocks and stood for hours watching the Crewe string put through their paces at the end of a longe or hitched to the drag or a sulky. If there was an answer to Kindly's trouble, and his own, it was nuzzling its oats, rollicking on the fallow turf or trotting up and down before his eyes, if only he had the shrewdness to see it. He did not deceive himself for a moment with the thought that he might go outside for something to take the place of Helen of Troy. He knew instinctively that though Kindly's cure lay in a horse, it would be hopeless to attempt to force his purse in order to salve his heart. Spontaneity, surprise, joy in possession of an undreamed treasure—all these must Bimbo wrest from the gods that his intuition might come to full fruition.

And here was horseflesh in plenty. He began at the bottom. The two colts and the filly came in for first consideration, but they were too young; they represented altogether too long a wait. He discarded them with a sigh, but finally. There was quite a class of two-year-olds. These he mulled over in his mind during long wakeful hours and then watched for as many more as they were paraded before him in every type of harness from the dishabille of a hackamore to silver tabs and patent-leather blinkers. But never once did his own hands itch to grasp the reins with adept touch and send a message quivering down the oldest telegraph line known to man. Then came the hacks, and last of all the coach horses.

Crewe's four-in-hand of dappled grays was famous on two sides of the Western ocean. They had carried off more blues than any one combination of horses is entitled to, if the indoor sport of showing teams in harness is to endure. They formed a close corporation which was next door to a monopoly, and would have been cordially hated had they been the property of any man less beloved than Kindly. It was with this renowned team that he was scheduled to lead the coach parade through Central Park in a last effort to bring back the days when a coach and four had the right of way in the public's heart no less than on the road.

Bimbo watched them swinging by, hitched to the drag ballasted with every stable hand that could climb aboard. He knew these horses so well—every ripple and swell of their muscles; every shade of their color, in and out of sweat; every dapple, every hair! He knew their moods and their power, their infinitesimal failings and their transcendent perfections; be knew them as a mother knows her own young. Alas, he knew them so well that, though his eyes dimmed with pride at the staccato thunder of their passing, he did not ask himself even subconsciously if there was another such as Helen of Troy among them. They were not individuals; they were a team and gloried in the fact. Hence their extraordinary collection of decorations.

There remained only the waste—the outcasts of the stable, few in number, each marked by some bar sinister of ineradicable fault either in disposition or physical ensemble. These could not even be sold as from the Crewe string. They were doomed to be shipped away via the back door as soon as a nondescript auction offered the chance of an ignominious and unostentatious exit. Besides the Upper and Lower Paddocks, there was another inclosure, also a paddock, but never spoken of as such. It was called the pasture in a tone that made one think of cows. Here were penned the outcasts—the pariahs of the equine House of Crewe.

Bimbo climbed down from the perch from which he had been sampling the top of the cream in horseflesh and walked with dragging feet and lowered head toward the pasture. He walked as one without hope, but dogged in duty. Long since, he had abandoned all thought of casually picking out a winner by the exercise of sheer perspicacity and had fallen back by an unperceived transition to the ancient formula of deduction through elimination. He would not thus have named the process going on in his mind as he scuffed heavily along on his way to look over the despicable remnants of a great stable; he would have called it simply, passing up no bets.

He reached the gate to the pasture, folded his arms on its top bar, settled his chin on them and stared with lackluster gaze at the small bunch of blemished horses which was gathered in a hollow some distance away. At that range the most expert buyer would have been at a loss to pick and choose among them, but Bimbo needed to go no nearer. The mere sight of pastern, gaskin or hock, withers or buttock, was enough for him to reconstruct an entire tragedy. It was as he had foreseen. No glimmer of hope came to light his eyes which were rapidly turning glassy with despair. As he was turning from the gate, however, a form silhouetted against the evening sky on a near-by knoll, drew his attention only to throw him into a rage.

The object of his wrath was a magnificent gelding, steel-gray in color and gloriously dappled with shadowy spots as big as the palm of Bimbo's hamlike hand. To visiting horsemen he was a thing of indescribable beauty until they heard his name, and then he turned ugly by association before their eyes. He was a rebel of the first water and of uncertain age, but surely no chicken.

His splendid teeth, too freely shown, marked him as over four and under seven. His name was Highboy, and Bimbo hated him with a whole-hearted hatred.

Now, a word as to Highboy and how he had come unheralded and unpedigreed to the Crewe stables. The explanation lay in his color, dappled-gray, and in the fact that Kindly's scouts had orders to buy in every horse of that particular shade that came into the market, the only other qualifications being as to size and soundness of limb. It was specifically stipulated that temper was no bar; and, as it happens, Bimbo himself had been the joyful discoverer of Highboy at a sinister sale where no questions were asked or answered and prices were correspondingly low.

Kindly's theory was excellently conceived. His dapple-gray coaching team was the pride of his heart, and being subject to the ills of accident and age was constantly backed by a string of under-studies. He was not particular as to the temper of these supers, because, up to the advent of Highboy, he had been confident that he could handle all the spirits one skin could hold when bottled at the near wheel of a heavy coach and surrounded on two other dimensions by well-trained old-stagers.

But Highboy had kicked the stuffings out of this theory in five crowded minutes, and incidentally eaten a hole in the neck of his side partner before the excited grooms, swallowing their terror at the voice of command, were able to cast him free of harness and bit.

Since that day the rebellious gelding had lived a life of ease, all the more maddening to the conquered because his stable manners were perfect. He was easy to handle, loved to be manicured, curried and brushed, and would eat apples gently off the palm of a child's hand. Nevertheless and notwithstanding, no one had mentioned harness to him again. There seemed to be a general and tacit acceptance that Highboy's expression on that subject had been peculiarly final. Life, human and otherwise, also equipment, were too valuable in Kindly's estimation to be cast beneath the active feet of an equine cyclone that had cost only three hundred dollars in cash to the highest bidder.

Bimbo had been so elated at the moment of purchase, had brought the horse home in such a transport of pride and had so

Paul Brown

bragged of the price at which his astuteness had secured the prize of a season, that that miserable three hundred dollars immediately became a festering thorn in the flesh. The old trainer would gladly have wiped out the sting of defeat with three thousand of his hard-earned dollars had there been any particular method of so doing. But the iron of the situation went still deeper. Three lots of remnants had gone to the obscure auction block since Highboy's advent, yet he remained in slothful possession of bed and board.

"No, Bimbo," Kindly had said on the three occasions, "I can't do it, questions or no questions. It's on account of his gentle ways, you see. It might turn out that he would win some woman's heart and then break her neck. We'll just have to keep him, and at least he's easy to look at."

Easy to look at! As if that made things any better! Now, in the moment of his deepest despair of finding a cure for his sorely wounded master, Bimbo stared at the beauty of Highboy, at his perked ears, broad forehead, fearless eye, arched neck; at the glorious dapples that came and went under the flick of the sunlight; at the splendid bush of his sweeping tail and at the five straight lines of a perfect horse—four cannons and a level back. God help him, what a waste! Bimbo's eyes grew bloodshot with rage; his lips parted, he swore and from swearing sank to vituperation.

"Gelding! Bah! Lounge lizard! Mantel ornament! Father unknown; likewise mother! Good to look at as naked sin and rotten from the ground up! Parasite and blatherskite! Eunuch!"

Highboy pitched on his forefeet, flaunted his tail, threw up his widespread heels, insulted Bimbo, and then tore off to the farther side of the pasture, where he began to trot up and down, neck arched, nose in, ears pointing forward, hoofs spurning the sod and plume streaming on the wind. The old trainer's face turned purple with a fresh access of rage; he spat violently on the ground and turned his back on the grand-stand performance. That night, his bulky frame feeling unusually exhausted, he retired early, but not to sleep. The vision of Highboy persecuted him. How could anything so lovely be intrinsically so mean? Quite suddenly he came to a tremendous resolve. He would hitch Highboy to two tons of drag, with a board fence between him and the heaviest, staidest off-wheeler in the stable, and either break him or kill him or be killed. His own life had so lost its savor that he risked only the small end of nothing. Who would choose to live on with his mouth full of ashes when he might go down gloriously in combat with a mortal enemy?

The more he thought of the scheme the better it looked. Elimination of every other possibility had led him finally to Highboy. Anything which would change suddenly the status of the rebel must surely appeal to Kindly's dormant affection for horseflesh in the essence. Here would be spontaneity, surprise and joy in possession of an undreamed treasure, all rolled into one! What if he, Bimbo, should fail and die in the attempt? Well, there were times when a lot can be said for death as a boon. What if he should kill Highboy? He produced a grin in the dark which was a cross between a sardonic grimace and a gleam of pure glee. His sane judgment told him that Kindly would consider the event an economic relief. He could hardly wait for the morning, and thus thinking he slept and slept soundly.

Now, many a man has gone to bed with a problem and awakened to find its answer staring him in the face. Thus with Bimbo. He thought he had hit on a daring attempt at solution of his trouble on the night before, but when he awoke an idea stood waiting for him which for sheer boldness made his previous scheme seem faint-hearted cowardice.

It was as though the apparition of Highboy had been in reality an important message, an attempt at long-distance horse telegraphy, a hunch in the making, which had knocked and knocked in vain on the barred door of Bimbo's waking intelligence and then given up the struggle only to creep into the warm emptiness of his sleeping brain and fill the vacant apartment chockablock with its presence.

He did not stop to reason. He clambered out of bed and into his clothes by six of the clock, Eastern standard time. By seven Highboy was in his stall; by 7:30 he had munched two quarts of oats and by eight he was reveling beneath such a combing and rubbing down as had not been his portion in many weeks. By 8:30 he was in harness and by 8:35 Bimbo was beating it for the manor house as fast as his stumpy legs and stumpier breath would permit him to travel. He actually had the pleasurable illusion that he was flying. He burst into the morning room where Kindly, alone, was dejectedly eating a leisurely breakfast preparatory to catching the 9:05 for town.

The facial contortions induced by the emotions of disaster or great joy are astoundingly similar; consequently, and since Bimbo remained for a moment speechless by force of circumstances and the weight of his paunch, it was natural that Kindly should have picked the wrong answer to his trainer's inarticulate commotion and spoken as follows:

"If anything has happened to one of the horses, Bimbo, just shoot him and put him out of his misery. If it's anything else, use your own judgment. Whatever it is, don't bother me."

"I won't bother you, Mr. Crewe," said Bimbo, recovering his breath, "further than to request you to walk as far as the Upper Paddock."

Ordinarily the trainer addressed his employer as Kindly, except when before strangers or in the show ring, and the extremely formal opening of the interview should have warned Crewe that something unusual was afoot, something so formidable that it could not be carelessly brushed aside. His eyes assumed the vacant stare that on several recent occasions had proved so disconcerting to his secretary. With a shrug of his shoulders which looked more like a shrinking quiver, he turned on Bimbo.

"Get this straight," he said; "I'm not going near the paddocks, and, what's more, I'm not going to drive in the coach parade."

"Not—going—to—drive—in—the—coach—parade!" whispered Bimbo with a pause between each word, his eyes slowly bulging from his head.

"That's what I said," confirmed Kindly. His eyes grew vacant again. "I'm still trying to decide," he continued presently, "whether I'll show this year at all."

"Trying—trying to decide whether you'll show!" gulped Bimbo, amazement in his florid face and tears in his voice. Then suddenly he awoke from the trance into which his master's terrible words had plunged him. His bulldog chin shot out and his head up. "Listen to me!" he roared. "I've spoken to you as trainer to his boss and you wouldn't hear. Now it's Bimbo to Kindly and man to man. Listen to me! You're going to the Upper Paddock if I have to call the hands and carry you there. You're going now! Do you get that?"

"I heard you," said Kindly quietly. "You're fired, of course, Bimbo. I'm sorry."

"Fired!" snorted Bimbo. "Well, I don't care a damn if I am. Who minds being fired for five minutes? Will you come or do you still want to make it a ride?"

Kindly's eyes grew hard for the first time in the twelve happy years of almost brotherly companionship with his trainer. They became two points of steel which drilled Bimbo through and through. It was a look which in any other moment would have struck terror to his lion heart, but in this instance he took it so calmly that a shadow of doubt swept across Kindly's troubled face. But only for an instant. He drew out his watch.

"I'll come," he said shortly, "just for the five minutes it will take me to put Charlie in charge."

Side by side, and in silence, the two estranged friends, comrades in many a shared victory, left the house and walked briskly toward the stables; but with a difference. Kindly carried his head low, while Bimbo seemed to be striving to stretch his short neck to the heavens. His eyes protruded like the orbs of a crab as they strained forward for a first sight of the distant paddock, and were filled with a reaching anxiety which changed suddenly to complacent joy. His heart began to pound with something more than the labor of mere physical exertion.

"Hold it, boy!" he murmured inaudibly in exalted supplication. "Hold it, my beauty!"

The path to the stables led the two men close to the great Upper Paddock, which embraced the four-furlong practice track. As they approached the fence, Bimbo, in spite of himself, slanted stealthy eyes at Kindly; and Kindly, knowing that he was watched, kept his gaze subbornly on the ground. The consequence was that Kindly saw where he was going and Bimbo did not; Kindly stepped over a hose, while Bimbo tripped on it and all but came a purler. As he rushed headlong to catch up with his balance Kindly shot one glance across the fence and forthwith came violently to a stop.

The sight which met his eyes was the eighth, ninth and tenth wonder of the world. On the fresh green turf, well away from the track, stood the high English dogcart, two idle grooms and two horses, hitched tandem. The wheeler, a splendid bay, tried and true, was a bit restive from the chest up, tossing his head impatiently; but the leader, steel gray and darkly dappled, seemed posed in weathered Pentelic marble. From the straight-hanging plume of his tail, along the sheer line of his level back, over the curve of his arched neck and up to and including his erect ears, he was as fixed as a painting—only he lived. Waves of electric life throbbed from his still body to beat against Kindly's bursting temples.

"What horse is that?" he asked sharply.

"Highboy, sir," replied Bimbo promptly, without pausing to wonder at the question.

"How long has he stood like that?" continued Kindly, laying trembling hands on the top rail of the fence to steady himself.

"Since I told him to hold it while I fetched you," answered Bimbo out of the fullness of his faith. He sidled up to Kindly and suddenly all his pent emotions came burbling out in a volley of chatter: "Great balls of sweat, Kindly, don't you tumble? Don't you know he knows you're looking at him? Pride, by God! He's in the lead, ain't he? He's out and free; he's alone, not one of a level bunch. He's It, and he knows it just like you and me when we're on the box with the horn tallyhoing to make the people stare."

"You're right, Bimbo," gulped Kindly.

He was still in a daze; he was choking; he was at the very bottom of a translucent sea and he would drown if he didn't get to the top in a hurry. Up he came, and up. His shoulders began to straighten and his chest to bulge. All the blood in his veins started a race from his heels to his head. It was like the sap of springtime, hurrying back with youth to a stricken world. It lifted him, bore him swiftly upward until he shot out of the deep waters into the freedom of a new air.

"You're right," he breathed exultantly, staring hungrily at Highboy.

As though he had called, the sometime rebel turned his head with a slow, majestic movement and looked his owner square in the eyes. Instantly Kindly's body became vibrant. He slipped over the fence as smoothly as a snake over a stone wall, approached the horse quietly, and reaching out a steady hand began to caress him. Lowering his nose, Highboy promptly butted him in the chest and struck the sod a single sharp blow with his right fore hoof.

"I get you!" cried Kindly with boyish jubilation as he recoiled from the dignified and firm rebuff. "You mean 'Let's go!' "

He started toward the cart wheel, his arms extended and his fingers working as though they were in rehearsal for a half-forgotten play. The grooms moved forward, stood at attention and laid strong hands on the reins close to the bits. The horses quivered and pawed; bent their heads and cast them up again, almost lifting the grooms from their feet. Kindly sprang smoothly to the driver's box with a catlike alacrity astonishing in one of his generous build and recent age. He picked up the rug, wrapped it around his thighs in knowing manner, sank back on the high pad, leaned forward, gathered the lines and lifted the whip from the socket.

"Cast loose, boys," he said quietly, "and stand free."

The grooms complied and leaped aside; the horses shot forward on a bee line across the sward, moving in a swift but nervous, jerky trot. For a moment they pulled hard, tightening the wires, listening, ears back, for a message, and presently it came to them. It told of gentle, knowing hands giving them their will for a moment—velvet in the mouth for a moment—and then whispering steadily of the strength of steel. For that they had waited—the touch and call of the master. They heard and answered, eased their weight from the bits, pricked their ears forward and steadied down, freeing themselves from domination by obedience to the law. They became a glorious rhythm, a harmony, smooth to the eye, melodious to the ear.

They were making at right angles for the track and the fence, but Kindly had no intention of risking an expert turn. He bore down gently on the left reins as if he were guiding a commonplace bobsled. Gradually he brought the team around in a wide sweep to the track; and then, bit by bit, moment by moment, gave them their heads until they were racing along at a thunderous trot. Around they went and around once more. He eased them, let them go, eased them again, talking soft words to Highboy, getting acquainted, telling him confidential things in a low tone which suggested further intimacies and perhaps love in the near future.

As they passed for the second time the gaping stable crowd which had gathered around Bimbo, Kindly called out in a clear voice, "Open the gate!"

"No, Kindly," protested Bimbo. "Not to-day!"

His shout floated down the wind, weakening into a wail as he saw his master swing from the track to the turf and, with slip of rein and touch of lash, boldly venture on a broad figure eight. At the first turn Highboy seemed to check and waver, but in reality his lithe body was merely squirming to get a message and get it quickly—and it came.

"B-r-r-u!" Kindly caught up a six-inch loop over the middle knuckle of his driving hand. "Cluck! Cluck!" He let the loop go and at the same instant cast the whip's lash gently to Highboy's off shoulder. Into his full stride swung the gelding, leaning for the left swerve. Swiftly they made the small circle. "B-r-r-r-u!" again, slip of rein, lash to the other shoulder, "Cluck! Cluck!" and an all but perfect turn to the right. They came out of the figure eight and straightened. Bimbo forced back the gate with his own hands to give them the joy of the open road and the freedom of the wide world.

An hour later Kindly, perched on a stool, and Bimbo on a feed box, were assisting at Highboy's toilet after exercise. No words can describe the affection and admiration, amounting almost to awe, with which they regarded him. Kindly was still bubbling over with the feats of intelligence and intuition which the horse had performed during the morning's work-out and related them *seriatim* and over and over to his avid audience of one. But these wonders of technic faded into nothingness beneath the shadow of the great miracle of Highboy himself—Highboy as the triumphant vindication of horseflesh as an essence, one and indivisible.

"You may be thinking, Bimbo," said Kindly, "that he's been a leader before, away back somewhere in his stormy past; but I tell you he hasn't. I know it! I don't mean to say he jack-knifed on me. No; nothing so crude as that; but he asked questions all the time!"

"Did he now?" exclaimed Bimbo, even while he nodded his head up and down to indicate that he could quite understand the marvel. Half an hour later Kindly was still talking.

"I ask you, Bimbo," he was saying portentously, "what's behind all this business of coach and four, high cart, sulky or any bit of clean-stepping prettiness between the shafts? Why do we do it? Horse and man, why do we love it? I'll tell you. Just two things—exhilaration and admiration. Take one away and the other is spoiled. And don't forget the horses are in on both. You bet they are! They drain the joy from action and the nectar from the public eye. Look at Highboy here! Golly! See the coxcomb turn his head! What happened to him this morning? No; I don't want you to talk. I'll tell you. The same thing as has put many a pretty woman over the hurdles. Boredom and vanity in conjunction with the psychological moment."

"Sure-lee!" interjected Bimbo, spitting at a grain of oats and hitting it. "That's what he fell for!"

"Don't think I'm not giving you credit, Bimbo," resumed Kindly hurriedly. "I am, and your pay's raised 10 per cent from this day. Now, here's what I was saying, only clearer: The horse is the thing, of course; but what makes him show is the public eye, just the same as you and me when we're on the box with four reins in one hand and the whip at the salute. Do you get me, Bimbo? What I mean is, when there's no one left to cry 'Oh, look! Look!' as we come bowling along, and all we hear is 'Gee! See what's got away from Buffalo Bill!' why, coaching will be finished, metaled roads or no metaled roads."

Bimbo shook his head affirmatively.

"When you or me is on the box of a sharpish morning, Kindly, we be just kids—and the horses too."

"That's it," confirmed Kindly, rising from the stool to flex his muscles.

He opened and bent his arms with a snap; his eyes sparkled and his face radiated such joy that it seemed to illumine the stable with a golden light. He threw back his head and drew a long breath. Ye gods, what smells! Pungent oats and hay. Warm odors, more vulgar. The acrid smell of sweat and the sweet breath of horses. Leather—leather, bright and new; leather, worn and dry; leather, polished to the flower of old oak! Then his eyes fell upon Highboy and promptly filled with the illuminating moisture which is the visual distillation of happiness. He went to the horse, cast his right arm over his withers, pressed against him, caressed him. This time he was not repulsed. Highboy spoke to him with a whimpering whinny, curved his neck sharply and rubbed with his nose first Kindly's empty pocket and then his dangling and equally empty left hand.

"Heigh! Some one fetch me an apple, and fetch it quick!" called Kindly as his fingers crept along the bulging muscle beneath the mane and sought the two hollows behind the pointed ears. "What a hide, Bimbo! Baby's skin, here behind the ears of him. Not a blemish anywhere. All dappled silk, from eyes to buttocks. What a glory of a horse to be reborn, all in a morning, from a bit of understanding flattery!"

When Kindly finally wandered back to the house along toward one o'clock, still smiling from the depths of a happy daze, his wife greeted him with the following words:

"Why, Kindly Crewe! Did you miss your train? What on earth are you doing here? You know I never eat anything myself for lunch." And then as she really looked at him, "Oh, my dear, what has happened? Whatever it is I am glad!"

At the end of a week the office, which had been worrying itself sick over his sad and too continual presence, began to howl over his absence, as is the way of offices, and to predict dire results if he did not come to town by the first train or a flying machine. It pointed out that his many previous absences had been premeditated and consequently predigested by the monster organization, but this was different. There were deals to be closed; checks to be signed; papers, documents, that awaited his decision.

In the meantime—see Kindly and his tandem team seeking out the widest of the clay roads in the oak-and-pine belt. The oaks have turned; their leaves are red as pigeon's blood against the dark and juicy green of the everlasting pines. The air tingles and tinkles with the first pricklings of the frost. Look at Kindly, the youth of him! Shoulders squared, arms out, whip at the salute and Highboy in the lead. Up—up into the collar for the open stretch. Oh, the beauty of his action, the pride of his head, the joy and the spring and the drive of his stride! "I'm Highboy! Highboy! King of the road for a day!" and then—

"B-r-r-r-u Ho, my beauty! Up with your knees! Swing wide! Swing wide! Pipe the guy that's standing there to watch you take the turn! Cluck! Cluck!"

No slip of rein, no expert tossing of the guiding lash, for High-boy knows it all and more. Out he sidles, leans for the turn and flashes into line again, trotting free and wide, crash for crash with the hoof beats of the bay between the shafts. On they go, sailing along on whirling pin wheels of brilliant red, tempted to nick the outer edge of the foolish town—tempted and yielding. Not into the thick of the traffic. Oh, no! Just into the park and out again, to see the people stare!

Before Bimbo could scratch his ear, so to speak, show week was upon them and the Crewe string entered for a try at every class. Kindly drove, Bimbo drove, and Charlie, the head groom, nervously took his turn. They showed everything that wears leather for pleasure and in due course worked down to "Hack-neys: tandem." Long had been the debate waged between Kindly and Bimbo and back again as to just what Highboy would do in the ring and whether they should show him at all, always to come up against the blank wall of the question, "What if the judges call for a canter?"

Now a word as to cantering tandem, trickiest of all equine maneuvers, barring the *haute école*. The driver takes his team on the trot, straight at a solid barrier. At the very moment of the right-angled swerve the horses must change lead and break into a canter; but that is not all. Just one thing more: Leader and wheeler must start in step, hoof for hoof and stride for stride. The real question—the silent question behind all the spoken ones asked by Kindly of Bimbo and by Bimbo of Kindly was, "Can living man throw Highboy into a canter and bring him out again short of the Canadian border?"

"Well," concluded Kindly, "perhaps the judges won't call for it. They don't have to, and they haven't for three seasons on end. And what if they do? Perhaps Highboy will go through it once, just to show off. Anyway, I'm not going to try him out—not once; not even here in the paddock. If he killed himself or me before I trot him up and down under the noses of the boys who thought they had a laugh on you, Bimbo, why, I'd never forgive myself—never!"

The great day and the fateful hour came. There were five tandem teams and Kindly drove fourth. If the quantity and quality of the rattle of applause which followed the evolutions of the pedigreed bay and the brilliant dappled gray of unknown lineage meant anything to the judges, it surely meant another blue ribbon to the Crewe stables. Highly pleased with the world in general, himself and Highboy in particular, Kindly stepped briskly from the ring, looked at his watch and saw he must hurry to dress in time for dinner.

Friends stopped him right and left, some for a hasty word and some for the outline of the horse in history. They knew it was not in him to be brusque, and, one and all, they never missed a chance to take a leisurely warm bath in his smile whenever opportunity offered. Consequently, by the time he reached the outer lobby the best part of half an hour had passed, and as he stood there for one last handshake there came rolling out to him an uproar shot through with jabs of lightning in the shape of shouts of "Kindly! Kindly!"

Opening a way for himself with a plowing shoulder, he rushed back to the ring and for a single second stood transfixed. In the center of the tanbark was his best English dogcart with Bimbo on the driver's seat. In front of Bimbo was the wheeler, quivering but steady, and in front of the wheeler stood Highboy, erect on his hind legs and looking as high as the Woolworth Building as he thrashed around with his fore feet and madly tried to throw bit and bridle from his tossing head.

"So," raced the thought through Kindly's brain, "the judges called them back for a canter, after all, and Bimbo couldn't find me!"

He tore off hat and coat as he leaped into the ring, and in a moment was slipping up over one wheel of the cart as Bimbo, trembling and purple with rage, surrendered the reins and descended via the other.

"B-r-r-r-u! You dappled devil!" shouted Kindly.

Down came Highboy to all fours, deliberately turned his head all the way round and looked at his friend and master as one who would say, "So you're back where you belong, are you?"

Under cover of the ecstatic roar from the crowd, Kindly leaned over and spoke to the spluttering Bimbo:

"Oh, never mind that! I know what happened. They've called for a canter. Tell me quick, has he seen any of the other teams do it?"

164

P.B

"Three," answered Bimbo—"all rotten."

The bugle sounded. Kindly telegraphed a message along the tautened lines. The team sprang forward in unison and he began to talk aloud.

"Up with your knees, boys! Into your collar! Snap into it! Show them—show them how! Now! Hoop-la, Highboy! You've got it! Hold it! Hold it! Steady, boy! Whoa!"

The grooms sprang to the horses' heads. As he helped his master down, Bimbo chortled in a raucous voice, all malice forgotten, "What a canter, eh, Mr. Crewe? Oh, you Highboy!"

"The top of the cream, Bimbo!" answered Kindly, blinking the tears from his shining eyes. "Smooth as music and moonlight. I didn't do anything. Really, I didn't. He did it all himself. He isn't a horse at all. He's something God thought of just once."

"Well," murmured Bimbo reflectively, "I wouldn't lay quite the whole of it on God. If you'd heard some of the things I called him while he stood on his hind legs for five solid minutes, trying to paw holes in the roof, perhaps you'd get my meaning."

"Why, that's the very thing I was thinking of!" laughed Kindly with upthrown head. "He was made just for himself and me."

Two weeks later Kindly and his blue-ribbon team were back on the soft roads of the open country. The parchment leaves of the oaks were hanging on through the grim, cold winds of winter and the pines loomed big and dark above the bare, brown soil. But life ran with a surging note, high and full, through the veins of horse and man. They were coming in from a ten-mile tearing drive, and as of old the lure of town and people was strong upon them. Just a nick into the town, dash across the Boulevard, into the park and out again! This was the song of hoof and heart: "Rat-tat, tat-tat! Here we come! Look! Look! Aren't we lovely? Aren't we strong? And young, young, young!"

As they swept up to a crossing at a spanking trot, Kindly saw grouped on the left curb a shrimp of a man pushing a loaded baby carriage, and behind him his wife and two children of walking size. On the right was a narrow walk and the pronged iron fence of a great estate. To Kindly and the rushing horses it mattered not that the family group was greasy to look at and bundled in garments that poisoned the winter air. They were people—

people with eyes to see, ears to hear and hearts to leap in admiration.

Suddenly an icy chill shot through Kindly's extended arms. The man saw them, and yet he had started to cross with the woman and children strung out behind him! What on earth were they thinking? Didn't they know? Gangway! Gangway! Did they take a tandem in flying-wedge formation for a motorcar with horn, emergency brake and clapperty chains that could stop in its own length? In the terror of that instant Kindly grew hard, and rage seized him as he yelled at the top of his voice, "Heigh! You! Look out!"

He saw the man's face turn and leer at him with sneering lip as he kept on straight into the path of the flying team. Kindly's hands ate up the reins for a short hold. He knew he could lift Highboy, but never the wheeler. A baby, God help him! He could almost have killed the man with joy; but a baby! He had the lines at last, wrapped to his elbows. He braced his feet, bent his back forward to the coming strain, but never needed to pull. Highboy waited for no order; he shot straight into the air, leaped high, twisted violently to the side and fell, impaled to the heart on the sharp prongs of the iron fence. Wheeler and cart wrenched around to follow and crashed against his hanging buttocks, already quivering in the death throe. Kindly was hurled over and through the wreckage to find himself standing on numbed feet directly above the baby carriage and the rat-faced little man.

"Are you crazy?" he choked.

"You crazy," replied the stranger with alien accent, and walked on, uncurious, his family trailing stolidly behind him.

Late that night, when Bimbo came to the manor house to report that all that could be done in the way of cleaning up the pitiful mess had been accomplished, he found word that Kindly wished to see him in person, and followed the maid to the library with quaking heart. He expected to find his master an utterly broken man, but apparently Kindly had more than recovered from the actual shock of the disaster. Instead of breaking, it seemed rather to have added something to him. He was reading a book as Bimbo entered, and the eyes he raised from its pages were calm and warmly affectionate.

"Sit down, Bimbo," he said. "This isn't a business interview, though I may tell you of some radical changes in the classes of horses we are to breed from now on. What I want to do to-night is to talk about Highboy. I want to fix him for all time in my mind just as he was—the oneness and the pride of him—and I'll tell you why. He taught me something. That isn't it, either. He gave me something—something besides his life, I mean."

Bimbo nodded his bullet head solemnly and started to speak, but Kindly stopped him with a raised hand and continued: "You know, they say the heart can't remember for long the features of a face. Try to think of some one you've loved who is gone, and what do you remember? Some favorite photograph of that face and perhaps where it was taken. But Highboy didn't have features; he had points. A warm eye on a broad forehead. Let's remember that. Winged nostrils and a chest like an apron of silk. Clean forelegs that he could use like a boxer. Dapples! What dapples, Bimbo; big as your hand, each with the luster of a black pearl behind a silvery veil! A strong hide and in it himself, courage and rebellion, docility and rage, an unconquerable spirit—undying flame!"

Bimbo's eyes became suffused.

"Let up on that, Kindly," he said gruffly and in haste. "I just been burying of him."

"So you have," said Kindly, untroubled but with understanding. "Well, old friend, this is what I wanted to tell you: The ratty little man with the baby carriage was right. If only you could have seen his face when he said 'You crazy!' I am crazy; that is, I was crazy this morning. Don't eight million hooters blare the swan song I wouldn't hear? Haven't the metaled roads been tolling the death knell on us for a dozen years? And this is what Highboy did for me, Bimbo. He took the sting out of it. What a message! What a clarion call! What a sunset to our day of glory! God help us, Bimbo, what a curtain!"

Black Kettle[1]

By FRANK M. LOCKARD

ON A day in June, 1867, a wagon train owned by Mormons was passing west over the old Smoky Hill Trail. They carried with them a bunch of Kentucky Thoroughbred horses, which they were taking to Salt Lake for breeding purposes. Somewhere near the west line of Logan County, Kansas, Black Kettle and a band of Cheyenne Indians swooped down upon them, stampeded the stock which was grazing near camp, and left the Mormons with their loaded wagons and nothing to pull them.

Among these horses was a fine yearling stud colt that escaped from the Indians and joined the wild horses, which were plentiful on the prairie at that time. In the course of time this colt developed into one of the finest specimens of the equine family. Nothing to compare with him had ever been this far west. The Indians tried many times to capture him, and it was from them

[1]From *Black Kettle,* by Frank M. Lockard.

that the white men learned his history. The white men around Fort Wallace would speak of him as the Black Kettle colt, a name which stuck during his long life. His range, until he was thirteen years old, was in central Sherman County, where the city of Goodland now stands. During those years the old government road, known as Custer Road, ran through the center of Black Kettle's range and was much traveled by military authorities and also buffalo hunters, who sold their hides and bought their supplies at Peter Robidoux's store at the old fort. Very few ever traveled that road without seeing Black Kettle, and by the time he was five or six years old he was known to hundreds of men.

Black Kettle's chief distinction was his long mane and tail. His heavy tail was so long that more than a foot of it rested on the ground when he was standing still; and when he was running, it stuck straight out behind—making him appear to be about twenty feet long, when viewed from a distance. His mane reached nearly to the ground when he stood erect, and when he was in motion, with his head up, it lay along his back, making him appear about a foot higher than he really was. When he ran he was continually tossing his head. This movement puzzled me at first, but I soon discovered that he was throwing his foretop over his ears so he could see. That foretop, which reached below the end of his nose, completely shut off his vision when in its natural place. He was coal black and his glossy coat glistened like burnished silver; his movements were as graceful as the fawn, while for speed and endurance he excelled any other animal on these plains.

Wild horses ran in small bands, usually eight to ten in a bunch, all of them mares, except one, the leader. I have seen many bunches of twenty or more and when I first saw Black Kettle, in 1879, he had twenty-nine mares, which is the largest band I ever saw. There were only two colors, black and roan. Nearly all the mares were red roan. There was an occasional blue roan, but the latter at a distance looked black; and when on occasion we saw a bay, iron-gray or white, we always knew that they were animals that had escaped from immigrants or cattlemen. Among the females about one in ten was black, while the percentage of roans among the males was a little higher than that. The surplus males were driven out by the leaders and flocked by themselves, usually one, two and sometimes three together. There were hundreds of them on this prairie when I first came. These outcasts were called "dog soldiers" by the Indians, and the white men used the same name in describing them. The same name is used in describing an outcast among the Indians. A dog soldier had only one ambition, and that was to get a family of his own. They haunted the herds day and night, and the stud who had a family was compelled to keep up a continuous fight or lose them. For the most part these dog soldiers were roan and old blacks that could not fight any more. A roan with a bunch of mares was seldom seen. To be born a roan meant that a horse was doomed to celibacy. I suppose that was nature's way of providing for "the survival of the fittest."

For more than ten years Black Kettle was a conspicuous mark on this prairie. He was chased more often than any other horse. I have talked with men who knew him long before I saw him. Most of them had at some time tried to catch him. An early day captain of Fort Wallace, Homer W. Wheeler by name, conceived the idea of using the U. S. cavalry to aid in catching him. He came out with his company and surrounded Black Kettle one night. He had a scope of prairie about the size of a township in the circle with a soldier every half mile. His plan was to chase him inside the circle by sending in a fresh horse every hour and finally late in the day, when he was exhausted, to send in a cowboy and rope him. But Black Kettle went through that circle before he made the first revolution. Then Captain Wheeler marched back to the post. Shortly after this, while in the Robidoux store, Captain Wheeler was telling experiences in the presence of Ame Cole and others and wound up his story by offering two hundred dollars to any one who would bring him that horse, properly attached to the end of a rope. Here is where Ame Cole gets into the story.

"By G—d, Captain, I can walk the tail off the G— d—m horse in five days." And as Cole afterwards related the circumstances to me, Captain Wheeler replied by saying: "I consider the tail the most valuable part of the horse and would not give much for him without it." When Cole left Wallace the next morning it was his intention to catch Black Kettle and return in about one week.

When Cole left Fort Wallace, his plan was to crease Black Kettle and then hobble him before he woke up. (A shot through the top of the neck just in front of the withers would temporarily paralyze but not permanently injure a horse and was called "creasing.") But his partner, Grant, was opposed to fooling away any time on so uncertain a project. "Buffalo are plentiful on the river and might move on any time. Let us get a load of hides while we can." But Cole was obdurate, and the chase was on.

The wild horse can see, hear and smell a man farther than any other animal, and this country being flat and unbroken, it was only on rare occasions that you could get closer than one mile to a horse. As there were bands of them at frequent intervals, a man would be seen by some of them before he could get very close. And as soon as a man was seen by one, all others within a few miles knew it and were on the alert. Wild horses never move very far from their watering place and when being chased they run in a circle and never leave the home range. Usually that circle was small, as they never went more than ten miles to water. But Black Kettle had been chased so much that he became unusually smart and would sometimes run twenty miles in a straight line when badly scared. Another unusual thing, he had two watering places, one in the Wild Horse Draw, near the Smoky, and the other in a waterhole on the head of the Beaver. These two waterholes were twenty miles apart as the crow flies. Had Cole known this fact on the start, I might have a different story to write, but he learned it later.

I would like to tell you the remaining part of this story in Cole's dialect but I can't; so I give it in my own poor way. He found Black Kettle on a high prairie about ten miles southeast of Goodland. Black Kettle ran northwest, and in the course of an hour passed out of sight. Cole followed at a brisk walk and at times in a trot, until he felt sure he had gone as far as that band would go in that direction. Far away on the horizon, in all directions, he could see horses, but as he had no field glasses, he was uncertain which was his bunch. So he turned west and, after following a band until late in the afternoon, he found he was after the wrong horse. He turned toward camp feeling sure that Black Kettle would come to the Smoky for water sometime during the afternoon. Cole reached camp late, hungry and nearly famished

for water; and as he put it, "the only real quarrel I ever had with my partner occurred that night."

Early next morning he started out to locate Black Kettle. All day he tramped up and down the Smoky watching for him to come down, but night finally came and Black Kettle had not been seen, although many bands were sighted. That night Grant said: "Tomorrow we leave for the Republican," and Cole reluctantly gave in. The next afternoon as they drew near the Beaver, they unexpectedly came upon Black Kettle. Cole wanted to try him again, but Grant would not stop. Other hunters joked Cole about it afterward. He took it in good part but insisted that but for Grant he would have got Black Kettle. Cole intended to come back later and catch Black Kettle, but he never found time when he was in the mood.

My partner in these days was the late William Simpson. We were dealing in ponies quite extensively, and during the year of '78–'79 we spent most of our time around Wakeeney. The first settlement of Trego County came during that time, and a bunch of Chicago capitalists started the town of Wakeeney. Warren and Keeney were the promoters and by putting their names together the name Wakeeney was coined.

New settlers were arriving every day, and the demand for saddle ponies was brisk. We kept a supply on hand which sold readily at good prices. We talked of Black Kettle many times and whenever a buffalo hunter came in from the west our first inquiry was whether he had seen the horse or not. Our plans to capture him were discussed a thousand times, for we were cocksure of getting him later. Our experience in handling broncos had given us a conceited idea that no wild horse had any show whatever when we started after him.

During the time that we were at Wakeeney, word reached us that a pair of wild horses ranged on the high plateau, between the South Solomon and Saline. The center of their range was about twenty-five miles northeast of the town, not far from the northeast corner of Trego County. We went out to look them over. We did not expect to catch them but wanted to study them at close range, hoping to learn something that might be useful later when we got ready to catch Black Kettle. We found a beautiful pair of roans with a young colt following them. We chased them for two days but never got nearer than one mile of them. Their watering place was at the head of Wild Horse Creek, a tributary of the Solomon. Because of this the first settlers gave this creek its name. Some boys from down the river came out later and caught the colts, but the old ones were still there the last I knew of them, which was in the fall of 1880.

Late in the fall we returned to our home in Norton and at once began our preparations for the big wild horse chase. About December 10, 1879, we started following the Prarie Dog to where the city of Colby now stands. Here we struck a dim road leading southwest which had been made by buffalo hunters going to and from Wallace. We followed this road until we came to a water-hole in a draw, some two or three miles before we reached the Smoky. This was the first water we had seen since leaving the headwater on the Prairie Dog, just north of Dresden. As we had been without water for nearly three days for our horses, we laid up for a day to give them a chance to recuperate. Neither of us had ever been that far west except on the railroad. We had but little idea where we were. The weather had been cloudy with a good deal of fog, with the result that we differed about the direction in which this road was leading us, but while in camp at this waterhole we heard a train pass on the old K. P. and we then knew that we were pointing in the right direction.

Early next morning we came to the Smoky. We turned upstream, knowing that the headwater, which was to be our destination, could not be far off. Late that evening we came to an abandoned frame house, sitting back under a bank. It was only a shell without doors or windows. We afterwards learned that this house belonged to the XY cattle outfit. There was no one about, and from appearances there had not been for some time. Here we made camp and decided we would investigate. About three miles below we had crossed a wagon road which proved to be the old Custer Road, although we did not know that at the time; in fact, we did not know there was a Custer Road there, or elsewhere, but later discovered that it was the only landmark on this prairie. It served us many times afterward by pointing the way when we became bewildered on this vast expanse of level, flat country. Late that evening we sighted a bunch of buffalo coming into the draw south of camp. Simpson killed one, which supplied our wants in the line of fresh meat for the balance of the trip. This draw, we learned later, was called Wild Horse Draw, and it carries that name today. Next morning we rode south to a high point from which we could see over all the prairie north of the river, and with aid of field glasses we counted more than fifty herds of wild horses. There were more wild horses in Sherman County that day than there are tame ones today. This high point south of the Smoky we named Point Lookout, and it served us in several ways afterward.

Later, we set a post on this point from which waved a red undershirt, which could be seen through a field glass from the high points on the north prairie fifteen miles away. And during the following months signal fires burned many nights near this post to guide us to camp when darkness had caught one of us on the prairie.

We returned to camp, and after dinner we rode out north for the purpose of familiarizing ourselves with lay of the country. We felt sure that we were on Black Kettle's range and expected to see him any time. Several small bunches of horses were scared up and we watched them through the field glass as long as they were in sight. We then observed for the first time that the mares were all roans with a black leader—and each leader looked like Black Kettle to me. But later in the evening, after we had started for camp, Black Kettle himself came in sight. We had heard him described so often that one flash through the field glass settled his identity. That long mane and tail were plainly visible, although he was a mile off. I wanted to start right there and then but Simpson said, "No, it is late, and your horse is jaded now. Wait until morning." This I reluctantly did.

Just what our plans were, if we had any, I have forgotten. We had, in a way, studied wild horses and I suppose we had in mind a complete plan which we thought could not fail, but what it was has escaped my memory. Green and inexperienced as we were, I don't think we expected to rope him on the open prairie; so I think probably we intended to run him down and then drive him to Norton without catching him. So far as we knew, there was no corral within one hundred miles of us and I do not think it ever occurred to us that we would need one. We had talked to many men who had run wild horses but had never heard of anyone catching them except an occasional colt or cripple, but these stories did not discourage us in the least. On that first afternoon we had seen two or three hundred horses in the course of our twenty-five mile ride, and I think we expected to drive them all into our home corral at Norton before spring.

That night at camp our arrangements were gone over for the steenth time and Simpson decided to haul a load of cow chips out to Point Lookout, so that if I failed to return before dark, a signal fire would be burning to light my way home. I weighed one hundred and forty pounds at that time and was hardened to the saddle. I could ride a hundred miles without trying, and I had corn-fat horses that were as tough as I. At daylight next morning I was in the saddle, and two hours later I found Black Kettle. I started after him on a stiff lope, going at about ten miles an hour and held that same rate of speed for the next ten hours. As darkness closed down around me, I observed I was getting colder. A brisk wind was blowing and I noticed occasional snow flurries, which lasted for a moment. In order to make the load on my horse as light as possible, I had left my overcoat in camp. My plan was to drive Black Kettle toward camp in the late afternoon, and when night came, I expected to go in and get something to eat and mount a fresh horse in the morning. I had crossed the Custer Road two or three times that day but had paid no attention to it, as I felt sure that I knew in what direction I was going. The weather had been pleasant and I was delighted when I thought how easy it was to follow and finally catch a herd of wild horses. But even in fair weather the nights are cold in this altitude. After I stopped and got off my horse, I walked briskly to warm my stiff legs. It occurred to me that possibly I did not know the direction in which camp lay. I fed the horse some corn that I had in the saddle pockets and ate some cold biscuits that I had had for my noonday lunch, and as I was eating I walked around and around the horse to keep warm. When he finished his grain I was uncertain which direction I had come from; so I decided to remain there until morning.

I unsaddled my horse, and wrapping the saddle blanket around me, lay down. The blanket, being wet from the perspiration of the horse, was frozen stiff in a few minutes and I was not long in discovering that I would freeze to death if I remained there. So I put the saddle on the horse and started for camp on foot, leading the bronco. I had not gone but a short mile until I came to a shallow ravine. I supposed this led to the Smoky but could not recall having seen a draw in these parts before. I walked fast all night as I had to keep warm, but I was sure I was going toward camp and expected to arrive there any minute. When daylight came I found myself going down a broad valley with the bed of a dry creek through its center. I then supposed I had struck the Smoky above headwater and would soon come to water and camp.

It was cloudy and I had not realized that I was lost. I mounted the pony and urged him into a trot and kept up that gait most of the day, until, just as night was closing down, I came to the ranch of Johnny Buck on the Sappa, which I afterwards learned was near the southeast corner of Rawlins County. Here I spent the night and got food for myself and Mr. Buck explained that the Custer Road ran from Fort Wallace straight north to the Republican and directed me to follow the Sappa until I came to that road and then follow it to the Smoky. I reached the road that evening just at dark and got to camp at daylight. I walked most of the way, for my horse was completely exhausted.

Simpson was just coming in from Point Lookout, having spent most of his time up there for the three days I had been absent. He was so delighted at seeing me that he wanted to embrace and kiss me. "I had given you up," he said. "I supposed you were lost and probably dead." He had kept a fire going on the point for three nights and had spent most of his time during the day up there scanning the prairie with the field glasses, hoping I would come in sight. He had scarcely closed his eyes in sleep during the time, and I was in nearly the same condition, but it took us most of the day to recount to each other our experiences for the past three days. Finally I said, "If I had had a pocket compass I would not have got lost." "Sure," he said, "and we will have one before we start out again. I was going to start home today if you had not come, but we will go anyway," he said.

I protested and told him that I had Black Kettle jaded and now was the time to finish him, but he thought his nerves needed a rest; so back we went to Norton. During my three days' ab-

sence he had found the XY corral, which was only three miles
west of camp. I don't remember that we had thought of a corral
before but now that we had found one, we felt sure that all we
needed was a pocket compass; so we went one hundred and
twenty-five miles to Norton to get one.

We reached Norton late in December and spent the holidays
at home. About the 10th of January, 1880, we came back and
camped at the XY corral, beside the headwater of the Smoky, at
the point where the Dyatt ranch is now. We brought a wagon-
load of corn drawn by four horses, with Ed Maple as driver and
cook; also six corn-fat saddle horses, and a pocket compass. Our
previous experiences satisfied us that we knew the game perfectly
and that all the loose horses on this prairie were soon to be decorated with our well-known brand.

One of our delusions was that a tired horse meant a tame
horse, and, the wild horse being weak at that season, we had no
doubt that our corn-fat saddle horses would soon make them
tired.

A wise philosopher once said, "Experience teaches a dear
school." During the following weeks we learned many things that
can't be found recorded in Kansas history.

A few miles west of our camp on Goose Creek lived one Mr.
Johnson, known as Wild Horse Johnson. We heard that he was
the only man in the West who had successfully caught and tamed
a wild horse. So, before starting after Black Kettle again, we paid
him a visit. We found about fifty wild horses grazing contentedly
around his corral. We found him a very courteous gentleman and
he explained his system both of catching and taming. Before that
time we had supposed that a wild horse could be run until exhausted, but he explained that to run them down was impossible,
and even if you could, he said, they were worthless ever afterwards. "I follow them in a buckboard," he told us, "until they
become sore-footed and then corral them. Once in the corral,
I catch them and tie a clog to the front foot." A clog is made of
a forked cottonwood limb about two feet long; this is slipped
over the foot just above the hoof and tied with a rawhide thong
from the points of the fork. He would turn them out and once
or twice a day drive them into the corral to keep them tame.

After wearing the clog a few days they were again caught and the clogs removed.

Mr. Johnson drove his captives into the corral, thus giving us an opportunity for close inspection. Only a few of the leaders were wearing clogs at the time and all of them seemed as tame as the ordinary range horse. The wild horse at a distance looked much larger than these did from a close-up view, and this accounts for the many stories of large twelve hundred pound horses seen on the range in the early days. We inquired of Johnson if he had ever seen Black Kettle.

"Yes, and run him, too," was his quick response. "I chased him once for two days and then lost him; he has been run so much that he is very wild and cunning." He then admonished us not to bother with Black Kettle. "There are hundreds of horses on the prairie that are worth as much as Black Kettle," he told us. "There is nothing to him but his mane and tail. He weighs about eight hundred pounds and is getting old. Let him alone."

He told us many interesting incidents of cowboys chasing Black Kettle, and explained that by reason of this the horse was very wild and had a wide range. He had seen him often twenty miles from his usual watering place, which was Wild Horse Draw. He also told us the same story about Lieutenant Wheeler's chasing him with the United States cavalry that we had learned from Bill Street.

On our way back to camp we had a good laugh over Mr. Johnson's warning us not to bother with Black Kettle. We felt sure he wanted the horse for himself and greatly underestimated his size and value. Having seen the horse, we knew his size and value, or thought we did. We learned later that what Mr. Johnson told us was true in every respect, but it cost us much time and labor and some little humiliation to admit it.

We killed a Buffalo and two antelope in the breaks of North Smoky that evening on our way to camp, which supplied us with fresh meat for some weeks.

The only way to make the business of catching wild horses profitable was to drive the whole bunch. Even if your saddle horse had bottom enough to overtake them, the weak ones would drop out, and if any were captured it would be those of no value.

A man on horseback in the rear can't hold them together; that is always done by the leader. When the leader is crowded to fatigue, the bunch scatters and the first thing you know you are only driving one or two at most, and of course, if you catch one the others get away. Mr. Johnson explained this, but it did not impress me at the time. That night our arrangements for capturing Black Kettle were complete.

Early next morning we left camp, going north toward the point where Goodland now stands. I was mounted on a fleet, fat horse and was to do the running, Simpson following slowly on a big twelve hundred pound draft horse, carrying a half bushel of corn for the horses and a few biscuits for ourselves. A short five miles from camp we sighted through the field glasses Black Kettle with his bunch of roan mares quietly feeding on a piece of high ground about two miles northeast of us.

Simpson was to take up a permanent position on some high point, and I was to run Black Kettle in a circle around him. Knowing that these horses never went far from water, I felt certain I could hold them within bounds until they were exhausted and then the two of us would drive them into the corral. Keeping the high ground between us as much as possible, I approached the herd, riding slowly. While I was still a mile off, they saw me and moved away to the north.

I followed on at a stiff lope, going about ten miles an hour, but Black Kettle was going faster than that and gained on me rapidly and after a two-hour chase they disappeared in the brakes of the Beaver. An hour later I came to a waterhole where they had watered and from there turned west.

This waterhole is on the section line between sections 24 and 25, township 6, range 39, and had been a noted camping ground for buffalo hunters in past years, but I did not know that at the time; in fact, I did not know what stream I was on but supposed it was the Sappa. Little did I think that some day I would be farming in that neighborhood.

This famous waterhole has made a history to which I will refer later. Many an Indian fight occurred there; white men whom I knew were buried there. That land is now owned by Oscar Ramsey. I watered my horse and started southwest, and in a short time I saw Black Kettle quietly grazing about two miles west of me on the high prairie on the land now owned by Mr.

Fixsen. From there he ran south and crossed the Beaver, I following as fast as my bronco could run, being determined not to lose sight of him again. About mid-afternoon I came in sight of Simpson a little northeast of the present site of Goodland. The weather had been cold and crisp but not very uncomfortable.

About noon it became cloudy and a strong wind arose. By the time I reached Simpson, snow flurries were in the air and in a very short time the worst blizzard I ever experienced was upon us. We abandoned the herd and started for camp, but the fury of the storm became so intense that we soon lost all sense of direction. We came to a lagoon and decided to stay there. We began to gather chips but they were scarce and for the most part hid by the snow; yet we succeeded in piling up about one bushel and then decided to keep them until morning. We removed the saddles and fed the horses some corn; then, taking the saddle blankets, we wrapped ourselves as best we could and sat down on our small pile of fuel in an endeavor to keep it dry for future use. In those days men wore boots exclusively and cowboys shunned the hand-me-downs kept for sale by the frontier merchants and wore the fancy high-heel variety, made to order by the village shoemaker. A cowboy with high heels and a Stetson hat was dressed up. In the way of clothing nothing else mattered.

Simpson wore a pair of high-top alligator boots that fit the foot snug, and as we had no overshoes he was complaining of cold feet before darkness settled and the storm had reached its worst. Fearing we should lose our hats, we put them in the saddle pockets. To replace them we cut two strings about one foot wide off the end of a saddle blanket, each of us wrapping one around his head. Then, drawing the saddles over our laps and feet, we sat there eating frozen biscuits, contemplating what our fate was to be.

Whether I had any premonitions about our future during the long arctic night I don't remember, but at one time Simpson said, "I wonder how long our cadavers will remain here before we are found." Simpson had the appearance of a perfect specimen of physical perfection, but he was not; whether it was cold or heat, hunger or thirst, he tired out quickly.

I always thought if he had been alone, he never would have left that camp alive. He died a few years later while still a young man.

He talked very little that night and I don't think I said anything. Like James Whitcomb Riley, "I just kept a-thinking." When daylight came, the fury of the storm increased, the air was full of icicles that cut like a knife. After making several attempts we finally started a fire, which only lasted a few minutes. Simpson wanted to remain right there, but I went to work and saddled up both horses while he stood in the ashes of our small fire, trying to warm his feet.

Fortunately we were north of our camp and could go with the wind. (It was impossible to go against it.) I started on foot, leading the horses and thus breaking a path through the snow, Simpson rather reluctantly following. We had taken but a few steps when I heard him yell, "Stop."

When I turned back he was sitting down, the soles of both boots gone; he had burned them out while I was saddling up. We both wore corduroy pants and in addition I wore overalls. These I removed, cut them in two from crotch to waist, and tied the legs around his feet; then, taking a double blanket from under my saddle, I laid it across his horse and tucked the ends around his feet and slipped the stirrups over them. About mid-afternoon we reached camp. I had walked all the way and was not very cold, but Simpson was so cold and exhausted that he had lost all ambition and interest. We were stopping in a dugout near the XY corral and we found a good dinner awaiting us. Simpson's feet were so badly frozen that the loss of his boots made no difference, because he could not have worn them anyhow. He had a high fever that night and was threatened with pneumonia.

All interest in Black Kettle had passed out of my mind as we set about our preparations for returning home. As soon as the storm was over, we set out for Norton. The cook and I walked and as we passed along we gathered chips from the bare spots on the prairie and threw them in the wagon so that we could have a fire at night. The snow was deep and badly drifted, and our progress was slow. On the second day we reached the dugout of Andrew Jardine near where Colby now stands. We had passed near there on our way out but did not see it.

Early in May we left Norton for the annual round-up and proceeded to Pawnee Grove, where we spent the next ten days in gathering cattle, but before leaving home I had gotten together my supplies for another wild horse chase and, of course, took them with me to Pawnee Grove, as I planned to proceed from there to Sherman County and make one more attempt to capture Black Kettle. Having learned that the weakness of the wild horse was in his feet, I secured a buckboard, as I felt sure the practical way to follow them on this smooth prairie was in a light buggy, which enabled me to carry food and water for myself and team.

I started from Norton with three driving teams (good ones) and one saddle horse, a wagon of corn, and supplies for myself and cook, sufficient to last sixty days. During the round-up at Pawnee Grove there were present ten or twelve cattlemen with about forty saddle horses, and when they discovered my load of corn, they of course helped themselves and nearly all my groceries and flour were consumed by that outfit before we finished working the cattle. So it came to pass when I was ready to move on to Black Kettle's range I found it necessary to send my cook, Ed Maple, to Wallace for corn and provisions. These he secured from Pete Robidoux's store and then met me with the balance of the outfit at the XY corral on the Smoky.

There was considerable speculation at the camp at Pawnee Grove about Black Kettle, and the probability of my catching him. So when I started for the Smoky several of the men decided to go also. Marsh Parker of Jewell County had cattle on the Sappa that winter and was present at the round-up. He said: "If I ever see that celebrated horse, I will have to go to his range; you will never catch him." So he came along.

My youngest brother, Allen, had just arrived in Kansas that spring. Before taking up his work as a cowboy at Pawnee Grove, he decided he wanted to see a buffalo and the wild horses; so he came along. There were two or three other men in the party who had never seen a buffalo or wild horse, and as we neared the old camp ground on the Smoky there was considerable speculation among them about the probability of seeing a buffalo or getting a close view of the wild horse.

Somewhere in the Sappa draws near where Brewster now stands, we came suddenly onto two old buffalo bulls and after a five or six mile chase killed one and wounded the other.

This satisfied the boys so far as the buffalo was concerned. Later the same evening we sighted Black Kettle. He, with his fine bunch, was grazing on the high prairie near the old Custer Road. Although he was more than a mile away, all the men got a good view of him through the field glasses.

When we got to the XY corral, my cook was just driving in from Wallace with the supplies. I observed that he was leading behind the wagon a strange horse, which he said belonged to a cattleman at Wallace. "They are starting for Texas in the morning to meet three thousand cattle which are at this time on the trail coming to Kansas, and I have a job with them." So after supper he mounted his horse and rode away and I have never seen or heard of him since. He was a fine cook, and I was sorry to lose him but glad to see him get a position on the trail, as that had been his ambition.

His going was a disappointment in another way. My nerves were keyed up on the Black Kettle chase and I was anxious to be off but I could not leave camp until I had some one to care for the stock while I was out. So I was compelled to lie there and do nothing until the party who came with me returned to Pawnee Grove and sent a man back a week later. Billy Rogers of Norton came and remained with me the balance of the season. That week seemed long to me. Each day I rode out and took a look at Black Kettle and hundreds of other horses and wondered if I was ever to catch them.

I had so far received little encouragement. Not a man in Pawnee Grove believed I would succeed. Simpson had abandoned me and discouraged the enterprise as foolish, but I never worried for a minute. I was young and full of energy. I knew if I followed that horse long enough and far enough, some time he would give up and I meant to do that very thing, and did it.

Now a word descriptive of my equipment. In my open buggy I carried a five-gallon keg of water for the team, a gallon jug of water for myself, a frying pan and coffee pot. I brought a supply of bread from camp but made coffee and fried bacon each time I camped. I carried a Springfield rifle and a field glass, a pair of blankets and a slicker. When night came, unless I was near the home camp, I made camp on the prairie, put my team on the picket rope and went to sleep.

The next morning after the arrival of Billy Rogers, I set out for the chase. This was on June 2, 1880, but as the chase progressed, I lost track of the day of the week and month—when I got in, Billy set me right.

Within two hours after leaving home camp that morning I found Black Kettle, and the chase was on. I had learned that speed was not necessary; that if a horse was kept moving constantly his feet soon gave out. So I jogged along at the rate of about five miles an hour. For the first two or three days the herd ran away at sight of me and left me many miles behind, but on the fourth day I could see them limping along and only half a mile away at times. Late that afternoon they went to water in Wild Horse Draw, and I went to the home camp for a change of horses and a fresh supply of bread.

During the night it hailed and rained, which made it disagreeable. We had no fuel but buffalo chips and the reader will understand how near the impossible it was to build a fire with that kind of fuel when it was wet. So I went to the old corral and got some boards with which we cooked breakfast and baked a supply of sourdough biscuits for me to carry along.

This made me late in getting started and I drove many miles before I sighted Black Kettle again. The prairie was covered with water, the lagoons and draws were full. But late that afternoon and about fifteen miles northeast of the home camp, I found Black Kettle and his little herd quietly feeding near the old Custer Road. All signs of tender feet had disappeared, and he apparently was as wild as at the beginning and I followed him for five days before I saw home camp again.

The soft ground made it easy on the horses' feet and, there being an abundance of water everywhere, they moved back and forth half way between the Smoky and the Beaver. Try as I might, I could not get them within ten miles of the home camp. On the afternoon of the fourth day, the prairie having dried up, they began to go lame again.

They had been running nearly due east and west. After running about fifteen miles west, they would turn and go back over the same ground. I had been experimenting with them by driving them farther each day than they wanted to go. Late on the fourth day I had driven them east until we were ten or twelve miles east of the Custer Road. When darkness came, I made camp with the horses about a quarter of a mile east of me. I had killed an antelope that day; so I gathered some chips and cooked an antelope steak, which I found an appetizing supper, as I had been living on cold biscuits and bacon and only a limited supply of these.

Black Kettle had wanted to turn back for some time before we stopped. I had learned to read his movements, as he would stop and loiter a considerable distance behind the bunch when he wanted to change his course. His movements always indicated on which side he intended to pass when he turned, but I had kept them moving in the direction he expected to use when turning.

Early dawn next morning found me up and cooking another antelope steak. When it was light enough to see, I discovered they had gone around me during the night but had gone but a short mile west of me, where some of them were lying down, the others standing around, all of which indicated they were very tired. As I started after them they moved west, first in a walk but a little later as I drew near they broke into a trot, but did not appear to be excited or afraid.

This was the most beautiful morning I ever experienced. The atmosphere seemed to be impregnated with sweet perfume. I seemed to see hundreds of miles and on the high spots I could see clear across Sherman County.

I had driven only a short two miles when I heard something that sounded like distant thunder; the earth seemed to tremble, and as I looked about me, I discovered wild horses coming from all directions. Black Kettle broke into a wild run and other bunches fell in alongside of him. My team wanted to run and I let them out at full speed.

There was a magnificent scene spread out before me and I wanted a close view of it. I was also curious to know the cause, and as I looked out on that panorama, I could see horses coming from everywhere. The herds from each side came in close, then turned west alongside of Black Kettle. We had only run a short time when there were hundreds of them all abreast and running their best. Such a sight I shall never see again. The studs were busy keeping their bunches from mixing, although they were very close together. The almost military discipline of each bunch counted and each herd maintained its own individual number. There were many dog soldiers darting here and there, but they were driven off, and antelope by the hundreds joined in the chase.

After I crossed the Custer Road, I looked to the right and saw a herd of buffalos, about fifty in number, running parallel with the horses and a short time afterwards off to the left there was a small bunch, probably ten or twelve, which soon crossed over behind the horses and joined the other herd. They ran along in this direction for about ten miles and then bore off toward the northwest. These were the last wild buffalo that I ever saw.

Black Kettle was near the center of the long line, which extended half a mile on either side of him. Presently a young colt fell and dropped behind, and when the mother tried to turn back to it Black Kettle put her back in her place and kept her there. As I cast my eyes down the line I could see the little colts dropping behind. The studs paid no attention to them but kept the mares in the bunch by simply shaking their heads at them with their ears back.

We were going very fast. My team soon began to weaken but I applied the whip and kept as near them as I could. About this time I noticed the strangest mirage that I had ever seen. Those horses at times looked to be fifty feet high and then a golden mist would hide them completely; when I was on low ground, the mist seemed to lift so that I could see their legs, which appeared as long as telephone poles. This would only last an instant. Just a flash, and everything changed again and then for a minute the mist shut off the view of the horses, but on beyond I could see towers and spires of a great city.

When the mirage dissolved, I found the horses had separated; some went southwest and other bands were moving toward the northwest. Black Kettle had been in a pocket. He could not run fast enough to go around in front and I kept so close that he dared not drop back. Although he was weary and wanted to stop, he had held his place at the front. My team was exhausted and stopped as soon as I laid the whip away. I must have run thirty miles that morning and probably crossed Sherman County quicker than has ever been done since with a team and buggy. I had killed a team that was worth more than a hundred wild horses.

As I turned back I could see many little colts coming. I suppose some of them found their mothers, but the coyotes got a few of them.

After I had gone about ten miles, I came in sight of a horse standing on the prairie with two colts standing near him. As I came closer, I discovered the horse wore a harness. Then the mystery of the stampede was explained. Had I looked behind me early that morning I might have seen him coming, but I had no time to look anywhere but straight ahead. He had followed until he came to those little colts and had stopped with them, and as I drew near he came to my team. I tied him alongside and moved on toward camp. One of those colts followed for several miles and then turned back.

I moved along on a slow walk because my team could go no faster. Late in the afternoon I met a man on horseback riding bareback. I had been thinking as I rode along, "If I don't catch Black Kettle, I have found a pretty fair horse that will help pay expenses," but the man claimed the horse and soon satisfied me he was the owner.

I asked him his name and he said, "Call me Boney Joe; that's all the name I use in this country." He was camped at a water-hole in a Sappa draw near the east line of the county and only four or five miles from where I had camped the previous night. He had harnessed his team before breakfast and left one of them loose to graze. While he was eating, a bunch of wild horses crossed just below and his loose horse followed them. The rattle of the harness had caused their stampede.

Boney Joe said, "I knew if that old chain harness stayed on him I would get him again, because no wild horse would go near him." He went with me to my camp and spent the night there. Boney Joe lived at Wallace and was gathering buffalo bones for the market. A week later he moved up to my camp and remained there several days.

Well do I remember his description of the mirage. I must have been twenty miles ahead of him when that mirage showed the best. Yet he said he could see those horses running and hear them plainly. There must have been five hundred of them.

The next morning after the mirage I went northwest from camp and met Black Kettle as he was returning to his home range. I came onto him about twelve or fifteen miles from camp at a point near where Ruleton now stands. The horses ran for a couple of miles and then slowed down to a trot and kept that up during the day. They moved around in a circle on ground that was familiar. Toward evening I was driving close up to them, but that night it rained and the soreness in their feet seemed to disappear and they were nearly as wild as on the first day. During the next week it rained every night and their tender feet seemed to improve. I would probably have caught them just as soon if I had laid up during that rainy week, because as long as the ground was soft they could travel about as well as at the beginning.

When the prairie dried off, they soon showed sore feet and I was again driving them about where I pleased. I had now followed them more than twenty days and they were so tame I kept within one hundred yards of them and closer at times. I would drive them close toward camp each evening and spend the night with Billy, and as I would drive away next morning I would tell him I expected to corral them that day. Every day I would get them in sight of the corral but could not get them in. They would break back and run a mile or so and then stop until I came up again.

My best team was out of commission since the big stampede and my other teams were tired and slow. Wild horses are always led by the same mare, and right here I must tell you about Black Kettle's leader. When we had first looked them over the previous winter, Simpson had named the old mare Aunt Susan. He said she reminded him of an old lady by that name he once knew. She was a beautiful blue roan and about twelve years old and during her remaining years she was widely known as Aunt Susan. I shall have occasion to mention her often as my story nears the end. When the wild horse is excited, the male always remains between the herd and danger; so it happens that as you follow them he is always in the rear, except that on occasions he will run around in front to drive off dog soldiers or other danger that may appear, but he soon takes up his position behind and remains there. In all their movements he is in supreme command. By some signal which mystifies me Black Kettle would turn his mares in any direction he chose without seemingly making a move. I always thought he made the signal with his ears but was never sure. He could increase or lower their speed by a slight movement of the head, which was imperceptible unless you watched him very close. The lead mare kept her eye on him at all times but the balance of the herd had no responsibility except to follow the lead mare, and if one of them dropped out of place even for a few steps, the male was right there to put her back.

The XY corral was in a bend of the creek and I had difficulty in getting the horses to it. I had been holding them near it for several days but had not had them nearer than two hundred yards of the gate. One morning as I was getting ready to start, Billy said, "This is the thirtieth day you have run Black Kettle; if you don't get him today, you had better quit him and try another bunch." I told him I would corral him before night.

When I got out on high ground, I saw my bunch going up the slope on the south side of the river. I had never seen them on that side before, although I had tried to put them there several times. They were moving along in a slow walk, Black Kettle in the lead. Fifteen minutes later I was in front of them trying to turn them toward the corral, but, try as I might, I could not turn them. They would walk around me, part on one side and part on the other. I rode close enough to touch them with my whip. They would trot around me and move on in a walk. Black Kettle had lost all interest. His feet were so sore that he would stop for a moment once in a while and hold up one foot while part of the bunch had stopped and was acting as though they did not intend to follow; so I got behind and drove them along. I knew that if they separated they were lost. Black Kettle and Aunt Susan kept moving slowly toward Lake Creek, while I was doing my best to keep the balance with them. I lost several that day, mostly old mares and yearlings, because each wanted to go his own way, but I saved the best ones and might have saved them all if I had driven my best team that morning.

I was now in strange country. I did not suppose there was a corral between me and Fort Wallace, but no matter, my mind was clear: I was going to stay with them and trust to luck. Late that afternoon I came to a house and a corral. I afterwards learned this was the Bar Lil ranch owned by Kibbe and Edwards. Although I had never heard of their ranch, I was delighted to find it. After a few trials and as the sun was going down, I got the horses into that corral.

Could you have seen me then, you would have seen a proud boy. I would not have changed places with the president of the

United States, although I had had no dinner and my team was jaded. I felt like singing the national anthem and did it. I unhitched my team and put them on the picket rope and went to the house. There was no one about, and from appearances had not been of late. I looked around for something to eat but found nothing; however, in one corner was a comfortable bed. I turned in at once and was sound asleep. Some time later I was awakened by some one getting into bed with me. I did not suppose there was a man in many miles of me. The first conscious thought was that some highwayman was there to hold me up; the next was that the proprietor had come to throw me out, and as I began to apologize a voice said it was all right, sleep as long as you want to. I felt relieved but he talked a little. I don't remember whether I told him I had a bunch of wild horses in the corral or not, but suppose I did.

The first thing I did when I came out that morning was to take a peep into that corral to see if Black Kettle was still there. The horses were standing close together in one corner, seemingly contented and enjoying their rest. It then occurred to me that I had not eaten anything for twenty-four hours, and I felt the need of something stimulating; so I set about getting some breakfast. After drinking a pot of black coffee and eating a couple of sourdough biscuits, I felt better. The puzzling thing to me was what I was going to do with those horses, now that I had them. So far as I knew there was no one in twenty miles of me and for me to catch and hobble that bunch alone was impossible. So I decided to turn them out and drive them to the home camp. As Black Kettle had led them in the wrong direction all day coming back, I decided to tie him up and drive the mares alone and come back and get him. I was not an expert roper, but I caught him the first throw. He made a lunge at the fence and landed on top with his head and front feet on the outside. After struggling for an instant, he slid down on the outside and started north dragging my forty-foot lariat.

I hitched my team to the buckboard as quickly as possible and turned the bunch out. Aunt Susan led them straight north, and when I came up to them they were walking peaceably and slowly towards the Smoky. You would have supposed that drag rope would have kept them excited, but except when it touched one of them they paid no attention to it. Aunt Susan was in the lead, and Black Kettle brought up the rear; so it was seldom they noticed the rope at all. We reached the Smoky about noon and turned upstream towards the XY corral and camp. I had difficulty at times in steering them in the right direction but succeeded late that day in driving them into the big corral at the home camp.

So it was the end of the thirty-first day before I had them safe. I called Billy to bring the saddle. Although I was very tired and hungry, I decided I would ride Black Kettle that night; so we both got hold of the rope and snubbed him to a post and saddled him. I got on and rode him for a few minutes inside the corral. We left the saddle on him for the night and went to camp. The next morning we caught and hobbled a few of the leaders and turned them on the grass. We took Black Kettle to camp and kept him on a picket rope. Within a week they were all tame and never made us any trouble. Billy had Black Kettle eating corn from the start and within two days he was as gentle as a plow horse. Billy cut some horseshoes from a piece of rawhide and nailed them on Black Kettle with shingle nails. He wore those shoes for some time and they were a great help to his sore feet.

I had a saddle horse that was afflicted with Texas itch, and when we saddled Black Kettle we used a blanket that had been worn by that horse. Black Kettle was jaded and weak and the powers of resistance were low; so it came about that one week later Black Kettle had the itch. His hair began to slip and nearly all, including that mane and tail, came off. He was a sorry looking specimen. I worried about it, and told Billy no one would ever recognize that horse, and the boys back home would never believe it was he. Billy thought that the hair would grow back and he would look natural when we got home. Billy applied a coat of bacon grease and had him cured in a short time.

Billy was an expert at making lariat ropes from rawhide, also quirts and horsehair bridles. He made a fine bridle out of the hair of Black Kettle's mane and tail, which I used for several years. Black Kettle's new mane and tail were never long afterwards.

Tzagan

By CLEMENT WOOD

MIDWAY of the mountains that bound on the northwest the demon-land of Mongolia rises the stiff peak Jagisstai. On an icy August morning a troop of wild dun horses cantered briskly along the undulating road that led from its crest to the river valley below. This was the last herd of the tarpans, the wild horses of Tatary, ancient children of the untamed steppe, who have never known bit or bridle.

At their head loped Tzagan, the white stallion, undisputed lord of the herd. He was the only white tarpan within the long memory of wild horses; the rest were dun-colored, or at most mouse-colored, with dark mane and tail and legs. Tzagan's mane and tail were shining jet, his legs a suave black; but his soft white coat was a thing new to them. Soon after he was foaled he had been recognized as a prodigy, and shielded tenderly. He had grown agile and strong, a hand taller than most and heavier in build.

Old Taiga, the Forest One, the head stallion for long cold years, grew old as the white colt matured; at last his cunning dozed. The day came when Tzagan rubbed an inquisitive white muzzle against the graying one, then drew back, to neigh out the challenge for combat. A few bitter rushes and the age-withered head horse moved aside; young Tzagan swaggered to the van of the line and gave the signal for the advance. The tarpans at once looked to the White One to lead them; and a shrewd leader he had made.

Down the rocky road from Jagisstai, with its thick crust of snow, the horses hastened. The frozen whiteness crunched under their tread; at times the icy balls that formed on their hoofs broke loose, and rolled away over the brittle surface with a sound like crackling twigs. Around the shoulders of the ridge, in and out of the descending ravines, the trail zigzagged. Squirrels chattered from the squat green cedars, bullfinches flew with flaming breasts over their heads, white partridges whistled by. They passed scanty herds of bighorn and antelope, busily digging through the snow to the nutritious grasses below. To the side of the road writhed great balls of snakes; an occasional hare thumped casually away; a brown bear below giant boles of larches stared stupidly at their snow-cloudy passage.

As they reached a ravine that fed one of the headwaters of the river, Tzagan stopped abruptly, large head raised, nostrils twitching. His ears grew tense. They caught a far, faint whinny of distress, almost of despair. Across the ravine his keen eyes made it out at last—a cloud of black in a grassed clearing, a winged cloud, stridently squawking. Again the pitiful whinny.

A sharp neigh from the leader and the horses swerved into a steeper path that led into the very heart of the ravine. Across fallen larches they leaped and floundered, then over a burned area beneath leafless skeletons of trees. They forded an open stream, began a stiff climb. There was no sight or sound from the grassed clearing above; but they knew what they would find there.

Long before they had neared the place other eyes discovered it. On the top bald crag of Jagisstai, all morning, had sat a living thing, hunched and huddled toward the brooding east, facing away from the shrieking devil-winds that whirled over the Siberian steppes. His far eyes could pick out the lazy sources of streams that writhed through all enchantments to the drowsy swell of the Pacific.

Had he looked north he could have seen the headwaters of the river that crept under frozen horror to the frozen Arctic. An easy day's journey to the west and he would have found a stream that made its way through the locked Caspian and more populous seas, beyond the very Pillars of Hercules. A day's travel to the south and he would have encountered water that would know the Indian Ocean, and wash at the end the final polar floes. He sat brooding above the vast highland whence all the waters of earth are fed.

Good for them that no hunted Mongols, no avenging Tatars, came upon that lone living thing huddled high upon Jagisstai. They would have fallen to their faces in the snow in holy terror.

Paul Brown
'45

"Demon of Jagisstai!" they would have cried. "Spare us, spare us!" We will build you an *obo* of branches—we will build you a tower of rocks. Spare us!" And Zaberega, the living thing, the great hunched mountain-eagle, would have turned his eyes again to the swimming horizon, and at last vaulted upward to cleave heaven.

In frigid isolation, this icy morning, he held his peak. His hooded eyes, which could see beyond what men call sight, had observed the cantering passage of the wild horses down his valley road. Now they fixed upon the stir far down the rich head-plain of the river. The great throat lifted unconsciously, the eyes blinked rapidly. What should be moving in his domain?

It had been a long time since trespassers had disputed his suzerainty. In younger days he had had to fight back full-grown hawks from the fringes of the Gobi Desert; ponderous erns, the sea-eagles from the edge of the northern ocean. He had now no rivals. And yet this stir.

As if flung by springs of steel he catapulted into the air. His wings beat upward in a long slant, then sloped in an easy spiral down toward the grassed height. As he neared the ground, they dug more savagely into the stinging air. He knew now what he had to face—that blatantly cawing cloud of black bodies. His hurled passage warmed the air as he made the last low swoop and burned his tornado way into the noisy swivet of jet wings and red beaks.

Just before he struck, a few of them saw him—a wandering Indian pie, his black beak stained crimson; a great gray shrike, larger and more murderous; an evil old chough, claws gripping the poor horse's torn flank. There was red blood too on the chough's vivid red beak—she had hardly time to open it for a sharp scream of warning, when the eagle was upon her. One slash with powerful talons—the dead bird hurtled through the air. Right and left they rose in flying panic, all the hateful flock of pies and crows, ancient foes of the eagle folk. Zaberega, the winged demon, slanted and slashed left and right, with startling activity taking bird after bird in its flight.

The last one shrieked out of vision. Tired, deeply pleased, the eagle swung slowly back and lit on the ground a score of feet from the drooping horse.

It was a tarpan mare, he saw at once—a mare with a reddish-dun coat. Her bleeding back, where the dreadful birds had troubled her, was one vast spreading sore. Zaberega knew how these cowardly killers, that hunted only in winged clouds, fastened themselves to any horse or bull whose back showed the slightest wound, and scratched and pecked at it until it was an incurable thing; how they kept at their hateful killing until at last they gorged themselves upon the splendid creature.

He preened his ruffled feathers and muttered deep in his throat.

The mare was too drooping to raise her head and see her rescuer. She stood, patiently awaiting horrid death.

Zaberega turned to make a meal of the black bodies scattered over the ground. Ah! A wounded shrike, dragging itself below the grasses. One powerful pounce—one more foe gone. Here were glossy choughs, like feathered balls of jet with ruby beaks and feet; here were ungainly crows, glittering magpies. His curved beak tore cruelly into the warm meal.

He raised his head in sharp surprise; something drip-dripped from the beak upon a stone. Out of a dense cedar covert topping the rise broke the white head of Tzagan, the head stallion, his black mane streaming behind him. Another—a third—a dozen of the tarpans all at once appeared out of the fringing forest. Their feet clicked together; they poised uncertainly.

After a moment's scrutiny Zaberega continued his feeding.

Timidly Tzagan led the way closer. His black feet were printed deftly together, his black tail swished against his snowy coat. He neighed a salutation to the great demon-bird.

Grasping a dead chough in each claw, the eagle lifted from the grass, and flew back to the wind-bedeviled height of Jagisstai.

Tzagan's head drooped slightly. Delicately, whinnying a soft greeting, he neared the wounded one.

His sensitive eyes widened as he recognized the mare; a softer note sounded from his throat. This was Ulan, the Red One—once his favorite. She had been driven from them less than two months ago.

At the familiar whinny the mare lifted her tired head. She answered as well as she could—a feeble, discouraged response. The other horses thronged around her, exchanging their greetings. With horror they observed the evil thing on her back—the wide, bleeding wound.

A sudden unease shook Tzagan: he remembered his duty.

Head lifted, black mane stringing out on the chill wind, he trumpeted the call for the onward journey.

It was the time of the last Summer migration—you could have told that by the thinned hair of the horses. In Winter their coats were thick and soft, almost like a bear's; but as the warmer months came this fell away, until their underbodies were almost hairless, and only a sparse covering remained on back and flanks. It was now midway of the thinned season.

Again Tzagan neighed the advance.

They trotted after him, hoofs clicking on the rounded rocks.

Ulan, the red mare, started feebly to follow. She saw the herd drifting past her; she strained to keep up. The blood woke afresh on her back; her limbs would not respond to the commands of her will.

Out of the distant forest the menacing caw of shrike and chough sounded; the heavy black birds began to near the place again.

She struggled forward; a pitiful whinny died in her weakness.

Tzagan stopped, sensing the breach in the herd. He parted the others, cantering between them until he reached her side again.

As Ulan lifted her tired head to greet him, the first of the choughs flew greedily up; it lit on her unprotected flank. Her teeth showed in sickly fashion; the head sagged again. Dispiritedly her tail shook, a menace no longer.

Tzagan was different. Eyes blazing, the white head snapped at the first bird. An untasty mouthful of black feathers was his reward.

The chough flew mockingly out of reach, cawing derisive hatred.

More and more of the birds circled around Tzagan's head.

The other horses surrounded the mare again. They sought to nudge her on with them; feebly she responded. As she moved, her escort of death continued. The whole troop of horses slowed to her painful gait; several of the angered dun heads curved above her sick flanks, keeping the pies and crows at a safe aloofness. They came constantly from every direction, swirling above in a dense flock, jeering just out of reach of the snapping teeth.

At length there was grumbling among the foremost horses.

Tzagan sensed it as soon as it began. They must go forward with all speed to the northern grazing-place, the mutters told him; they had delayed too long already. He knew that his part was to direct this powerful will of his followers, or that they would choose another stallion to lead. A leader must lead, not his own way, but the way of the herd.

Again he tried to hasten Ulan's progress. The Red One drooped more and more.

The grumbling among the horses grew more open.

He could face them, and stay with the wounded mare. Let them go away without him—abandon his leadership.

No. His place was at the head of the herd.

A sharp neigh—Tzagan cantered lightly ahead. Gladly the van tarpans leaped after the flashing White One. One by one the others abandoned the hurt straggler. The birds flapped closer and closer. The last horse passed her.

Cawing discordantly, the birds came to rest upon the bleeding back. The mare's head bowed to the ground. The living death was again upon her.

The troop arrived at last at the final pass that opened to the long slope to the lower end of Lake Kosogol. Tzagan knew this demon country well—this land of sliding sand-demons. There were constant fallen larch-trees, that must be circled cautiously; underneath these, even below clear stretches of the turf, were miry swamps—still, hidden pools of putrefying water, where a horse might sink and never rise again. The swamp snakes rustled beside them; a lone red fox swayed on his haunches and barked mockingly.

The road turned upward. There were no more quagmires, but instead a path along the top of a precipice, paved with cobbles and small stones that rolled deceptively from under their feet, and threatened to throw them over the great split in the hills. At times the very road melted away beneath them, in great ugly slides of stone and sand; it was all they could do to leap to scrambling safety, when one of these unexpectedly opened under their very way.

A small army of goldfinches whistled past the cautious steps of the tarpans. A white ermine snaked close to the ground across their path. In the willows below they could see a drove of wild camels munching phlegmatically. A flock of cranes cut between them and the sun.

Unnoticing, the horses continued this last rise.

Ah! The fringing valley at the head of the Kosogol in full sight! Now for a wild gallop down the ultimate slope to the rich grazing below.

But Tzagan stopped uncertainly. His feet lifted and dropped in perplexity. Here—before him—the old way, but altered. A vast cuplike depression sliced across the path—a wide new slide. Above the road were sharp gray rocks, steep and hard to climb; these curved in a great horseshoe to the firm path more than a hundred yards ahead. Sagging below this was the queer sink of sand and stone, with gray rocks again at its lower left end, and the precipice beyond that. Trees sprawled in ungainly fashion upon it; several lay on their sides, torn, impotent roots whitening in the air. It was all strange, all new.

Behind him crowded the others, eager to get down to the lush grass below. The foremost horses nudged him speculatively.

Circle around the top?

But they might be injured in the wild, rocky scramble.

Go back a few miles, and cross above?

The nudges grew more definite. He made up his mind to try it.

One tentative hoof went forward, then another. It seemed firm enough.

Cautiously he began to make his way across it.

The sliding demon heaved abruptly beneath him. His front legs slipped in to the hock, then to the knee; he felt the ground yield below his back feet. He tried to leap aside; the viscid sand held. He was moving, at increasing speed, toward the top of the abyss.

He became acutely aware of the other horses. A young stallion was a length below, at his right; behind his left flank was a third one, the Wood Mouse, a clever, timid tarpan, named also from his color. Tzagan tried to leap forward, and gained a doubtful yard. At the same moment, he sensed the Wood Mouse's backward spring to safety. A second afterward Tzagan heard the despairing sound as the stallion below, in a vain effort to leap out of the sand, stumbled over upon his side. A quick glimpse out of

Paul Brown

the corner of his eye showed the thrashing legs, the anguished head. as the quickening masses of sand and rock began to cover him with hissing clatter.

Tzagan thrust all power into his legs and sprang. Almost out of the depths. His front hoofs struck a stone; he leaped again— and into deeper sand, sliding ever more rapidly. Again, again he tried.

He was tiring now; it took all of his energy to remain upright. Far behind he caught the troubled whinnies of the rest of the troop. There were choked sounds below him.

He had veered around now, and faced down-hill. In full view was the body of the lowest stallion, desperately floundering beneath its crushing load of sliding death. The distance between them increased rapidly.

Tzagan's feet were poised together below him as well as could be. The treacherous sand was well above his knees. If he could only remain upright until the bottom was reached, and then leap free.

This hope fled swiftly. He saw the last despairing heave as the lowest horse was rolled over the edge of the precipice. He heard the dreadful clamor of the rocky mass pouring in a cataract over the sheer edge of the great clove—the sound of tree-boughs crackling and breaking as the stallion's body ricocheted to death among them.

Queerly enough, his part of the slide was more sluggish than that to the right. Ahead, he could see where the stream turned before him, avoiding the obstruction of gray rocks. If he could reach them——!

Cautiously he began to work himself farther to the left in order to be swung as close to the stones as possible. They were a kind of rock wall, that made the slide veer away to the right and narrowed its lower end. In his eagerness he nearly lost his footing. A great rock bounded across his shoulder; he shivered in pain. Desperately he steadied himself upon his feet; the inevitable tug of the sand dragged him again to the right.

Here—right at him—hardly four feet away—the gray rocks. One desperate drive with his legs, all his power pushing into the yielding mass. He felt himself lifting out of it. One wild second spring—he hurled himself sideways against the gray crags. A leg tripped on the nearest rock. He fell, rolling over twice. Against an uptilted slab of stone he came to rest. Just beyond this gaped the final drop of a thousand feet.

Weakly he pulled himself up, legs trembling from exertion and excitement. Over the edge his glazed eyes peered. The stallion below was out of sight. The sand-slide poured by, dropping deafeningly into the void. Far below the screaming caw of chough and pie.

So near to death—and now so far from it!

Skirting the left end of the slide, he set out painfully up the rocky wall that had meant such amazing salvation. As he stepped his shoulder stung. There was a damp feeling, a drip on the rocks when he paused to rest. He sniffed at it—it was the red water that comes when the skin is broken. Shaking his head clear, he neighed once toward the top of the hill, and continued on his way.

At the far end of the wide curve at the top, he came upon the others. In their eyes was fear, that might easily turn into panic as they watched his approach. This could not be Tzagan, who had disappeared in the rumbling death!

He whinnied reassuringly.

Their white muzzles smelled of him; their warm tongues licked the wounded shoulder.

Back with his own again!

He resumed the lead, and took up the march down to the grazing-ground beside the lake.

Out of the woods he heard the harsh chatter of rook and chough. At first he did not heed it; evidently they had found some new victim. Over the backs of the horses they flew and slanted until they had reached the head of the line.

Suddenly he felt a sharp pain on his shoulder. One of the birds had dashed against him, ripping with red beak at the red wound.

Viciously Tzagan snapped back.

The chough veered away.

From the other side a second one slashed at him.

Throughly infuriated, he champed back. The other horses aided in this.

More slowly than the first stages of their journey, they came down to the grassy ground at the head of the lake.

The horses lowered their muzzles for the ample grazing.

But Tzagan, the White One, found it impossible to crop the sweet, soft food. The ominous birds circled slashingly around his head, ever more and more of them. His full energy was needed to deal with them.

Then began dreadful days and nights for Tzagan.

Again and again, that first afternoon, he sought to lower his head, to nibble at the delicate grass. Each time half a dozen of the winged murderers seized the moment to stab into the living flesh. They were always at him. Evening found him unfed, wearied, pain-racked.

It was a little better after the sun had gone. At least he could doze.

Toward morning he dispiritedly cropped at the nearer grass, which the herd had already gone over. Dawn came all too quickly, and with it again the flying menace.

That day and that night—the next day, the next night—endless days, endless nights—passed in the same horrid fashion. The wound was worse now and spreading—that he knew. At night he ate as best he could, but his strength was no longer up to that of the rest of the herd.

He was still regarded as leader. But long ago he had dropped back toward the rear, weakly proud that he could keep pace with the poorest of the cantering hoofs. The other horses did what they could to aid him; but they must eat sometimes, and the devil-birds never rested.

Day by day it grew harder to keep up. The day came when he was last in the line. Far ahead the Wood Mouse was leading. There had been no battle with the formal change of headship; Tzagan was too ill to dispute his sick abdication.

The cloud of winged death never left him, from the thin gray bud of dawn to the blankness of night. Even in day-bright moonlight a few overgreedy birds stayed to plague him. Only in the scant black hours was he his own at last; and he was too tired and drowsy to eat much at this time.

The day came when the last mare in the line loped away, and Tzagan could not follow. The birds descended in a jubilant cloud upon him, tearing at his very life.

He backed against some trees, snapping with all his vigor at the menacing claws. The low boughs were partial protection; without

this they would leech to his very back. With sick despair he heard the thud of the last hoofs dying away in the distance.

Alone—abandoned.

His thought was all of Ulan, the red mare. By now, long ago dead, on the grassed clearing below Jagisstai, the peak of the demon. Pictures of her dreadful plight bewilderingly passed over him, strangely blurred and altered. He seemed to be the red mare, torn to death.

A faint wave of denial swept over him. At least he could still slash with his tail and snap with his teeth.

His blows grew feebler and feebler.

It was only a matter of how long he could hold out. There would come a time when he could not.

Day after hideous day he stood, backed against the screen of trees, fighting back the hovering death that gave him no moment's rest. The evil hordes were always upon him; their evil odors pained his sensitive nostrils. Harder and harder the effort to snap back; it had been many days since he had eaten a full meal. And food was life.

He crept out in the black of night and cropped what herbage he could. One morning dawn came before he knew it; he was still far from the trees. The hordes of slaughter gathered unexpectedly. A killing half day he snapped back, keeping them away as best he could. His legs trembled from the pain of the vast hurt, extending now across his shoulders and almost to his tail.

Noon came, and tiring afternoon. His head rose slower each time; ever more feebly he fought away the tearing death.

Suddenly his body stiffened with strange hope. He sensed a stir of deliverance.

Out of the menacing air it came—the whir of great beating wings, the cyclone breath of passage, as the demon-bird, Zaberega, swept down among the cowardly killers. The great pinions fanned his back as they swept over him. He felt spasmodic clutchings as the birds, too late, sought to rise. Right and left Tzagan saw bodies fall amid cawing screams of terror. The eagle slew a score before the last of the enemies had made a panicky escape.

For the first time in weeks Tzagan knew life that was not torn by the talons of death.

The trees. He must reach them before the killers returned. He started his trembling journey; Zaberega, as if understanding that his presence was relief, drifted along beside, pouncing upon the foolhardy shrike or chough that ventured out again.

The trees were hardly a hundred yards away now. One satisfied, menacing scream, and Tzagan heard the great wings thrash the air as the demon-bird soared off to his lone peak.

At once he grasped what this might mean. Glazed eyes fastened to the distant trees; he sought to master and hasten his weak steps.

The rooks and pies cawed their summons. Closer, closer, came the sound.

Desperately he pushed forward. Worn knees suddenly betrayed him; he staggered sideways, and fell heavily, his chin striking a projecting stone. The tired body rested a moment on the old earth. It was so easy to give up, to die. Now as well as later. He was tired, tired.

A piercing pain in his shoulder—the winged fiends again! Inflamed eyes hardened to terrible determination. He pulled up to his feet and set off at a feeble canter for the last hope of life.

The rooks and pies dashed against his face, ripped his back, clung to him like evil river-leeches. This time he did not fight them away; all energy must be saved for the final yards. Before him the trees. And, more than that—he blinked his eyes painfully to make sure that they were not deceiving him—more than that, a cave—a hollowed opening below a great rock—a slight cave, hardly his height. It might mean shelter. With every ounce of reserve in his body, he held his legs to the torturing canter. Death tore at his life. He stood this, determined to make the shelter, or die.

He made it.

Here—just before him—the scooped-out place, barely higher than his neck. With despairing briskness he slued his body around and began to back in. The birds, realizing that their prey was trying to escape, screeched and shrieked. The low top of the caveway struck the birds clinging above his tail, and rasped them off. Sharp, burning pains shot through him at their last wild clawings. Farther and farther in he pushed; he could feel the living body of one bird caught between his sore back and the cave's top. He arched his body; the bird, breath squeezed out, slid past his flanks to the ground. Vengeful hoofs ground it into the soil.

He was entirely within it now but for his head. There was no more room. The birds whizzed back viciously, seeking to tear his face. Summoning what little strength was left, he snapped at their approaching threat and kept them off. There was at least no wound on his face that they could claw.

It was late afternoon. Until after dark the magpies and crows massed in front of the cave entrance, waiting for him to come out. There was one especial chough, an old fellow, larger than the rest, gleaming jet body contrasting bravely with scarlet beak and scarlet feet, that planted himself on the ground right before Tzagan's face. The baleful bird eyes, below a feather torn rakishly awry, watched for some sign of weakening. If he could wait, the old chough seemed to say, so could they.

At last the sun drowsed below the hills. The chill vacancy of night strode eerily over the basin. One by one the birds flopped away.

He was all alone.

His legs gave; he sagged forward to his knees. His head collapsed to the half-frozen ground. His eyes closed.

After a half-hour's rest he managed to rise again upon his shivering legs. Step by step he staggered out of the cave. Every instant he expected the birds to hurl their punishing beaks upon him. No; black night was his protection. By some dim supersense he knew that the moon would rise after a few hours. He must make the most of this short space; the terrors might return in the false dawn of moonlight.

Just beyond the cave's mouth commenced the grass. Hungrily his weary lips crunched the succulent stems. At length he had his fill. Not far to the left, he remembered, there was a stream. Quietly he trudged over and drank. He did not go farther; if there was to be life for him, it lay in that cave; he must always be within reach of it.

At last the moon washed the sky gray. Guzzling another drink, he cropped his way back to the hollow scooped below the big rock, senses alert for the onrush of the birds.

They did not come.

For a few hours he dozed; then he ate again, before the gray promise of dawn brought back the jeering enemies.

Day after day passed the same way. A few of the birds tired of the long wait; there was one day when only half a dozen stayed with him; evidently the rest had found a slaughtered prey near by. The next day most of them were back again. Always just below his nose squatted the old black chough, one feather still rakishly awry, gleaming scarlet beak waiting for scarlet food.

One morning Tzagan was slow in returning to the cave. The birds came at him before he reached it, tearing him. As he backed wildly in, the big chough, with the feather aslant, flew in ahead and sought to claw him from behind. With firm assurance the horse closed up the opening with his body. Methodically he kicked backward, once—twice—thrice. Ah! On the third kick he felt his hoof strike something yielding, squirming. One horrid scream of anguish. His hoofs danced the body of the would-be murderer into the rocks. White throat lifted, black mane tossing as it had not for days, he neighed victory—victory! Here was one enemy who would not plague him again.

After that the birds were more careful. There was more than one morning, when he was tardy in his return, that several tore the wounds open again. Never as bad as at first, however. Day by day he grew stronger, more able to travel; day by day the birds grew more doubtful as to this meal that had once seemed within their very beaks.

More than six weeks passed. The Winter chill came into the air. There would come a day when the tarpan troop would return up the grassy bank of the lake and seek again the southern fields beyond Jagisstai. Meanwhile, below the healing wound the Winter hairs, thick and soft, like the covering of a bear, were pushing their way. The hour came when he knew there was no more open wound—only healing scabs. The hour came when the last of these dropped away, and he was whole again.

But still the crows and choughs waited; still Tzagan was unwilling or afraid to come out, so used had he become to this imprisonment from the threat of clawed day.

It was a morning in late October when the horse's nose wrinkled at an unexpected odor upon the wind out of the brooding east. His ears pricked up, his senses sharpened acutely.

In scattering alarm the black birds rose. Some flew away, others settled a short distance away, in cawing uncertainty.

Down the wind came the sound of faint neighings. Tzagan, strangely excited, pranced up and down in the narrow caveway.

Across the grassy plain he saw them at last—the tarpan herd, the wild horses, with the Wood Mouse dancing along in the lead.

He took two or three uncertain steps forward. He was out in the sunshine of day for the first time in two months. Speculatively the crows observed him: one or two flung themselves upon his twitching flanks and sought to bury their beaks in the thick, matted hair. His teeth clicked vigorously at them; they jawed out of sight into the far woodlands.

The horses loped ever closer.

Alone, before the cave, the white tarpan stood.

There was a sudden whinnying from the front ranks. A hundred feet from him they came to a stop; intent doubt was on their faces. A sudden noise and they would have wheeled and galloped off in veritable panic. A white tarpan! There had never been but one; and he was dead long ago, pestered to his death by the punishing birds.

He neighed the old greeting.

There was an answering neigh, half joyful, half unbelieving.

Delicately he stepped out. The sun shone on his bright black mane and tail, on his shining black legs; it spangled on the tangled mat of thick white hair covering the rest of his body. He came to a stop ten feet away from the Wood Mouse.

Threateningly the darker stallion raised his head; a red glaze came across his eyes. He approached the stranger, menace in his bearing.

Tzagan did not move. The other turned, and neighed the command for all to fall in and resume the journey.

Out of the sky came the far whir of great wings. Black against its brazen deeps, they could see the high blur of Zaberega, the demon-bird, returning to his aerie on the crest of Jagisstai. The sight of the familiar eagle brought back to the Wood Mouse remembrance of those days when he was only a follower and the White One the leader. The great wings passed out of sight. The dark stallion eyed the other in some perplexity.

Cruelly Tzagan held his eye until the usurper looked down at the ground. Then, lifting his throat, until the wind sprayed out his mane like a black pennon of victory, the White One trumpeted the call to advance. A bit sullenly, the Wood Mouse ranged himself behind the old leader, so strangely returned to them. A sudden clatter—the clicking hoofs struck the pebbles of the way again— a swirl of dust.

Up the long road the herd of wild horses cantered, with Tzagan, the White One, back with his own again.

Chiquita

By BRET HARTE

BEAUTIFUL! Sir, you may say so. Thar isn't her match in
    the county;
Is thar, old gal,—Chiquita, my darling, my beauty?
Feel of that neck, sir,—that's velvet! Whoa! steady—ah, will you,
    you vixen!
Whoa! I say. Jack, trot her out; let the gentleman look at her
    paces.

Morgan!—she ain't nothing else, and I've got the papers to prove
    it.
Sired by Chippewa Chief, and twelve hundred dollars won't buy
    her.
Briggs of Tuolumne owned her. Did you know Briggs of Tuo-
    lumne?
Busted hisself in White Pine, and blew out his brains down in
    'Frisco?

Hedn't no savvy, hed Briggs. Thar, Jack! that'll do,—quit that
    foolin'!
Nothin' to what she kin do, when she's got her work cut out
    before her.
Hosses is hosses, you know, and likewise, too, jockeys is jockeys:
And 'taint ev'ry man as can ride as knows what a hoss has got in
    him.

Know the old ford on the Fork, that nearly got Flanigan's lead·
    ers?
Nasty in daylight, you bet, and a mighty rough ford in low water!
Well, it ain't six weeks ago that me and the Jedge and his nevvy
Struck for that ford in the night, in the rain, and the water all
    round us;

Up to our flanks in the gulch, and Rattlesnake Creek just a-bilin',
Not a plank left in the dam, and nary a bridge on the river.
I had the grey, and the Jedge had his roan, and his nevvy, Chi-
quita;
And after us trundled the rocks jest loosed from the top of the
cañon.

Lickity, lickity, switch, we came to the ford, and Chiquita
Buckled right down to her work, and, afore I could yell to her
rider,
Took water jest at the ford, and there was the Jedge and me
standing,
And twelve hundred dollars of hoss-flesh afloat, and a-driftin' to
thunder!

Would ye b'lieve it? That night, that hoss, that 'ar filly, Chiquita,
Walked herself into her stall, and stood there, all quiet and drip-
ping:
Clean as a beaver or rat, with nary a buckle of harness,
Just as she swam the Fork,—that hoss, that 'ar filly, Chiquita.

PB

That's what I call a hoss! and—what did you say?—Oh, the
    nevvy?

Drownded, I reckon,—leastways, he never kem back to deny it.

Ye see the durned fool had no seat; ye couldn't have made him a
    rider;

And then, ye know, boys will be boys, and hosses—well, hosses is
    hosses!

The Horse of Hurricane Reef

By CHARLES TENNEY JACKSON

THE mares are for whoever is man enough to take them," retorted Jean Abadie from the bow of the barge which the towing launch was shoving into the mud shoal on the bay side of Île Dautrive. "Rojas has given them up. The white stallion killed his son, Emile, four years ago. No man of the camps around here will land on this reef; he has a name, that wild white devil!"

"You see, M'sieu Lalande, it is not stealing," added Pierre as he stopped the motor and looked at the stranger in the stern seat.

"It is stealing," grunted Joe Lalande, "else why do we come under cover of a storm to rope the colts and mares? Well, no matter. Once we get them aboard and up to the Mississippi plantations, I will show you something, you shrimp-seine Cajans. Throwing a rope, eh? Over westward they never yet showed me a horse I could not break."

The two seine-haulers from Sanchez's platform looked at him doubtfully. "Over westward," to the men of Barataria Bay, began at the dim marsh shore and stretched to infinity. A native never ventured so far; out there anything might be possible. But no man had faced the exiled king of Dautrive reef. Pierre muttered again how they would get the young mares—they would first shoot the white stallion. It was the hurricane month; they knew well enough that an obliterating sea would come this week over the dunes and marshes. Old Rojas, living with his grandchildren, orphaned by the white brute's savagery, on the far west point of the island, would never know what happened to the five mares and colts. More than once the gale off the Gulf had left the shell-beached *chenaies* far up the bay strewn with the dead cattle of the people of the reefs.

The big Lalande laughed as he followed through the salt

2 1 9

grass to the first low dunes. "Shoot him! You'll shoot no horse with me! You say he's so bad; show him to me! I'll rope and load him, too, my friends, or he will finish me. If we lift Rojas's animals we take 'em all."

The Cajans laughed in nervous disbelief. Lalande, a native also, who had returned this season to haul seine in Sanchez's company, might have been a great man with the pitching broncos he told of, but Rojas's great white stallion—well, this boaster would see! The brute would allow no seine-crew to land on the Île Dautrive; they told of his charging upon the fishing-skiffs clear out to the surf line. Sanchez, the boss, had shot him once as he fled to his lugger, leaving the bleeding stallion to rend and trample an abandoned seine.

Grandpère Rojas, in his camp across the shoal depression that cut through the reef, had never tried to reclaim the wild mares and the colts of the white stud's breed. The generations of them lived on the coarse reef grass and the rain pools; an oysterman had no use for horses, anyhow. His son, Emile, had tried this foolish experiment of raising horses on the reef, and given his life under the stallion's hoofs. *Grandpère* had shrugged and let the breed go wild; yet, as Lalande muttered when Jean and Pierre proposed to use his skill in lifting the younger animals, the horses were his to the scrawniest colt. But Lalande had come. He would show the shrimpers; and even if they only roped and dragged the least unruly to the barge, Lalande could break them and Pierre sell them on the plantations. Yet it was horse stealing. Lalande would not gloss that over, but something else had drawn him here—the stories the islanders told of the white stallion's savagery.

"Old Rojas's son, I will be the avenger," he grunted, sullenly, and came on the day Pierre had chosen for the secret raid.

Abadie had stopped on the sandy trail broken through the mangroves to the top of the sand ridge. "Bon Dieu!" he whispered, pointing. "His track, Lalande! Big as a bucket! *Eh bien!* I'd rather face a hurricane than this white tiger!"

Lalande had stepped out in the open sand patch. From here the dunes fell away to the Gulf beach. Already the sea was rising. Between Dautrive and the outer bar curious, oily currents were twisting in unwonted directions, and beyond them the surf broke

Paul Brown

in white, serried teeth gleaming against the black southeast. The sky was ribboned in black lines streaming northerly; the wind came in fitful smashes against the mangrove thickets and then seemed sucked up to howl in the writhing clouds.

"There'll have to be quick work," muttered Pierre. "I tell you this is bad, this sea. We waited too long, M'sieu Lalande. We better be back across the bay, and try for the colts another time."

Lalande's gray eyes narrowed surlily. He straightened his powerful figure above the wind-slanting bushes. The two other raiders had crept back through the brush. It was disconcerting to find the animals crossing their trail behind. "If he smells a man he will never let up on us, Lalande," muttered Jean. "Kill him, then!"

The white leader had crossed the trail of the raiders. He turned, broke through the brush, and gained the ridge forty yards from them. Lalande could see him now against the black skyline very plainly. A tremendous brute towering above the others, his shaggy mane flowing backward in the wind, his muzzle outstretched, his neck tensed until the powerful muscles bulged the satin skin. He was suspicious; he stood there a challenging figure to the storm, but his eyes were roving watchfully into the thickets as a tiger scenting prey.

Lalande glanced back. His comrades had slunk below the mangroves. They were brave, hardy men of the hurricane coast, but the evil name of the sea horse of Île Dautrive seemed to hold them nerveless. The horse was coming on along the top of the ridge slowly crashing through the brush with alert glances right and left. His pink nostrils quivered, his iron-gray tail raised and swept in the wind puffs.

"They will shoot," muttered Lalande. "If he trails them the cowards will shoot." And he stepped more in the open, and then shouted, "come, thieves, let the colts go! I will need you on the throw-line to check and choke this brute!" Breast-high in the windswept thickets he was laughing and coiling his rope. This was a foe for a strong man who boasted!

The great horse suddenly upreared with a neigh that was like the roar of a lion. No man had so much as ever put finger on him; he had beaten the brains from one, broken the leg of another; and smashed two seine skiffs in the shallows for invaders.

He had been the lord of the reef. Now he reared again and again as he plunged through the mangroves watching for the fugitives as a cat would a mouse under a flimsy cover of straw.

His satiny flanks were toward Lalande; apparently he had not yet discovered the man behind him in this hunt for the others. And then, out of pure panic as the white stallion broke near him, Jean Abadie fired. Lalande cursed and sprang down the slope of dunes after them. He knew he would need their help when he roped this horse; it was no starveling cayuse of the Texas range. But he saw now that the two islanders were skulking for the boat in the last fringe of the mangroves. They would never make it; out in the open the white stallion would crush them both ere they covered half the marsh grass, unless, indeed, they killed him.

The brute saw them now; he swerved in a tremendous rush below the man on the higher sand. Lalande was whirling his rope, and when he heard the hiss of it through the air he laughed, for he knew the throw was true.

"*Eh, bien,* devil! You and me!" He went down sprawling, seeking a root of the tough mangroves to snub the line. He caught one, then it was jerked out; and he went trundling and rolling over and over through the sands hanging to the lariat. He might as well have roped a torpedo. The horse was in the open now rearing and bucking, but with his savage eyes still on the fugitives. They were floundering through the water. Jean was jerking the mooring-lines from the barge, and Pierre poling the launch back from the swamp grass. The stallion was surging on with the line cutting deep in his neck, but they could not see this in the welter of spray he threw in his charge.

Joe Lalande was on his back in the high grass, bruised and dizzy from his ride on the throw-rope. It was lying out taut through the grass; and for a time the man did not stir. The stallion was plunging somewhere out there, still implacable with fury to get at the shrimpers. Then Lalande heard the first throb of the motor. They were getting away, leaving him, then? They must think him killed—a good end for a braggart who would rather fight the stud than steal the mares!

He lay in the grass listening, without even resentment. The wide reach of the bay northward was flecked with white surges rising between those curious oily bulges of water, the first stir of the creeping tides which come upon the Gulf shores before the hurricane winds. Lalande remembered enough of his boyhood among the island folk to know that. Pierre was right; they had waited too long for this week of storm to raid Rojas's wild horses.

He crept around on the jerking line. Above the grass billows he saw the brute. He was whirling madly in the shallows fighting this strange, choking clutch on his neck. Then he charged back up the dunes, and Lalande barely had time to lie out on the end ere he was dragged again. But when the stallion plunged into the thickets, no human strength could hold. He felt his fingers breaking in the tangle of rope and roots, his face ground into the sand and pounded by showers of sand from the brute's hoofs.

Lalande staggered to his feet presently, cleared his eyes, and followed a crashing trail over the sand ridge. Northward he saw the launch rocking its way across the pass with whiplike streamers of wind hitting the water beyond. Everywhere the coast folk would be debating whether to quit their platform camps and take to the luggers or trust to the oaks of the *chenaies* and their moorings. The hurricane month, and a sea coming up past Cuba! Île Derniere had vanished under the waves; La Caminada gone with six hundred souls; these were traditions of the coast, but the natives knew what a hurricane tide meant on the low, loose sand islands that fringed the Louisiana swamps.

Lalande paused on the highest ridge. There was that sullen glisten of the sea, cut through with patches of white, and the green-back horizon gaping to east and west and blotting out with gray squalls. The great wind had not come yet beyond these first squadrons. The big man shrugged as he regarded it. The hurricane tide was shoving frothy fingers out over the shoals. Across the sandy stretch westward he could just see the shack camp of *Grandpère* Rojas on the highest ridge of Dautrive. A few ragged oaks showed white against the sky. The old man ought to be leaving with his orphaned grandchildren, taking his stout oyster lugger and making for the solid land fourteen miles north across the bay.

"It is no place for little ones," muttered Lalande in the Cajan patois. These people never will leave quick enough before the storms. I can see the old man's lugger still riding behind the point. He is a fool, Old Rojas, afraid to put foot on this end of the reef

because of the white stud, but stubborn against the sea which comes like a million white horses."

He went warily on the crushed trail. That throw-rope would foul somewhere in the mangroves; that stallion would choke himself to a stupor, for not all the strength in the world can avail against lungs bursting for air. Then he saw the mares. They were huddled in a hollow of the dunes, the colts about them as if confused, uncertain, their shaggy coats ruffled in the wind. That wind was moaning now, high and far; not so bad here on the reef, but striking in slants on the sea as if the sky had opened to let an arrow loose. A hundred miles away as yet, that Gulf hurricane wind, but mounting; sixty, eighty, a hundred miles an hour—a hundred and twenty-five in the bursts that presently drove the sand dunes into smoke.

The rim of wet sand beyond the dry, hummocky space was covered with sheets of black water racing from the surf line, breaking on the shoals.

And here Lalande saw what he had sought. There was the white mound in the ripples. With a cry he dashed for it. The horse was down. He had not thought it would come so soon. But the end of the trailing rope had fouled a great driftheap, and the brute had kept on charging and fighting until he choked and fell in the first wash of the sea. The slip-noose was bound to cut him down if he kept on hurling his weight against it, Lalande knew.

He wished he had seen the last magnificent fight against it on the sands; but now he walked quickly around the fallen brute, and knelt to touch his distended, quivering nostrils. The eyes were shut but bulging under a film. The great sides were heaving, a rumbling groan found escape somehow; it was as if the mighty heart was breaking with a last throb against this mysterious power choking its strength away.

"Eh, soldier!" whispered Lalande, and felt high on the horse's neck.

A sudden apprehension took him. Perhaps the thong had killed the renegade? He did not mean that; he was filled with a great exultant joy in this savage. He had stalked and subdued him alone! He stood above this outstretched, trembling body in the first sea ripples, laughing.

"Come, boy! The fight's not done yet! Not the end yet." He

twisted his fingers into the taut rope, forced on the dragging driftwood, and eased the tension bit by bit. The rope was buried in the white skin; he worked hurriedly, fearing it was too late.

"Come, come; this will not do—" he was whispering into the stallion's tense ear, fighting at the rope. Then came a fierce, convulsive blow, an explosive sigh, a struggle, and the stallion lay quiet again. He was breathing in great, resurging sighs. His filmed eyes opened slowly. Lalande kept on patting his muzzle while he hitched the noose into a knot that would not choke again. He did not know why he did this, only it seemed fair. He was looking close into the brute's eyes which were beginning to glow with sense again; and to withdraw the choking hitch seemed only justice.

Lalande stood up and looked down at the white stallion. The water was roaring out there now. The skyline was blown white as feathers. The mangroves were slanting; and he suddenly realized that the wind was hard as a plank against his cheek. Not bursting, but steadily lying against the land. There was no rain, yet the air was full of water streaming in white lines through a growing darkness.

"Get up!" he shouted. "The sea is coming. This is no place to be! Comrade, on your feet!"

And the great horse did so. First plunging up, but with his haunches squatted in the water as he looked slowly about. Then to all fours and standing with his tail whipped about on his heaving flanks. He seemed watching that wall of blow water from the Gulf. Watching steadily, undaunted. The sands under the racing froth seemed trembling; one could hardly see the mangrove dunes not a hundred yards away.

Lalande swiftly turned his eyes from the ridge at a sound. It had seemed a shriek above the tumult. Then he leaped, and the wind appeared to lift him above the shaking earth.

For the great stud was on him. Upreared above him, a shaggy hoof coming not an inch's breadth from his skull.

Just a glimpse of those red, savage eyes; and the impact of those huge feet almost upon his own. Then Lalande ran. The hurricane wind flung him onward, but he could hear the rush of the white stallion. The entangled rope checked the charge only enough to allow the man to hurl himself into the first mangroves, crawl under them in a whirlwind of rising sands, and keep on crawling. When he stopped he knew the horse was crashing in the thickets hunting him. He saw him as a wraith against the sky, plunging his head low to ferret out his enemy, blowing explosively and hurling the tough mangrove clumps aside.

Lalande kept on his stealthy crawl. He lay, finally, in a water-riven dusk under the lee of the dunes, listening. *"Dieu!"* he panted. "I said, a soldier! The hurricane could not stop that hate of men!"

For half an hour he did not move. The brute had lost his trail. And when Lalande crawled to the top of the dunes he could not stand. All over the weather side the sea had risen. It was white. White, that was all he could say. And the wind? It did not seem a wind, merely a crushing of one's skull and lungs. When he tried to turn away it threw him headlong, but he got to his feet on the northerly, lee side of the sand ridge and fought on.

The sand was dissolving under his feet, and now he saw the water of the bay streaming by him. The inner marshes were gone; the hurricane tide was on, and sixty miles inland it would rush to batter on the cypress forests and the back levees of the plantation lands. Lalande had no illusions about Île Dautrive—he had been a lad on this coast—but he kept on, for the highest ridge was at the western point. Across the sand shoal, beyond this point, was still higher land, a clay fragment in which grew a few stout oaks. By these Old Rojas's camp had stood. It did not stand there now, thought Lalande. Nothing built by man on the reef would stand. *Grandpère* and the children of the man whom the white stallion had killed must certainly have taken to the lugger—escaped before the hurricane tide rushed upon the flimsy shack. Surely, yes. Rojas was no fool!

Lalande kept on, clinging to the thickets when the worst clutch of the wind was on him. The roaring of it all was so steady that actually he seemed in a great silence, as if a new element had enveloped him—a normal thing, this shock and unceasing tenseness of feeling and of sound. Through it he strode steadily himself, a strong man with neither fear nor curiosity—a mere dull plunge on to the last foothold of that reef which was churning to gruel behind his steps. He could not miss the point; there was no other spot to reach, and the hurricane was guide as well as captor.

And his mind was upon the lord of Dautrive Island. "He will go. Perhaps he is gone now. And the mares and colts, all off the reef by now." And a grim satisfaction came that the white stud had turned on him at the last. It was fine to think of. The savage had not cringed. "I do not want anything that can be stolen," he murmured, and spat the sea spray from his sore lips. "His mares and colts, he fights for them—that devil!"

And he began shouting profane, fond challenges and adulations to his conqueror somewhere in this white chaos of a night. A whipping wisp of scud was that charging shape above the torn thickets; any single shriek of the storm, his trumpeted challenge in return. Lalande boasted to his soul that he was seeking his foe; if it was the last stroke of his hand he wished it raised to taunt the white, oncoming devil.

Even the storm glimmer had faded when he felt the water shoaling from his armpits to his waist. This was the west point, the highest, and here, with hands locked to the stoutest of the mangroves, he would have to let the sea boil over him as long as a strong man could—then go.

On the western high point at last, and nothing to see, nothing to feel but the submerged bushes and the earth dissolving so that he had to keep his feet moving to avoid each becoming the center of a whirlpool.

"It is a storm," Lalande grunted. "Two white devils on this reef." He remembered seeing spaces of mirrored calm, peaceful coves over which they told him orange trees had bloomed in cottage yards of the reef dwellers. The sea had devoured the islands in a night, dug the hole, and lain down in it like a fed tiger. Lalande, crowded closer to the stouter thickets, put out his hand in the dark. He touched a wet, warm surface, heaving slightly.

The skin of a brute. He smoothed the hair in the rushing water, felt along. A wall of steely flesh broadside to the tidal wave. Lalande softly slipped his hand over the huge round flank. The water was swirling about them both to the man's armpits now. Lalande knew. They were on the highest point, but ahead lay the shoal pass. The sea was eating away this point; what was left was sinking, flicked off into the meeting currents around Dautrive and swept inland. The island would be silt on some cane planter's back fields forty miles up the Mississippi delta within the week.

But for the last of his domain the lord of Dautrive was fighting with his last foothold. The white devil of the sea was doing what man could not do. Lalande laughed in the blackness. The stallion could not feel his soft touch in all that beating welter of sand and debris churning around him. He rested his arm across the un-seen back—the brute would think it was a driftwood branch. The man stepped forward. There was no other foothold now, it seemed. He reached his hand to the shoulder, up to feel the stiff, wet mane. He laughed and patted the bulged muscles.

"We go, you and I," he grumbled. The mangroves were slatted out on the tiderush, tearing loose, reeling past them. "Eh, friend? The last—"

And then he knew that the horse had whirled, upreared in the blackness with a scream of fury. Lalande sprang to the left, into deep, moiling water.

He felt the plunge of his foe just missing him once more. But another body struck him and then was whirled off in the meeting tides. He collided with a colt in the dark; and now he guessed that the white stallion's breed had been gathered on the refuge shielded to the last by his huge bulk against the inexorable seas.

They were gone now. There was no more foothold on Dautrive either for the exiles or the man who had come to subdue them. Lalande knew he must not go with the tidal wave. It was death anywhere out there. The water would rush fifty miles inland over the battered reefs. So he fought powerfully back to get a handhold on the mangrove thickets through a whirlpool of dissolving sand.

But the man could not breast those surges through the dark; he felt himself driven farther back in a tangle of foam and debris, and suddenly came a whiplike tightening about his legs. He was dragged under and out across the current until he fought down to grasp this thing that had him.

It was his throw-rope, the new and heavy line that he had brought to conquer the white stud that the island men feared. Lalande plunged up and along it. The rope was tight and surging athwart the drift. When he got his head above water he knew he was clear of the disintegrating sand point, overwhelmed by the rollers in the pass and stung by the spray, but moving.

An unseen guide, a mighty power was drawing aslant the inshore tide. Lalande hauled along until he felt the rhythmic beat of the stallion's stroke; along until he touched his flank. When he could put his hand to his long mane Lalande laughed. He hung there, and felt the brute plunge higher at this contact. Once, twice, and then the stud settled to his fight.

The lord of Dautrive could not shake him off nor rend him with teeth or hoof. He was being ridden through the blackness and the sea.

Lalande began shouting. He could not resist the impulse of defiance; the great horse had been merciless to him on the island, so now he howled at him whenever he could keep the salt water from his teeth.

"*Eh, bien!* Big fellow, you see I am here! If you go, I go! Lalande is with you—devil! Fight! Fight on; a man is on your back at last. A last ride, too, white devil!"

For he had no hope of anything except to be battered to a pulp by the driftlogs and wreckage in the pass or drowned over the flooded marshes. But the stallion would not give to the northward tide, always he kept fighting to windward and westerly. When he plunged on these tacks Lalande swung out straight over his back, but clinging lightly and calling his taunting courage to the brute.

"The west ridge," muttered the rider. "He knows that, the oaks and the clay soil. If anything hangs together in this sea it will be that." So he clung in the dark. Nothing but the incessant battles of the horse's broadside in the hurricane tide kept that feeling in Lalande's heart that the swimmer was trying to cross the pass to Rojas's oak grove. The white devil was blind in the white sea, but he remembered that. Lalande could feel the leg strokes steady and true even when the waves lifted or buried them, or when they were half drowned in the whipped foam among patches of reef wreckage. The man was fighting at this debris to keep it from the stallion's neck when he felt something else streaming along his flanks. It appeared to be submerged bushes or thick, long grass twisting about beneath them. And there was a changed note to the hurricane's tumult.

Lalande swung up on the stallion's back, listening. The swells of the pass were slower here, huge and strangling, but not with the fierce rush they had battled. The horse was swimming more to seaward, almost head on now, and once he arose as if his fore-feet had struck the earth.

"He has found the marsh," muttered Lalande. "Night of wonders; nothing else!"

Still that powerful, steady stroke under the man's clinging limbs. The brute was seeking whatever land might be above the water. Then Lalande began to think, as again he felt the forefeet touch bottom.

"Then we fight again, eh, tiger? Shake me off and come at me! Make the oaks and we'll see!"

The horse plunged past a torn oak stump which smashed him in the side. He was in water to his withers, but Lalande knew he was climbing. He got a foothold, leaned against the tide rushing through the oak grove, and kept on. Against the man and horse there crushed another trunk, denuded of leaves, swinging by its roots, staggering them with its blows. The sea was over this also, Lalande knew. If it came higher there was no hope here.

Then the stallion stopped. He stood belly deep in the lee of another oak trunk which Lalande could feel in the utter dark And the man sat silent astride the white king of Dautrive who had lost his domain and his subjects. He moved his legs across the heaving flanks—a sort of stealthy challenge. He wanted the white stud to know that he, Joe Lalande, was there astride him. He laughed and leaned to pat the unseen arch of the neck.

And then again came that furious, uprearing plunge of the great brute. His head came about in a side blow, his teeth tearing at Lalande's face as the rider swerved out under this twisting, maddened attack. He heard that trumpet cry again of the wild horse seeking him as he dragged himself about the oak tree in the water. He stood clutching the rope, trying to make out the brute's form.

Then he knew that the swells riding through the twisted oaks were slowed; the yelling of the winds more fitful, higher; and a sort of check came to the clutch on his body against the tree. Lalande seemed to stand in a frothy eddy as if the sea had stopped running and was foaming to an apex about him. And he knew what it meant, the moment that always comes in the Gulf hurricanes. The wind was dying off and changing. The sea could do no more. It had piled its flood as far inland and as high as even

its strength could hold. Its whirling center was now over the coast, the wind whipping fitfully, now southwest, westerly, northward, and beginning to rise again. But there came one moment when it was almost a calm, silence except for that roaring in the sky.

"*La revanche,*" muttered the man. "Now comes the worst—the rush of the tide back to sea. The good God help them all, these Cajans who have not found refuge up the bay. *La revanche*—that is when they die!"

He felt about his oak trunk, wondering if it were still rooted firmly. The white stallion must be just about the torn branches, for Lalande still had the trailing line. And then came something that numbed him with uncanny fear. A voice out in the dark, a child's cry among the oaks.

"*La revanche! Grandpère,* it is coming! Get the lines the other way, *Grandpère*—"

Lalande went plunging toward the spot. "*Nom de Dieu!* It is not possible? Rojas!" He shouted, and stumbled among wreckage of trees and timbers around his waist. "Rojas, you are in the grove?"

A dim light glowed behind a blanket. He saw a boy had snatched this moment of the falling wind to try the lantern. When Lalande waded to the spot an old man straightened up on the other side of a sunken raft. Upon it, under the blankets, were lashed the forms of Rojas's children, the orphans of Emile, who had once sought to tame the white horse of Île Dautrive. Old Rojas held the lantern close to his white beard. He seemed as frightened as was the small boy by the stranger's coming.

Old Rojas had been trying to spike a cross-piece to his shattered raft. His lugger had been smashed in the first reach of the hurricane, and he had torn up the planks of his camp floor to build this refuge anchored to the biggest oaks of the grove. They knew what to do, these Cajans of the reefs, when they were caught by the hurricane tide. Cut the mast from the lugger and drift inland, seize an anchorage before the dreaded *revanche* took them seaward; or if not that, hang to one's oak stumps!

Lalande did not waste the precious moments with a single question.

"A brave fight, old man. I see you made a brave fight! Give me your raft-lines. The other way around now, and to the stoutest trees. This sea, it is like a mad tiger when it has to go back defeated! Come." He took the mooring-line and plunged off in the waist-deep froth.

"Day of wonders!" mumbled old Rojas. "A man on the reef—living! A big man, strong after the hurricane! It is impossible!" He went hammering his raft as it surged and plunged by his shoulders, ordering the youngster to make himself fast once more in the life ropes which held them all to the shaking planks. There was no whimper from the four children. They raised big dark eyes staring from *Grandpère* to the strange man who was battling back in the first seaward rush of the waters to make them fast against *la revanche*. The wind was smiting again. It appeared to fall out of the blackness to the north, blast after blast, rising swifter, smiting the piled-up waters, hurling them over the reef islands with thrice the speed they had come in.

The dim lantern went out. The fugitives tied themselves on again. If the worn lines held and the raft kept together they might live. "Name of Names!" grumbled old Rojas. "A man coming to us out of the sea? He said he would make fast for us. If not, my children—well, we must trust him."

Lalande had struggled off into the new rush of the wind with the raft-lines. They were frayed and ragged. He made them fast to his own new throw-rope. He would get this rope off the stallion somehow, and make it fast to the big oak. If not—he shrugged, well, then, nothing! Every wreck of a lugger, plank of a camp, driftlog, tree, that was loose would be miles in the open Gulf to-morrow to eddy endlessly in *la revanche*.

The old man's mooring-lines would not reach the big oak. Lalande had thought that, combined, they might last the night out, but the sea and wind were whipping fast on him in the dark. He had to plunge out shoulder deep to the tree, feeling of his line.

"The white devil is there and quiet," he grumbled. "If he would let me slip the rope from his shoulders and tie it to the tree!" He breasted the brimming tides over the submerged isle past the oak, his hand cautiously out to the dark. "Devil!" he called softly. "This is for Emile Rojas's young ones. The rope, devil! We've fought, you and I, but now let me have it."

The line was tight past the oak stump. The weight of the raft was already coming strongly on it as the tide began to seethe through the shattered grove. Lalande could hardly keep his feet, or his eyes open against the bitter spray. Then he was off his feet; he was hanging to the line, fighting out on it, calling to his foe, reaching for him. The brute must be swimming now, for the footing had gone from under them both.

Lalande felt a plunging on the line. It was too late now to hope to get the rope to the oak. The fighting horse was on it, and it began to give slowly past the man's hands. *La revanche* was bearing them on, the raft, the man, and the white devil who was its sole anchor, now. Lalande clung with one arm to the oak and drew in on the line. The dead weight of the raft had its way. The bucking, plunging brute, now touching the ground, now surging in the tide, was being drawn to him. Lalande began to call again. He had a great sense of pity for the stud. There were things that could not be withstood even by his lion heart; yet even the sea might not conquer except for this choking drag of the raft that held Rojas's grandchildren.

Lalande touched the stallion's muzzle now, coming on fighting with the obstinate ferocity of a white shark. He crouched in the crotch of the oak and held out his arms to the stallion's neck. When finally the brute crashed upon the sunken oak, Lalande reached his fingers to the cleft where the throw-rope cut into his neck. He dragged on the line, vainly trying to ease that tension. Once he thought of his knife; he might cut that choking grip from the white stud's throat. Then Lalande lay back in the crotch above the plunging hoofs and eased the great head above his own shoulder. Dragging on the line with all his power he kept up his whispering as the hurricane tide rushed under them, swinging the oak on its roots, twisting it seaward, and sucking the earth away in whirls where Rojas's house had stood.

"I tell you we are still here, you and I," called Lalande after a while. "You and I, devil! You and I—smashed up together, my face against your own! *Eh, bien!* Be quiet, Emile Rojas may be watching his children, and you in this storm? Remember that, white devil, you have returned for them!" He laughed and shouted in the dark, his arm about the neck of the horse working his fingers under the rope, trying to take some of the strain upon his own flesh and bone. And presently he grumbled, "And remember, also, I am not a thief. Not a thief, eh?"

They clung that way five hours, until the crest of *la revanche* was passed. The sun even got through the huge rifts of black clouds streaming south by the time old Rojas stirred about from his creaking raft in the scrub oaks. Everywhere a brown, dirty, sullen sea setting out, flecked with drift and wreckage, and of all Île Dautrive nothing showed but these few battered, branchless trees.

The stout old man waded waist-deep from his raft where now Emile's young ones sat up stiff and drowsy from the sea's nightlong flailing. He followed his mooring-line out to where it sogged under water by the big oak. The eldest boy had stood up looking after him.

"Grandpère!" screamed the lad suddenly. "Look! The white horse has come! By the tree, with the man!"

Old Rojas waded and struggled there, too astounded to speak. The sight was a queer one, indeed. The white horse was drawn against the oak-crotch, pinned in there, in fact; and the rope from his neck also crushed the strange man against his shoulder. Joe Lalande appeared to be crucified against the satin coat of the stallion. But he lifted his free arm faintly when the old man floundered near them.

"M'sieu?" gasped Rojas. "You here?" He had to touch Lalande's drenched body ere he could believe that the man lived. Then he fell to loosening the slacked rope so that Lalande lurched down from the horse's neck into the water where he could hardly stand but clung to the tree trunk watching the animal. The rope had cut through Lalande's arm and shoulder until it made a long red-scarred mark from neck to elbow. He could not speak for a time from his salt-swollen lips.

"Yes, I am here," he whispered at last, and staggered weakly.

"Name of God, the white horse!" cried the old man. He put his hand out to touch the smooth side, but as if fearing him even now. Lalande was trying to discover whether or not the heart of the white stallion still beat; and then he turned away, his eyes closing wearily. He seemed to be shaken by a sob, a grief that the islander could not comprehend.

"What's the matter, M'sieu? We are safe; the boats will find us. *Le bon Dieu!* that was a storm! I have never seen a greater on this reef!"

Then he looked curiously at the still form of his old enemy. *"Eh, bien!* It took a white sea to kill this white devil, my friend!"

"It was not the sea," grumbled Lalande. "The touch of a rope on his neck, M'sieu. I saw his heart break last night, but it was for the children of Emile. A rope and the touch of my hand upon his neck, they were not to be endured, M'sieu." Then Lalande turned away, as if speaking to the lord of Dautrive against the tree: "At least you must know this, white devil, the hand on you was not the hand of a thief."

Royal Cream Horses and Ponies[1]

By SIR HUGH GARRARD TYRWHITT–DRAKE

A CREAM horse to many people—and people with experi‑ ence—is any horse the colour of cream, such as a black dun (a dun or cream-coloured horse with black mane and tail), a silver dun (the same horse with a silver mane and tail), a dun horse with a black stripe down the back and often two or three short stripes across the front leg below the elbow, the colour of the wild horse; but all these horses have dark skins.

The sure test of a real cream horse is a pink skin—the same as that of a "white" man—and blue eyes, sometimes known in black horses with white points as a "wall" eye.

The only other horse that ever has a pink skin is a white-born horse—one that is white when born and unlike a grey which is always black when foaled and gradually turns white with age.

Milk-white or cream-coloured animals have always been prized above the ordinary coloured ones. Sacred, royal, or at least used by the highest in the land, possibly on account of their conspicu‑ ousness, more probably because of their scarceness.

German authorities assert that the Cream Hanoverians had a common origin with the breed known as *"Die gelben Pferd von Ivonach"*—cream-coloured horses seem to have been held sacred by the German tribe from a very early period. Tacitus, in his *Germania,* wrote: "It is peculiar to this people to seek omens and monitions from horses. Kept at the public expense, in those same woods and groves are white horses, pure from the taint of earthly labour; they are yoked to a sacred chariot and accompanied by the priests and the king or chief of the tribe who note their neigh‑ ings and snortings."

The most famous of all cream animals were (and I say "were"

[1]From *Beasts and Circuses,* by Sir Hugh Garrard Tyrwhitt-Drake.

with regret) the "Royal Hanoverian Cream Ponies"—a most misleading description, because the so-called "ponies" were horses from 15.2 to 16.2 with good bone and considerable strength, as was very necessary to enable them to carry out their duties, but of this anon.

Records shows that in 1773 there was the large stud at Hanover of no less than 546 cream horses.

I am one of many that hate to see old customs die out, and I must own that when I heard in 1921 that the royal creams were to be disposed of from the Hampton Court Stud and the Royal Mews I felt that some of the glory of our royal processions—and where else in the world can such beautifully-horsed and perfectly-turned-out royal carriages be seen—had for ever departed.

I know this view was also taken by many others, particularly colonials, who felt that in the Royal Creams our King had something in the horse-flesh line that no other royal or republican state could boast of.

In these days of expense and necessary economy it is not to be wondered at that they had to go. A royal team—and such was only used on full-State occasions, coronations, jubilees, funerals and opening of Parliament—consisted of eight stallions, and to be sure of such a team being available, four more in reserve, in addition to a breeding stud of at least eight mares and various young stock were absolutely necessary. A very heavy outlay to horse one carriage possibly four or five times a year.

I have already mentioned the size and necessary strength of these animals and for the following reasons. The Royal Coach to which they were harnessed weighs four tons, the State harness—red morocco with gilt "furniture"—weighs over 1 cwt. per horse, and in addition each of the four near-side horses had to carry a postilion.

And now to deal with the history of the Royal Creams.

Commonly known as Hanoverian horses ever since King George I of England (and King of Hanover) brought them with him from Hanover in 1714, they were probably at any rate originally Spanish. According to tradition, the original cream horses were presented by Queen Isabella of Spain in the fifteenth century to various German knights, mostly from the Thuringenwald, as rewards for services rendered in the Queen's Army.

The great Spanish painter, Velazquez, painted many equestrian portraits, the horses depicted often being cream-coloured.

From the year 1714 to 1921 they were always used for all full-State Royal Processions by the reigning King or Queen of England with the one exception of seven years, when Napoleon having entered Hanover confiscated a team of creams and used them attached to his carriage for his triumphant entry into Paris. This is said to have so annoyed George III that for seven years they were not used for the English State Processions.

Their peculiar colour was aptly described by Napoleon, who called them his *"chevaux café au lait,"* the general colour being a milky cream—not a yellow as in dun horses—with the mane and tail darker and exactly the colour of a well-milked cup of coffee.

It is not to be wondered at that by 1919, when I first had anything to do with these horses, they were not only delicate and unbred, but that there was great difficulty in getting the mares to produce foals at all.

I had had a good deal of experience in breeding cream ponies (10½ to 12½ hands) from pure coloured stock, and because I had not enough pure mares, by experimenting with other coloured mares, to produce cream foals at either the first or certainly the second generation. Because of my experiments I was asked to advise the Crown Equerry as to the best fresh blood to introduce to produce Royal Creams with more stamina than the descendants of horses into which no fresh blood had been introduced for centuries.

My advice was to obtain good hunter or coach-horse type mares, black or silver dun in colour, and on no account duns with the black stripe down the back, as I had found from my own experience that such a colour is almost impossible to eradicate, though the main colour of the progeny may be almost bay, or even blue grey, the stripe persists! Some four or five mares were obtained, either black or silver dun, and the results at the first foaling bore out the truth of my experiments, and every foal was pure cream in colour. True, the type and even the colour varied; those from the hunter type were somewhat light in bone, those from the heavy coach-horse or vanner type a bit hairy-heeled, *all* were deficient in the great characteristic of the original creams—the Roman nose. It stood to reason that the next cross was certain to produce cream foals, and by being three-quarters instead of half-bred much better in type.

It was at this time that the decision to get rid of the creams was made. The Royal team of eight were distributed to various golf links to horse their light rollers, etc.

I was honoured by a gift from H.M. the King of a yearling stallion, "Amorist," and two yearling mares, "Amity" and "Amour," though the latter soon died.

The rest were either destroyed or sold, and I obtained a three-year-old "half-bred" stallion, "Scarcroft," a mare with a roach back and an old stallion.

"Scarcroft" I broke to the Haute Ecole, and used as a procession horse, the old stallion continued in harness with a dun, beside which he trotted along and never would "pull an ounce."

And what of the Royal Creams to-day? I am afraid most of the old stallions are dead. I believe Lord Lonsdale has some half-breds, a well-known old established circus firm has two or three of the same, and I have the rest—the only pure-blooded stud in the world—and I fear from difficulties I have encountered the last two foaling seasons that ere long fresh blood will again have to be introduced or they will die out.

As horses the Royal Creams are delicate, rather stupid with good action in front and not bad behind, much better than the black Flemish horses, which they rather resemble except in colour.

As a relic of the horses of two or three centuries ago they are of great interest, and I hope it will somehow or other be kept going, though in these days it is somewhat difficult and expensive.

And now I come to the real *ponies*, 11 to 12½ hands. Their claim to the title of Royal is based on the fact that they were used by Her late Majesty Queen Victoria in her bath-chair at Windsor, when advancing age made such a vehicle useful, and they were obtained as follows:

Lord George Sanger's circus was commanded to give a show at Windsor, and the Queen was so taken with the miniature creams that she wished to purchase some. Lord George refused, but asked to be allowed to present two, which request was granted, and a mare and foal in due course were sent.

The original cream was a Welsh pony bought by Sanger while

244

touring Wales, and from this stallion were bred all the cream ponies owned by them. In colour they are facsimiles of the big Royal Creams, though a trifle paler, and with the mane and tail matching the body colour instead of being two or three shades darker.

Up to the year 1911 they were in the hands of the Sanger family only. In 1913 I heard of a four-year-old stallion, the property of the late Mr. Hales (who supplied Drury Lane and many other theatres with stage animals and who had just died). I hurried off to try and buy this pony, only to find it had just been sold. I at once applied to the new owner only to find again he had just sold it. To the newest owner I then went, and was at last able to buy "Prince," the third purchaser of him in seven days. He was a typical cream pony, eleven hands high, beautiful mane and tail and plenty of bone (he had been ridden by Mr. Godfrey Tearle who was over 6 ft. high) in a Chinese play in London.

Unable to get a cream mare, and always interested in colour breeding, I began to look round for what I considered suitable mares to produce anyhow in the second or third generation cream foals. For this purpose I was given a roan Shetland, which for the first two years produced pure creams, then a roan, then a dun and I discarded her. Another friend gave me a dun Shetland with a black stripe down the back. Three foals she produced *all* her own colour with the black stripe complete. I should have realized that this, being the real wild horse colour, would be sure to predominate. I did not then, but I do now!

I went to Bampton Fair and bought some Exmoor mares, browns and one chestnut. The former produced browns, and the latter a dun, which when put back to its cream father produced pure cream foals every time.

By this time I had sufficient creams to discard all other colours, and I have bred from this stock ever since, my present stock numbering nearly fifty.

They are charming ponies, quiet, sensible, and very hardy. The mares live out all the year round, dropping their foals in the park without any assistance whatever.

The only "work" that my ponies do is at Christmas, when they are much in demand to horse "Cinderella's" carriage on the stage in pantomime. Under the glare of the footlights they appear a milky white. Of course on the stage they have a wonderful time, two, four or six, according to the number of the team to draw a light skeleton carriage less than a hundred yards a day. They are petted by all the artistes and chorus, and come home so tame and on the look out for bits that one cannot walk through the park where they are without being mobbed by the whole crowd.

Dark Child

By EDWARD NORTH ROBINSON

AFTER Dark Child left the paddock, I followed and went across to the infield to get away from the crowd. I didn't want to think about the race at all, but I couldn't help thinking about it all the same. Like always, Dark Child started slow and was well back at the turn. In the back-stretch he began to move up; coming slowly, like it was awful hard. In the turn he was still far back, and it didn't seem possible for him to overtake the front line. But you could see he was running for all he was worth. Coming for home, he was still driving forward hard. And when I saw him trying so hard, a lump came into my throat.

Then it happened. Even though I knew it was going to happen, I couldn't look. I closed my eyes and everything got strange. I felt something inside me turn over.

This happened the year they built the wonderful new tracks in New England, and Yanks, who, they said, had hardly ever seen a horse, had gone mad about racing. All the time that year men kept coming around buying horses, until my father, who runs a feed store in Thomasville, began to say, joking, he was going to move up North, too, because pretty soon there wouldn't be any horses left in Kentucky any more.

But he didn't joke much. He was worried. I wasn't sure why; only I knew it came over him when we heard that my brother Lefty had quit working for Mr. Van Horn and started training horses for a man called Kapnick. I asked my father what part of Kentucky Mr. Kapnick came from, because I'd never heard of anybody talk about his farm. "He don't come from Kentucky; he don't come from nowhere," my father said, walking away.

When I tried to find out about Mr. Kapnick from Anselm, who is an old nigger that has forgot more about horses than any white man ever knew and who knows about anybody on the tracks, all he would say was that Kapnick was a low-down no-account.

Well, when I heard that, I felt awful bad, because my brother Lefty was about the swellest guy anybody ever had for a brother. It was him who taught me to ride Dark Child when he was the most promising two-year-old in Kentucky.

Maybe exercising a horse like Dark Child don't mean nothing to you. Well, that's probably because you're a Yank, and don't know nothing much about horses, and can't understand why it is I feel the way I do. I know Yanks who talk, talk, talk about how they was positive sure such and such a horse was going to win, and say they were going to bet as much as one hundred dollars on him, without even going around to the stables to see what that horse looked like. More than that, I've heard about Yanks who bet on horses with bookies by telephone, without even going to see the race. I've heard them talk, and they don't care nothing about the horse they bet on, they don't care who owns him, where he's from, or what color he is, or how he steps. They don't care about a thing except that he wins the race.

So, if you're a Yank, then there's some things I got to tell you about horses, so you will be able to understand why exercising a horse like Dark Child meant so much to me. Sometimes, though, the way I feel about a horse worries me, because the way I feel is the way some niggers like Anselm feel, and it makes me wonder if I wasn't supposed to be born a nigger.

Right off, I want to say there is only one way to learn about horses. I don't care how many races you've seen or how much money you've bet, unless you've really lived with horses, then you can't understand about them. Like I have with Dark Child. I don't mean you've got to be like that with every horse to know about him, but if you haven't lived with some, then you can't understand about any at all.

Ever since I was old enough to walk out to the farms from town, where our house is, I began going to see the horses exercised in the morning. I don't think there is anything finer than watching horses running. Especially early in the morning, when the turf is black with dampness and the air is sharp and clear and the sun feels good, shining on your back as you sit on the top rail watching the horses working on the track and listen to the nigger swipes talking and laughing. And there isn't anything finer than this in the whole world, unless you're lucky enough, like me, to be small, so you can get up on a horse yourself and take him out on the track and go slop-jogging around to unflex his muscles. And then, after a lap or so breezing, you climb up on his neck, cluck to him, and it is wonderful to feel him cut loose, to feel the power of his running, the fresh morning air sharp in your face and the horse going like hell-fire for the pure love of running.

That's the way it was when I rode Dark Child. I don't know what it was that happened inside me, but something did. When I'd stretch out along his neck and let him go, and then feel all the power and drive of him under me, the way he would respond, trying to go faster and faster, I just was sure he was going to be a winner. Maybe even the greatest horse who ever ran. It used to make me ache to ride him, because he would run so hard when I wanted him to run. He was the most obliging horse I ever knew. He would react perfect to the slightest pull on the reins, and if I wanted him to run, I would just cluck at him and he would give all he had.

Maybe he tried so hard to please partly because he was a gelding, and partly because he was not a pretty horse and never got a lot of attention from people, like some of the pretty colts did. He had awful big feet and big bones all the way through, and when he walked, he carried his head down between his knees and shambled like a sleepy milk horse. He wasn't proud at all but meek and gentle.

Dark Child was one of those horses who think more of you than just that you bring them oats. I know, because after I would feed him and finish doing chores and start away, he would stop eating and stick his head out of the stable and whinny at me. He always wanted to be petted. If I was working around in his stall, he would keep turning around, rubbing his head against me, as affectionate as a kitten. I got to think an awful lot of him, and when they sent for him up North, that was how I came to go North too.

It was during the summer, when we were hearing all sorts of talk about how insane the Yanks had gone over racing and how wonderful the new tracks at Pomfret Park and Salt Meadows were, that Mr. Van Horn himself came down to the farm to look the horses over to get some to take up North. One of those he took was Dark Child.

Anselm and I were both glad when Mr. Van Horn selected him, even though he did nothing as a two-year-old. All along, Anselm had said he was going places as a three-year-old. Anselm said he was too rangy to untrack fast enough to win in two-year-old sprints, and that was why he had done poor last year. But Anselm said that when he started running a mile and a mile and a quarter, then he was going to town. Anselm is so smart that he can most often tell what a foal is going to look like even before he is born. I never knew a white man what could do that.

After Mr. Van Horn took Dark Child and the other horses away, there was only the yearlings left. The farm seemed deserted, and I began to feel an all-powerful urge to go North too. I knew it wasn't any use asking my father if I could go, because he'd say I was too young. That's the way my father is. There isn't anything in the world he likes better than horses, and it nearly broke his heart when he had to stop training, going from track to track, on account of his asthma, and settle down. I can remember him talking to Lefty and me about all the horses he had trained and about all the tracks they had run at—about Tropical Park and Bowie and Churchill Downs and Saratoga, and in Cuba too. But then he'd say what an awful life it was, and after Lefty had gone he used to talk about me being a lawyer or a doctor, and he'd try to make me eats lots of food, so I'd be too heavy to ride, which I wanted to do more than anything in the world.

One day I saw that Dark Child was entered at Niantic and I could hardly wait for the next day to come to find out how he would do. Only all the time I was sure he would win, and I told Anselm so. Anselm said he would win all right, so long as he didn't get boxed up in the stretch turn, which is bad at Niantic, it is so sharp. Although I was positive sure that he would win, when I read in the paper that he did win by two lengths and driving hard, something funny happened to me. All the words blurred together like the white posts do when you're riding fast close to the rail. I couldn't see the words at all, only a vision of a big black horse flashing by the judges' stand in the bright sunlight while thousands of people were looking and cheering. Right then it was that I knew I had to go North. I just had to see Dark Child win.

The only person I told about running away was Anselm. Because you can trust a nigger not to tell on you. It wasn't hard. I just kept my ears open to hear when somebody was going to ship some horses, and when I heard that Colonel Saunderson had a carload going, why, I just went too.

It was in the middle of the morning when I got off the horse car at the track. There were rows and rows of barns. Even though I knew there were over two thousand horses there, I didn't think it would be so big. Although it was at a quiet time, there was an awful lot of people and niggers around—more, even, than in the whole town of Thomasville. I was hungry, so I found out from some boys pitching nickels where the restaurant was, and went there and had a piece of Catawba melon, a stack of wheat cakes with maple sirup and sausages, coffee, two pieces of pie and a bottle of milk. I felt better then and went out to look at the track.

It was beautiful. Clean and well kept, like a park. The infield was all grass, smooth as a lawn, except for the tan-bark strip where the horses crossed to the paddock. On the opposite side was the big grandstand, with rows of flags on top, flying in the breeze. In front was the judges' stand, all glassed in, and across the track the tote board. Even so far away the grandstand looked awful big, and I wondered where all the people came from to fill all the seats.

I didn't look around any more because I wanted to see Dark Child. It wasn't hard finding Mr. Van Horn's string. His colors ran the whole length of a barn, and right away I recognized old King Knute looking out of his stall. It seemed mighty good to see the horses again. There was Jim Dandy, with his Flying Don, short-hitched to keep him from pacing; a couple of new fillies I didn't know; Black Devil, who was out of the same dam as Dark Child; and His Royal Highness, who never once ran first, yet lots of times second or third. But Dark Child wasn't there.

I walked the length of the barn again, but he wasn't there. Then I met Monty, one of Mr. Van Horn's niggers. He wanted to know how come I was there. I told him, to see Dark Child run, and Monty agreed he was doing some powerful running. When I asked him where he was, he wanted to know where I'd been all my life if I didn't know my own brother was training him for Mr. Kapnick and that he was supposed to run that afternoon; only he probably was scratched, because he pulled up lame last time out.

I had to do some tall hunting and ask two niggers before I found where Kapnick's horses was. It made me worried when I heard that Dark Child was lame, not because I wouldn't see him run that afternoon, but that he might have to go back to the farm, because when a horse with weak pasterns like him goes lame, it's bad news.

Finally, I found him standing in his stall with his head down and different looking—not sleek any longer. Then I saw he was standing with one leg in a tub of ice water, and all at once I knew they were trying to get him ready to run, and it made me ache to see him standing, so quietly and of his own accord, holding his leg in the ice water.

Just then a man came with more ice in a bucket and dumped it in the tub. I asked him where Lefty was, and he asked me what the cripes I wanted. I said that I just wanted to see him, and when would he be back?

"Back?" he said. "He ain't been yet!"

"Where is he?" I asked.

"Up at the Town Inn with a dame," he said, "and if it's any·thing to you, that's where I'd be, too, if I had this three-legged gold mine."

I felt bad because it sounded like my own brother Lefty was campaigning Dark Child. I didn't believe it and started away. As I was going, a shiny car swung around the other end of the barn, and I saw my brother and another man, both dressed up swell, get out, and in the car I could see two women dolled up like movie actresses. I felt ashamed and went away quick, so they wouldn't see me.

That afternoon I went over into the infield to watch the races. Dark Child was running in the fourth. When I was riding up from Kentucky in the horse car, it seemed like I couldn't get there fast enough to see him run. But now, after finding out his condition, I kept wishing the fourth wouldn't come, and I kept telling myself that when Lefty saw how bad his leg was, he wouldn't let them run him.

It was a mile race, so the start was right in front of the grandstand. From the infield, I could see all the people in the clubhouse and grandstand milling around, and there was more than I thought could be in the whole world almost.

When the horses paraded out, Dark Child looked homely beside the rest. He shambled along with his head down, following the horse in front of him just like he was supposed to do, without any fuss or capers. The marshal in his red coat paraded the horses way up by the clubhouse and then back by the grandstand and down into the stretch. It seemed as if he would never get them to the barrier. I couldn't understand why he walked them so far.

All the while the people were rushing to the betting windows and the announcer was urging them to hurry and not get shut out. Finally the horses were at the barrier. After about three minutes, the starters got them in line and the bell rang and they broke off almost together. Right away, a filly called Cleo went to the lead, followed by a mare from the Baywood Stables, and then four bunched up, and Dark Child trailing with the rest. Most of the horses were new to me and I couldn't make out the silks without any glasses, so I couldn't tell exactly how they went into the far turn. But it was about the same order, with the filly leading and Dark Child well back. That was because he wasn't able to untrack fast. The minute I saw him come up on the backstretch, I knew he would win. Going into the turn, he was fifth and coming strong. But suddenly he stumbled and his jockey went off, flying. In the grandstand there was a loud noise from the people. The field passed Dark Child. As they did, he started after them. Then a funny thing happened. Instead of chasing after them, he turned around and went back to where his jockey was getting up. Himself, he didn't care about winning. He only ran because his jockey wanted him to.

After they led Dark Child across the infield, I followed. When they got to the barn I went right up to him and patted him.

Right off, he knew me, and I could see how glad he was to see me, rubbing his sweaty head against me and whinnying softly. When they took his bandages off and I saw the swelling, I knew he was through running for a good long time.

I didn't care if Lefty would come and send me home any more, because I felt so fond of that horse I would rather be back home with him than up here with all the others.

Lefty didn't come until after all the races were over. He came in the car with one of the same women. They sat in the car for a while and didn't notice me standing by the stall, because they were arguing about something. And then I heard Lefty start swearing at the woman about betting, and the woman swearing back like I never heard a woman talk before.

At first, when he got out of the car, he didn't see me. When he did, he said, "What are you doing here?" I told him I wanted to see Dark Child run. And he said, "Well, you seen the stumbling dog run all right, didn't you?" Then he wanted to know if the old man had got tired feeding me and sent me. I felt awful to hear him talk like this. I told him no. "Well," he said, "now that you're here, you can stay until the meeting is over." I told him that I thought I'd stay a few days and go back maybe with Dark Child. "What the hell do you mean—back with that dog?"

"He's lame," I said.

"Lame," he said, laughing. "Of course, he's lame. He was lame when we got him. But he still can run. Kid," he said, "take the hayseed out of your hair. You ain't down on the farm no longer."

I didn't know what to say. If I didn't know this was Lefty, then, from his actions, I'd know it wasn't Lefty. I wanted to go somewhere away, but I didn't want to leave Dark Child.

The next day Lefty came out with a big man who wore glasses. They looked at Dark Child's legs, and the big man said it was bucked shins and the only thing to do was have him fired. I heard Lefty arguing, saying, "But, doc, I'll have to lay him up for a month." Then the big man, who, I figured, must be a horse doctor, got mad and told Lefty to go to hell and do what he wanted, because if he hadn't earned enough on that horse without hollering about laying him up for a month, he ought to get out of racing.

I was glad he said that. I almost wished he'd put Lefty off the track for a while.

The next morning Lefty and the horse doctor and another man came. I saw the electric firing irons and knew they were going to try to pull the muscles back by firing him. I had never seen a horse fired before, and I didn't want to see them do it to Dark Child. But Lefty made me stand by his head and pat him. The first thing they did was to paint him below the knees with something that smelled like hospitals.

Dark Child didn't seem to care at all what they did, just so long as I kept patting him. He hardly moved, even when they cut open his legs and injected the irons. He just stood quiet and let them do anything. All the time I kept saying to myself that it didn't hurt him, because his legs were numb. After it was done, the doctor gave him a smack and said it was a good job and ought to last until next year.

When the meeting closed, Lefty left me there with Dark Child and he went to Pomfret. It was about a month before the next meeting would open up, and that was just about how much longer it would take for the wounds to heal. Almost everybody went away and, as Lefty came down only twice, I would have been awful lonely if it hadn't been for Dark Child.

A few days after the next meeting opened, Lefty ran Dark Child for the first time since he was fired. He wasn't the favorite, but the odds on him were low. Like always, he got away slow and began to make ground in the backstretch. When his jock started driving him in the turn, he came up more. In the stretch he pushed up with the leaders. Toward the finish he was running neck and neck with Chatterfol. In running so hard, Dark Child looked like he was coming apart. At the last few yards he just seemed to throw himself forward like he would die, even, to win for the boy riding him. And when I saw him trying so hard, I just felt that there wasn't a gamer horse living.

The finish was so close that nobody knew who won until the numbers flashed. It was Dark Child who won. When they led him into the winner's circle, he looked as though he would topple over, he was so all in. Standing there, he didn't seem to have any interest at all in winning. He just stood quiet, to be unsaddled and led away.

Three days later Lefty entered him again. This time the handicapper put seven pounds more weight on him. The race was a mile-and-seventy yards. When I led him out to go across the infield, I knew he didn't want to go. He wasn't a fighter or a show-off, like some horses who love to race. Mostly you can tell them by the cake walk they do in front of the grandstand. Dark Child hated racing. I could tell. But he came along just the same. He never caused any trouble.

He was the favorite this time. But the trackmen realized he was carrying a lot of weight, and most of them knew about his bad legs, so they stayed off him. Again he started slow, but he broke clean. And he ran the same way, stretching out and driving all the way in the backstretch, to come up with the leaders. Then, under the constant hammering of his jock, staying right up there around the turn, to give everything he had in the stretch and win by a nose.

Not until I led him away after the race did I realize how tired he was. It wasn't only that he was all lather and sweat and twitching muscles. It wasn't just the exhaustion of one race, but a tiredness from too many races without resting.

I couldn't understand why Lefty kept running him so often. I knew he did it for the money, but what I couldn't figure was why he kept running him continually, instead of resting him and training for a big purse. Because he was only a three-year-old, and if he was built up instead of being run so much, he could

become a great horse and maybe win twenty-five thousand dollars in one race, even. I knew he would be a great horse, because he was big and perfect to train, and because he had courage. Why Lefty ran him like he was, I didn't know, and I began to think about it all the time, trying to figure out why.

One day I found out. I had just brushed Dark Child and was putting a stable blanket on him to protect him from the horseflies, which were bothering him bad. As I bent under him to reach the blanket strap, a big horsefly stung his near foot and he kicked, nearly clipping me. Then I saw the same fly light on his other foot, and he didn't move at all. I wouldn't have thought about it, only I remembered how that was the foot that Lefty was always looking at. So I looked at it close and I couldn't see anything the matter with it; only somehow it didn't look healthy. I got thinking about what could make it look like that, and all at once I thought of something that just made me sick. It was the thing, my father said, any man who did to a horse ought to be shot for. Even though I couldn't believe what I was thinking, I had to know, because I was so crazy over Dark Child.

So I got a horse-blanket pin and unbent it, so it was like a lancet. Then I went into Dark Child's stall. Bending over from where I stood in front of him, I stabbed him in his right shank. The horse-blanket pin went in deep, but he didn't move. It didn't hurt him, because all the nerves had been cut out. And that was why he didn't go lame any more—because no matter how sore he was, he couldn't feel it. Pretty soon his hoof would be dead, and that was why Lefty kept running him all the time—because where the nerves were cut out, his hoof would become more and more brittle, and it was only a question of time when it would break off.

It was all clear then. But suddenly everything became foggy, and I thought of what my father had said to both me and Lefty about any trainer who did such a thing to a horse. I couldn't realize it was my own brother Lefty who had done it. Like a flash, I remembered how quiet and peaceful it was walking between the poplars at the Van Horn farm, and how Anselm was the smartest nigger who ever lived, and how Lefty and I used to listen to him talk about the gloriest sport that there ever was, horse racing, and the sound of the frogs in the marsh by the railroad at night. And it seemed a long time ago. And I remembered the way my father's feed store looked, with my father sitting in the office, and mash feeders and drinking fountains for chickens in the show window, and these things were all clear and fine.

But at the same time, ugly and jumbled together, was the crowd of people pushing one another and fighting to get to the ticket windows, the niggers lying drunk at the track stables, the women dolled up fine, but acting like bad women, the white trash hanging around the restaurant, bragging and drinking, the tote board flashing and the people shoving one another around. All this was jumbled up and spinning in my head.

Then Dark Child rubbed against me like he was always doing, and I just threw my arms around his neck and cried.

The next day when Lefty was saddling Dark Child in the paddock and I was there holding his head and the people were crowding around the paddock rail, looking at their programs to see what horse was the one they'd bet on, I saw Lefty look down at Dark Child's right foreleg. He looked up and saw me watching him, and he knew that I knew. Without saying anything he walked away and left me there with Dark Child.

Like I said, after the horses left the paddock, I went into the infield. And Dark Child started to run hard in the backstretch and the far turn, coming slowly, like it was awful hard. And that was when it happened. And I couldn't look at first.

When I opened my eyes, Dark Child had got up and was hobbling on three legs, with the hoof of his right foreleg flopping. His jockey was up too. And some men were running toward him from the infield, and pretty soon they got to him so he wouldn't try to walk. Then the big man who was the doctor went out, carrying his bag, and when he got there he made the men hold his head down while he jabbed something in his neck. Then they let him go, and he stood there weakly, trying to rub his head against the doctor, balancing on three legs for a while and then toppling over.

The next day they dug a grave out in the infield and had a funeral just before the first race. And before they pushed him into the grave, the announcer read over the loud-speaker, while church music was playing soft, what a fine horse Dark Child was and how much the people liked him, and he told about how much Dark Child liked to race and how he died a death that was fitting for a gallant horse to die, and he said a lot more while the music was playing softly and all the people stood watching to see the men with poles push Dark Child into the grave.

But all the time I knew what the announcer said was all lies, because he didn't like to race, and the only reason he tried so hard was because he wanted to please somebody. He didn't care anything about winning. He only ran because he wanted some-body to pat him. And all of a sudden I began to hate horse rac-ing, and betting on horses, and the people pushing around, and the fat judges sitting in the stands smoking big cigars, and the ritzy people in the clubhouse with their fancy clothes, and the amount of money bet flashing on the tote board alongside the numbers for the horses, and the announcer's voice urging every-body to hurry and get their bet in.

Then, inside me, I felt awful sick, and I knew I would never be a rider at a big track and I didn't want to see any more races. I just wanted to go home.

Paul
Brown
'45

Cinderella and Warrior[1]

By LORD MOTTISTONE (GENERAL JACK SEELEY)

WARRIOR was born within sound of the sea at Yafford, in the Isle of Wight, just twenty-six years ago to-day. His lovely black thoroughbred mother, Cinderella, had been taken along the coast road from my home at Brooke about three weeks before his birth. I well remember "Young Jim" turning up at 9 o'clock one morning, on a long-legged three-year-old, and announcing that he was going to lead her over to that famous little establishment at Yafford where so many good horses have been bred.

I had just returned from the South African War, where all of us young men thought we had become preternaturally observant. Each one of us who had commanded advance guards of mounted men during that long struggle, in which we learned to admire our enemies more and more, thought himself the embodiment of Sherlock Holmes. No doubt it was true that anyone who had the lives of a squadron of men and horses committed to his care, leading them forward in that mysterious country—the High Veldt of South Africa—did, indeed, have his wits sharpened to an extraordinary degree.

In August 1902 the yeomanry regiment to which I belonged, the Hampshire Carabineers, was in camp on Salisbury Plain. I had been promoted to command a squadron on my return from the War, and was sitting on the top of Silk Hill, having been ordered to plan a field-day for the following morning.

I was surveying the well-known landscape with my 24-diameter telescope, the present of a famous deer-stalker, which was of constant value to me in South Africa and in the late War, and has been ever since. On my left, as I sat there with my Arab pony, Maharajah, a little cloud of dust caught my eye. The tele-

[1]From *My Horse, Warrior,* by Lord Mottistone.

scope showed me that it was a man galloping at great speed. As he drew nearer I saw that it was an officer in khaki uniform mounted on a black horse with long mane and tail. They passed within three hundred yards of me at the foot of the hill, and I recognised the smooth effortless gallop of a perfectly trained thoroughbred on terms with his rider.

My father had told me that he would give me a charger. My mind was made up. This must be my charger! Clearly the man would not be galloping like this, all alone, unless he knew that his horse was perfectly sound in wind and limb, nor would he be sitting so easily in the saddle unless he were sure that his horse would not attempt to run away with him.

So I jumped on to Maharajah's back and galloped sideways down the hill to try to catch him up. Eventually the black thoroughbred, as I made it out to be, slowed down, and I ranged up alongside the rider.

This was our conversation:

"Would you sell that horse of yours?"

"It isn't a horse, it's a mare."

"I'm sorry, but will you sell that mare?"

"Well, I might."

"How much?"

"Seventy pounds."

"I would have given you ninety or a hundred; but will you ride over to my camp at once?"

"You're an odd young man."

"I'm sorry, but you have a lovely mare."

"Yes, she is a lovely mare. The kindest thing I have ever known."

So we rode back over the hill where I had been sitting, and down to the camp. On the way he told me something of Cinderella's story—how she was a clean-bred mare from County Leitrim, how he had bought her for £60, six months before, from the famous Mr. Field, of Chichester, how she was almost human, and would follow him about like a dog. As he talked Cinderella would cock one ear back, and listen to his voice.

And so we rode down to our camp on that glorious August morning, and jumped off at my tent.

My faithful orderly of South African days, Smith, came forward and took both horses, and I invited my guest inside to have a whisky and soda. While we sat there waiting for it to come, I asked him again:

"Did you say seventy pounds?"

"Yes, I said seventy."

I wrote him a cheque for eighty and handed it to him.

"But why the extra tenner?"

"Because I am going to keep your lovely Cinderella here, and you can ride back on some other horse which I will lend you."

He laughed at my enthusiasm, and accepted the cheque, protesting as he rode away on the pony I lent him that he would send me back ten pounds any time that I wished.

So Warrior's mother came to belong to me, and, in a curious way, so far as there can be true affinity between man and horse, I to her.

Her story is romantic, and ends on a sad note, but on this first day, without doubt, it can be said that it was a happy chance that brought us two together.

How well I remember on that summer's morning, in camp on Salisbury Plain, leading my new charger to the horse-lines, where about four hundred other horses were tethered by a headstall and a hind leg to long ropes pegged down to the ground. I saw Cinderella looking at me all the time and wondering what was in store for her. By great good fortune, tethered on the very end of the rope was my white Arab pony, Maharajah, that I had ridden constantly for a year and a half in the South African War. He had left the Isle of Wight with me at the end of 1899, and after much trekking over the South African veldt, and many battles, which we now regard as small, but some of which we then regarded as very important, he had returned with me once more in 1901.

Maharajah whinnied when I came up to the horse lines, then looked round, and saw the beautiful, coal-black mare with the glossy coat and clear, wide-open eye of the Arab. I wondered what would happen, and expected the worst, for Maharajah, like all horses who become friendly with men or women, was jealous of any rival. My faithful groom and orderly, who had been with me and Maharajah during our long service together in South Africa, accompanied me on this adventure. We both made en-

dearing remarks to Maharajah, but I could plainly see a wicked look in his eye. I handed my sleek new thoroughbred to Smith, and told him to tie her up to the head-rope four feet from Maharajah while I went forward, patted his neck, and tried to explain to him that he had a nice new friend coming to see him. He trembled a little, and refused a lump of sugar which I had brought to offer him in order to effect a friendship. Then I stepped back while the tying up of the headstall and the hind leg was accomplished.

Cinderella never turned her head to look at Maharajah, nor did Maharajah, four feet away, pay the least attention to her. Then I made a mistake. I went forward and fondled Cinderella's head and ears, and with a pat for Maharajah turned about and walked away. I had not gone ten yards when there was a scream; Maharajah had broken his headstall, and had caught Cinderella's wither firmly in his teeth! I dashed back to them, and they were soon separated. It was the first and last occasion on which they quarrelled, for, from that moment, they became inseparable friends. When I rode one the other followed; I have never known two horses so deeply attached to one another.

From that moment Cinderella was my constant companion and friend until the outbreak of the recent War.

She came back with Maharajah and me to the Isle of Wight, where she was to spend most of her life. Whether it was the change from being one of a "string," that hateful phrase, to being one of two in constant touch with her friend called the "owner," I do not know, but the fact is that this lovely, docile, black thoroughbred became so devoted to me that she could not bear to leave me. My elder children will testify that whenever she saw me she would jump out of any enclosure, even over an iron railing, in order to join me.

As Maharajah became too old to attend manœuvres and staff rides, Cinderella took his place. When I became a Minister, Cinderella came to London with me, and I used to ride her every morning to the Colonial Office, after a gallop round the Park if I got up early enough—a rare occasion. But she did not like London, and was never really happy there. Of course when the Parliamentary recess came we enjoyed ourselves thoroughly in the Isle of Wight, riding over the downs or galloping over the sands at Brooke and Compton, and sometimes taking a day with the Isle of Wight Hunt. But although she could gallop fast, and jump well, I knew she did not care for these days with hounds. What she really loved was to be alone with me in the sun or the rain, and, above all, in the great south-west winds. It was in days of storm that she sprang to life; she loved the strong west wind. I see her now with distended nostrils, black mane and tail streaming, galloping through the gale and rejoicing in her strength.

Meantime her comrade, Maharajah, the white Arab, whom she had first met on Salisbury Plain, and who had been her constant companion in the Isle of Wight, while they were turned out together on the cliff as often as might be, slipped up one frosty morning, crossed his legs and broke his neck. The school-children were all looking on, and Maharajah loved to give them a show, jumping over imaginary obstacles, galloping on his forelegs while whisking his hindquarters round and round as only Arabs can do. It was in doing this particular trick that he slipped on the icy ground and met his end. Cinderella was looking on too; she was broken-hearted, and wandered listless and gloomy for day after day, refusing to take any food offered to her.

Then "Young Jim," my constant adviser in anything connected with horses, had a great idea. Obviously so wonderful a creature should have a child, and so in 1906 she was mated with a horse named Likely Bird. She went to Yafford for the event, and, in due course, a handsome son was born within sound of the sea. "Young Jim," and all concerned, thought this was the best foal ever seen, but, unfortunately, the brilliant young thing caught a chill of some kind, and died suddenly, to the disappointment of the Jolliffe family, and to the real grief of his mother, Cinderella.

I saw her often at this time, and, though it is difficult for human and equine creatures to communicate with each other, I like to think that she was somewhat consoled by our interviews in those grass fields stretching down to the sea at Yafford. But more real consolation was provided by another mate. This time it was Straybit who was destined to be the father of her foal.

Straybit was an exceptionally bright chestnut. I never saw a better-looking horse. By breeding he had every advantage. His father was Burnaby, his mother was Myrthe.

One very interesting episode in his life occurred in the spring of 1909. He won the Lightweight Race at the Isle of Wight Point-to-Point, the same race that his little son Warrior was destined to win, after four years of the Great War, in 1922. On both occasions "Young Jim" was the successful rider. In the December after he won the Isle of Wight Point-to-Point he went to the blood-stock sales at Newmarket, where he was bought at a good price by the Austrian Government. I have heard that he was a very successful sire, and sometimes I wonder whether Warrior may not, in the course of the War, have met, at fairly close quarters, his half-brothers and half-sisters, or even his father himself. We do know that the Austrians provided a great number of horses to the German army, so such a happening is not impossible.

However, the main importance of Straybit to Cinderella and to me lay in the fact that he was the father of Warrior.

How well I remember receiving the telegram at the Colonial Office, where I was then installed as Under-Secretary of State, announcing:

FINE CHILD FOR CINDERELLA BORN AT YAFFORD THIS MORNING. BOTH DOING WELL.—JIM.

My private secretary brought me the telegram, and looked at me narrowly. He was an austere man, R. V. Vernon, a most distinguished civil servant, and until lately our financial adviser in Iraq. I shouted with joy, and then turned on him and told him that Cinderella was a mare. But as he retired demurely I knew that he did not believe a word of what I said!

Yafford is one of the most delightful places that one could choose to possess as a birthplace. The thatched farm buildings where Warrior was born look just the same to-day as they did twenty-six years ago, even to the chickens scratching in the yard outside.

In due course Warrior was weaned, and with his mother roamed the fields at Brooke and Mottistone, till she once more resumed her duties as my charger.

Then, in August 1914, Warrior went to the War with me and Cinderella was left behind in the Isle of Wight, turned out in the big grass fields adjoining Brooke and Mottistone, wherever the pasture was best. Again, as when Maharajah was killed, she became listless and moody, missing not only me, her friend for twelve long years, but her son with whom she had been, with some intervals, for more than four years past. My children did their best to look after her, and to cheer her up, but for the first month or two she seemed inconsolable. However, the World War had a curious consequence for Cinderella and provided her with some consolations.

Warrior and I having gone to the Front, Cinderella spent most of her time alone, turned out in the great field called "Sidling Paul." Now my father had a good breed of very powerful cart-horses, in which he took a great interest. One thing that made it necessary for these cart-horses to be very strong was the existence of the Brooke lifeboat. It took ten horses to haul the heavy boat on its carriage along the loose sand to the point of launching, but even with ten horses, unless each one was powerful, and they all pulled as a team, the boat was liable to get stuck. Such a team was always forthcoming in my father's time, and, indeed, until a year ago, when we replaced the horses with a tractor.

I suppose things were a little disorganised in September 1914, but, whatever the explanation, a very fine entire cart foal was turned out on "Sidling Paul" too. No doubt it was assumed that Cinderella was much too old to have another child, but it happened otherwise.

When I came home on short leave in the summer of 1915 almost the first question I asked was, "How is Cinderella?" The children replied with glee:

"Cinderella has had a baby and we have christened it Isaac."

"Why Isaac?"

"Well, we thought she must be almost as old as Sarah was in the Bible! Come and see him."

So we walked up to the paddock between the house and the church. There was Cinderella, who, seeing me, neighed and cantered up. Sure enough she was followed by a young foal. It had a sweet little head, as all foals have, but the most comically hairy legs and heels! I fondled Cinderella as she rubbed her head against my shoulder, while the foal surveyed us both with interest. I could not help laughing when I looked at its hairy legs, and I am sure Cinderella was hurt, for she turned away from me, and licked her child's shoulder. However, I called him endearing names, and made him suck a lump of sugar, so that Cinderella resumed her equanimity, and walked back with me towards the house.

I went through the kissing-gate into the garden and was walking up the path towards the house when I heard a rat-tat behind me. I looked round and saw that the foal had jumped the iron railing, and was trotting up to us, to the consternation of his mother, who realised that she could not follow.

However, we soon lifted the kissing-gate off its hinges, and restored them to each other.

I had to return to France two days later, and so saw no more of Isaac; and, to my infinite regret, I saw but little more of Cinderella either, for the end of her story is sad. She was devoted to her quaint child; the very fact that everyone laughed about the episode made her more than ever determined to be kind to the little animal. My children and the farm bailiff concur in saying that they never saw a mare so devoted to her foal. But shortly after Isaac had been weaned, his passion for jumping was his undoing. In trying to jump a very high fence out of the paddock he caught his forefeet, fell, and broke his neck.

So Cinderella was more than ever lonely, except for the constant attention of the children.

I did not see her again until 1916. It was late on a summer's evening, and pale shafts of sunlight shone through the trees. As soon as I reached home I asked the children how was Cinderella? They said she seemed rather feeble, and was in the field by the church path. So I walked up there, and saw her, standing very erect with arched neck—I suppose she had heard my step on the gravel path. I gave her a shout, our agreed shout, and she looked my way. I gave another shout, and then she knew. But this time she could not canter; she trotted up to me and gave me a greeting so affectionate, so moving in its intensity that I can never forget it. I talked to her for a long time, stroking her nose, before turning home.

Early the next morning my son Patrick, then a little boy of eleven, came knocking at my door and shouting:

"Daddy, there is something wrong with Cinderella."

I jumped up, and ran out to the field where I had left her the

evening before. There, lying on the church path, was Cinderella. I knew at once that she was dead. I suppose that for all that long year she had waited to see me.

It was Sunday morning, and we had to pass her body on our way to church. Soon after midday I received the inevitable telegram, which all who served in the War will still remember so well, ordering me to return at once. I left immediately and got back to France the same night. On the Monday Cinderella was buried.

It was at the Battle of Amiens that Warrior met his great adventure. We fought many little rearguard actions, at one time covering the French Corps commanded by General Diebold. I well remember one of these days, I think on the 26th March, sitting on Warrior on a little bridge over a stream, giving orders to Colonel Macdonald, commanding Strathcona's Horse. A single shot rang out, fired from the rushes quite near to us, and Macdonald's horse fell dead. His horse's nose and Warrior's were almost touching, but it is wonderful to be able to record that Warrior did not flinch although he knew full well the dangers of rifle-fire.

I had Akbar and Patrick with me as well as Warrior, and had acquired another horse to take the place of St. Quentin, who had been killed at the Second Battle of Cambrai. So I rode Warrior on about every third day during this period.

On the morning of the 27th March Warrior had a most extraordinary escape. I had stabled him the night before in the drawing-room of a little French villa which was still completely intact—so much so that I remember giving him his corn on a small ormolu table.

At dawn the next morning I stood in the square of the little village dictating orders to my brigade major. The Germans, who were not far off, perceived that the village was occupied, and opened fire with a big naval gun. Almost the first shell that came over our heads hit the little villa fair and square and exploded inside, knocking it completely down except for one corner.

I said to Connolly: "I am afraid that is the end of Warrior." But, no, there was his head poking out from the few bricks still standing, with the joist of the ceiling resting on his back.

We started to try to pull the bricks away, but before we had got very far with it, Warrior made a supreme effort and bounded

out. As he emerged the joist fell, and the whole of the remaining corner of the house collapsed in a heap.

Except for a little lameness from having carried most of the weight of the top storey, Warrior was none the worse, and I rode him all that day.

On the night of the 29th March we camped at a little village called Boves near the main line from Paris to Amiens. Things looked very black then. I knew that if the Germans reached the ridge covering Amiens, the French and English armies had orders to fall back, the French on Paris, the English on the Channel Ports.

Next morning early, General Pitman, who commanded our division, woke me where I was sleeping close to Warrior under a wall. He told me that the German advance had continued, that they had captured the vital Moreuil Ridge, but that our infantry were holding on, much reduced in numbers, to the left of Moreuil village, which was for the moment held by the French. He directed me to take my brigade in that direction in order to help the infantry, and to cover their retirement when it became necessary. His last words were: "Don't get too heavily involved; you will be badly needed later."

Again, as at the Second Battle of Cambrai, I jumped on Warrior and galloped forward with my brigade major, Connolly (who had succeeded Geoffrey Brooke, promoted to command the 16th Lancers), my aide-de-camp, Prince Antoine, and my signal troop.

Although he must have been weary, Warrior put up a good gallop, and we clattered into the little village of Castel in fine style. There were a good many bullets flying down the road, but by turning to the right behind some houses we were in complete security.

By great good fortune I found the French divisional commander there. It seemed to me quite clear that unless we re-captured the Moreuil Ridge it was all over with Amiens, and probably with the Allied cause. I told the Frenchman this, and he agreed with me, but added that my little brigade could not possibly achieve it. In this he was wrong, as the event proved, but the main thing was that he sent orders to his men to hold on to the village of Moreuil on our right.

Sitting there on Warrior's back I decided to attempt the apparently impossible—to recapture the Moreuil Ridge.

Warrior was strangely excited, all trace of exhaustion had gone; he pawed the ground with impatience. In some strange way, without the least doubt, he knew that the crisis in his life had come.

At this moment the colonels of each of my regiments came galloping up as we had arranged. I dismounted and gave Warrior to Corporal King to hold. We consulted briefly, and orders were written for the attack. Then they galloped back to rejoin their regiments, the leading one, the Royal Canadian Dragoons, being only half a mile away.

The plan was that I should cross the little river separating Castel from the Bois de Moreuil with my staff and my signal troop, and, as the brigade advanced, should go forward with the signal troop and plant my little triangular red flag at the point of the wood. Our infantry were only some four hundred yards from this point, and were firing into the wood. It seemed clear to me that under cover of their fire I could do this vital thing, and establish the flag and headquarters at the point of the wood so that every man could see, as he passed our infantry front line, that the first phase of the battle had been won.

Now comes the wonderful part of the story as it concerns Warrior. As I have said elsewhere, after nearly four years of war Warrior had learnt to disregard shell-fire, as being part of ordinary war risks, but he had learnt to show great respect for rifle-fire, and would always try to swerve to right or left in order, as he clearly understood, to reduce the danger from it. But this day all was changed.

I bade farewell to my French comrade, and mounted Warrior. As I rode round the corner of the little house behind which we had been consulting into the main road of Castel, Warrior took charge and galloped as hard as he could straight for the front line. At the bottom of the hill, where we were in dead ground, I induced him to slow down to a trot as we crossed the stream by a little half-broken bridge. Then up the opposing slant we went, still out of direct view of the enemy, and across a field of winter wheat. A hundred yards beyond us was our own thin front line of infantry, lying down and returning the enemy fire.

Paul Brown

There were about twenty of us all told when I halted Warrior for a moment and looked round to give final orders. I turned in my saddle and told my comrades that the faster we galloped the more certain we were of success, that I would tell the infantry to redouble their fire as we passed through them, and that the day was as good as ours. But I could hardly finish my sentence before Warrior again took charge.

He was determined to go forward, and with a great leap started off. All sensation of fear had vanished from him as he galloped on at racing speed. He bounded into the air as we passed our infantry, and I remember shouting to a young infantry officer just on my left: "Fire as fast as you can."

There was, of course, a hail of bullets from the enemy as we crossed the intervening space and mounted the hill, and perhaps half of us were hit, but Warrior cared for nothing. His one idea was to get at the enemy. He almost buried his head in the brushwood when we reached the point of the wood at the chosen spot. We were greeted by twenty or thirty Germans, who fired a few shots before running, doubtless thinking there were thousands of us following.

Corporal King jammed his lance with the red flag into the ground, the survivors of my signal troop jumped off their horses and ran into the wood with their rifles, and the first phase of the battle was over. It was perhaps an odd way to use a signal troop, but it was the only thing to do.

But what I must record, and it is indeed the truth, is that so far as I am concerned the credit for this wild adventure, which succeeded in so miraculous a fashion, was due not to me, but to my horse Warrior. He it was who did not hesitate, and did not flinch, though well he knew the danger from those swift bullets which he had seen kill so many hundreds of men and horses all around him in the preceding years.

It was a wonderful day. The main attack swept up and the wood was soon filled with galloping Canadian horsemen. Both sides, ours and the Germans', seemed to be filled with some extraordinary exaltation. Neither would surrender. Again and again these brave Bavarians and Saxons too, and men from every part of Germany, surrounded and wounded, would continue to fire, but, on either side, not one man would hold up his hands and surrender. One determined Bavarian, with a sword thrust right through his neck, raised his rifle just level with Warrior's near shoulder, and had a last shot before he died.

Such was the spirit of the men who took part in this desperate action. So it was with the horses, and especially with Warrior, who, as all my surviving Canadian comrades will testify, was an outstanding example to all on that fateful day.

Another tribute to the heroism of the Canadian Cavalry Brigade was that paid by Marshal Foch himself, Commander-in-Chief of the French and British armies on that day. Here are his words: "On the 30th March the Battle was at the gates of Amiens, and at all hazards it was necessary to maintain the union of the armies. The Canadian Cavalry by their magnificent attack first held the enemy in check, and then definitely broke their forward march. In great degree, thanks to them, the situation, which was agonising at the beginning of the battle, was restored."

I never look at Warrior without remembering that he had a part, and so far as I was concerned, the main part, in achieving that success.

NOTE: Warrior lived to the ripe old age of thirty-two, retired in clover on the meadows of the estate on which he was born. When he could no longer endure the harsh English winters without suffering, Lord Mottistone reluctantly had him put to death.

Under the Joshua Tree

By HENRY HERBERT KNIBBS

WAY out there where the sun is boss,
  Under the Joshua tree,
'Long came a man on a played-out hoss,
  Under the Joshua tree.

Says he, "I reckon I'm a ding-dang fool
For gettin' het up when I might stay cool:
If you are a hoss—then I'm a mule,"
  Under the Joshua tree.

"The sink's gone dry and the trail's gone wrong,"
  Under the Joshua tree.

"I'm gettin' weak—and you ain't strong,"
  Under the Joshua tree.

"As sure as my name is Jo Bill Jones,
We got to quit right here," he groans,
"And the buzzards 'll git our hides and bones,"
  Under the Joshua tree.

Now that hoss wa'n't much on family pride,
  Under the Joshua tree,
But he aimed to save his old gray hide,
  Under the Joshua tree.

He says to hisself: "The world's gone dry,
But there's no sense quittin' while you can try,"
So he cocked one foot and he shut one eye,
  Under the Joshua tree.

Bill Jones went crawlin' round and round,
  Under the Joshua tree,
Diggin' like a dog in the bone-dry ground,
  Under the Joshua tree:

But the hoss stood still on his three feet,
Lookin' like he was plumb dead beat,
Till he seen his chance—and he done it neat,
  Under the Joshua tree.

Ole Bill he riz right in the air,
  Under the Joshua tree,
And oh, my gosh, how he did swear!
  Under the Joshua tree:

With a hoss-shoe branded on his pants
He let three whoops and he done a dance,
While the ole hoss waited for another chance,
  Under the Joshua tree.

UNDER THE JOSHUA TREE

Ole Bill stood up, for he couldn't sit
    Under the Joshua tree,
And he rubbed the place where the hoss-shoe lit,
    Under the Joshua tree:

Says he: "By Gum I'm a-seein' red!
And I'm blink-blank sure that you ain't dead—"
And it wa'n't no cooler for what he said,
    Under the Joshua tree.

He forked that hoss like he's never been
    Under the Joshua tree,
His head was thick, but his jeans was thin,
    Under the Joshua tree:

He pulled out slow, but he made the ride,
With the ole hoss thinkin' to hisself, inside,
"I put in a kick, and I saved my hide,"
    Under the Joshua tree.

There ain't no moral to this here song,
    Under the Joshua tree,
If you don't go right you'll sure go wrong,
    Under the Joshua tree.

But settin' and lookin' at a ole hoss-shoe,
-And figurin' luck will pull you through,
   Don't always work—there's hoss-sense too,
     Under the Joshua tree.

The Look of Eagles

By JOHN TAINTOR FOOTE

I HAD waited ten minutes on that corner. At last I ventured out from the curb and peered down the street, hoping for the sight of a red and white sign that read: "This car for the races." Then a road horn bellowed, too close for comfort. I stepped back hastily in favor of the purring giant that bore it, and looked up into the smiling eyes of the master of Thistle Ridge. The big car slid its length and stopped. Its flanks were white with dust. Its little stint that morning had been to sweep away the miles between Lexington and Louisville.

"Early, aren't you?" asked Judge Dillon as I settled back contentedly at his side.

"Thought I'd spend a few hours with our mutual friend," I explained.

I felt an amused glance.

"Diverting and—er—profitable, eh? What does the victim say about it?"

"He never reads them," I confessed; and Judge Dillon chuckled.

"I've come over to see our Derby candidate in particular," he informed me. "I haven't heard from him for a month. Your friend is a poor correspondent."

The gateman at Churchill Downs shouted directions at us a few moments later and the car swung to the left, past a city of stables. As we wheeled through a gap in a line of whitewashed stalls we heard the raised voice of Blister Jones. He was confronting the hapless Chick and a steaming bucket.

"Fur the brown stud, eh?" we heard. "Let's look at it."

Chick presented the bucket in silence. Blister peered at its contents.

"Soup!" he sniffed. "I thought so. Go rub it in your hair."

"You tells me to throw the wet feed into him, didn't you?" Chick inquired defensively.

"Last week—yes," said Blister—"not all summer. Some day a thought'll get in your nut 'n' bust it!" His eye caught the motor and his frown was instantly blotted out.

"Why, how-de-do, Judge!" he said. "I didn't see you."

"Don't mind us," Judge Dillon told him as we alighted. "How's the colt?"

Blister turned and glanced at a shining bay head protruding from an upper door.

"Well, I'll tell you," he said deliberately. "He ain't such a bad sort of a colt in some ways. Fur a while I liked him; but here lately I get to thinkin' he won't do. He's got a lot of step. He shows me a couple o' nice works; but if he makes a stake hoss I'm fooled bad."

"Huh!" grunted Judge Dillon. "What's the matter? Is he sluggish?"

"That wouldn't worry me so much if he was," said Blister. "They don't have to go speed crazy all at once." He hesitated for a moment, looking up into the owner's face. Then, as one breaking terrible news: "Judge," he said, "he ain't got the class."

There followed a silence. In it I became aware that the blue and gold of Thistle Ridge would not flash from the barrier on Derby Day.

"Well, ship him home," said Judge Dillon at last as he sat down rather heavily on a bale of hay. He glanced once at the slim bay head, then turned to us with a smile and said, "Better luck next year."

I was tongue-tied before that smile: but Blister came to the rescue.

"You still like that Fire Fly cross, don't you?" he asked with a challenge in his voice.

"I do," asserted Judge Dillon firmly. "It gives 'em bone like nothing else."

"Yep," agreed Blister—" 'n' a lot of it goes to the head. None of that Fire Fly blood fur mine. Nine out of ten of 'em sprawl. They don't gather up like they meant it. Now you take old Torch Bearer—"

I found a chair and became busy with my own thoughts. I

wondered if, after all, the breeding of speed horses was not too cruelly disappointing to those whose heart and soul were in it. The moments of triumph were wonderful, of course. The thrill of any other game was feeble in comparison; but oh, the many and bitter disappointments!

At last I became conscious of a little old man approaching down the line of stalls. His clothes were quite shabby; but he walked with crisp erectness, with something of an air. He carried his soft hat in his hand and his silky hair glistened like silver in the sunshine. As he stopped and addressed a stable boy, a dozen stalls from where we sat, the courteous tilt of his head was vaguely familiar.

"Who's that old man down there?" I asked. "I think I've seen him before."

Blister followed my eyes and sat up in his chair with a jerk. He looked about him as though contemplating flight.

"Oh lord!" he said. "Now I'll get mine!"

"Who is it?" I repeated.

"Ole Man Sanford," answered Blister. "I ain't seen him fur a year. I hopped a hoss fur him once. I guess I told you."

I nodded.

"What's he talking about?" asked Judge Dillon.

And I explained how Old Man Sanford, a big breeder in his day, was now in reduced circumstances; how he had, with a small legacy, purchased a horse and placed him in Blister's hands; how Blister had given the horse stimulants before a race, contrary to racing rules; and how Mr. Sanford had discovered it and had torn up his tickets when the horse won.

"Tore up his tickets!" exclaimed Judge Dillon. "How much?"

"Fifteen hundred dollars," I replied. "All he had in the world."

Judge Dillon whistled.

"I've met him," he said. "He won a Derby thirty years ago." He bent forward and examined the straight, white-haired little figure. "Tore up his tickets, eh?" he repeated. Then softly: "Blood will tell!"

"Here he comes," said Blister uneasily. "He'll give me the once over 'n' brush by, I guess."

But Old Man Sanford did nothing of the sort. A radiant smile and two extended hands greeted Blister's awkward advance.

"My deah young friend, how is the world treatin' you these days?"

"Pretty good, Mr. Sanford," answered Blister and hesitated. "I kinda thought you'd be sore at me," he confessed. "While I didn't mean it that way I give you a raw deal, didn't I?"

A hand rested on Blister's sleeve for an instant.

"When yoh hair," said Old Man Sanford, "has taken its color from the many wintuhs whose stohms have bowed yoh head, you will have learned this: We act accohdin' to our lights. Some are brighter, some are dimmer, than others; but who shall be the judge?"

Whether or not Blister got the finer shadings of this, the sense of it was plain.

"I might have knowed you wouldn't be sore," he said relievedly. "Here's Chick. You remember Chick, Mr. Sanford."

Chick was greeted radiantly. Likewise "Petah."

"And the hawses? How are the hawses? Have you a nice string?" Blister turned and "made us acquainted" with Old Man Sanford.

"Chick," he called, "get a chair fur Mr. Sanford. Pete—you boys start in with the sorrel hoss 'n' bring 'em all out, one at a time!"

"Why, now," said Mr. Sanford, "I mustn't make a nuisance of myself. It would be a great pleasuh, suh, to see yoh hawses; but I do not wish to bothah you. Suppose I just walk from stall to stall?"

He tried to advance toward the stalls, but was confronted by Blister who took him by the arms, smiled down into his face, and gave him a gentle shake.

"Now listen!" said Blister. "As long as we're here you treat this string like it's yours. They'll come out 'n' stand on their ears if you want to see it. You got me?"

I saw a dull red mount slowly to the wrinkled cheeks. The little figure became straighter, if possible, in its threadbare black suit. I saw an enormous silk handkerchief, embroidered and yellow with age, appear suddenly as Old Man Sanford blew his nose. He started to speak, faltered, and again was obliged to resort to the handkerchief.

"I thank you, suh," he said at last, and found a chair as Judge Dillon's eyes sought mine.

Paul Brown

We left him out of our conversation for a time; but as the string was led before him one by one the horseman in Mr. Sanford triumphed. He passed loving judgment on one and all, his face keen and lighted. Of the colt I had just heard doomed he said:

"Well-made youngsteh, gentlemen; his blood speaks in every line of him. But as I look him oveh I have a feeling—it is, of cohse, no more than that—that he lacks a certain quality essential to a great hawse."

"What quality?" asked Judge Dillon quickly.

"A racin' heart, suh," came the prompt reply.

"Oh, that's it, is it?" asked Judge Dillon, and added dryly: "I own him."

Mr. Sanford gave one reproachful glance at Blister.

"I beg yoh pahdon, suh," he said earnestly to Judge Dillon. "A snap judgment in mattehs of this sawt is, of cohse, wo'thless. Do not give my words a thought, suh. They were spoken hastily, without due deliberation, with no real knowledge on which to base them. I sincerely hope I have not pained you, suh."

Judge Dillon's big hand swung over and covered one of the thin knees incased in shiny broadcloth.

"No sportsman," he said, "is hurt by the truth. That's just exactly what's the matter with him. But how did you know it?"

Mr. Sanford hesitated.

"I'm quite likely to be mistaken, suh," he said; "but if it would interest you I may say that I missed a certain look about his head, and moh pahticularly in his eyes, that is the hallmark—this is merely my opinion, suh—of a really great hawse."

"What kind of a look?" I asked.

Again Mr. Sanford hesitated.

"It is hard to define, suh," he explained. "It is not a matteh of skull structure—of confohmation. It is—" He sought for words. "Well, suh, about the head of a truly great hawse there is an air of freedom unconquerable. The eyes seem to look on heights beyond our gaze. It is the look of a spirit that can soar. It is not confined to hawses; even in his pictures you can see it in the eyes of the Bonaparte. It is the birthright of eagles. They all have it. . . . But I express myself badly." He turned to Judge Dillon.

"Your great mayeh has it, suh, to a marked degree."

"Très Jolie?" inquired Judge Dillon, and Mr. Sanford nodded.

I had heard of a power—psychic, perhaps—which comes to a few, a very few, who give their lives and their hearts to horses. I looked curiously at the little old man beside me. Did those faded watery eyes see something hidden from the rest of us? I wondered.

Blister interrupted my thoughts.

"Say, Mr. Sanford," he asked suddenly, "what did you ever do with Trampfast?"

"I disposed of him, suh, for nine hundred dollahs."

Blister considered this for a moment.

"Look-a-here!" he said. "You don't like the way I handled that hoss fur you, 'n' I'd like a chance to make good. I know where I can buy a right good plater fur nine hundred dollars. I'll make him pay his way or no charge. What do you say?"

Mr. Sanford shook his head. "As a matteh of fact," he stated, "I have only six hundred dollahs now in hand. Aside from having learned that my racing methods are not those of today, I would not care to see the pu'ple and white on a six-hundred-dollah hawse."

"Why, look-a-here!" urged Blister. "All the big stables race platers. There's good money in it when it's handled right. Let a goat chew dust a few times till you can drop him in soft somewheres, 'n' then put a piece of change on him at nice juicy odds. The boy kicks a win out of him, maybe; 'n' right there he don't owe you nothin'."

Once more I saw a dull red flare up in Mr. Sanford's face; but now he favored Blister with a bristling stare.

"I have difficulty in following you at times, suh," he said. "Am I justified in believing that the word 'goat' is applied to a thoroughbred race hawse?"

"Why, yes, Mr. Sanford," said Blister, "that's what I mean, I expect."

The old gentleman seemed to spend a moment in dismissing his wrath. When he spoke at last no trace of it was in his voice.

"I am fond of you, my young friend," he said. "Under a cynical exterior I have found you courteous, loyal, tender-hearted; but I deplore in you the shallow flippancy of this age. It is the fashion to sneer at the finer things; and so you call a racin' thoroughbred a goat. He is not of stake quality perhaps." Here the voice became quite gentle: "Are you?"

"I guess not, Mr. Sanford," admitted Blister.

"Never mind, my boy. If man breeds one genius to a decade it is enough. And so it goes with hawses. Foh thirty years, with love, with reverence, I tried to breed great hawses—hawses that would be a joy, an honoh to my state. In those days ninety colts were foaled each spring at Sanfo'd Hall. I have spent twenty thousand dollahs foh a single matron. How many hawses—truly great hawses—did such brood mayehs as that produce? How many do you think?"

Judge Dillon gave Mr. Sanford the warm look of a brother.

"Not many," he murmured.

"Why, I dunno, Mr. Sanford," said Blister. "You tells me about one—the filly that copped the Derby fur you."

"Yes; she was one. And one moh, suh. Two in all."

"I never hear you mention but the one," said Blister.

"The other never raced," explained Mr. Sanford. "I'll tell you why."

He lapsed into silence, into a sort of reverie, while we waited. When he spoke it was totally without emotion. His voice was dull. It sounded somehow as though speech had been given to the dead past.

"It has been a long time," he said, more to himself than to us. "A long time!" he repeated, nodding thoughtfully, and again became silent.

"In those days," he began at last, "it was the custom of their mistress to go to the no'th pastuh with sugah, and call to the weanlin's. In flytime the youngstehs preferred the willow trees by the creek, and there was a qua'tah of a mile of level blue grass from those willows to the pastuh gate. She would stand at the gate and call. As they heard her voice the colts would come oveh the creek bank as though it were a barrier—a fair start and no favohs asked. The rascals like sugah, to be sure; but an excuse to fight it out for a qua'tah was the main point of the game.

"One year a blood bay colt, black to the hocks and knees, was foaled in January. In June he got his sugah fuhst, by two open lengths. In August he made them hang their heads foh shame— five, six, seven lengths he beat them; and their siahs watchin' from the paddocks.

"In the spring of his two-year-old fohm he suffered with an attack of distempah. He had been galloped on the fahm track by then, and we knew just what he was. We nuhsed him through it, and by the following spring he was ready to go out and meet them all foh the honoh of the pu'ple and white.

"Then, one night, I was awakened to be told that a doctoh must be fetched and that each moment was precious. I sent my body sehvant to the bahns with the message that I wished a saddle on the best hawse in the stable. When pahtially dressed I followed him, and was thrown up by a stable man. . . . .

"There was a moon—a gracious moon, I remembah—the white road to Gawgetown, and a great fear at my heart. I did not know what was under me until I gave him his head on that white, straight road. . . . Then I knew. I cannot say in what time we did those four miles; but this I can tell you—the colt ran the last mile as stanchly as the first, and one hour later he could barely walk. His terrific pace oveh that flinty road destroyed his tendons and broke the small bones in his legs. He gave his racin' life for his lady, like the honest gentleman he was. His sacrifice, howeveh, was in vain. . . . Death had the heels of him that night. Death had the heels of him!"

In a tense silence I seemed to hear a bell tolling. "Death had the heels of him!" it boomed over and over again.

Blister's eyes were starting from their sockets, but he did not hear the bell. He wet his parted lips.

"What become of him?" he breathed.

"When the place was sold he went with the rest. You have seen his descendant race on until his name has become a glory. The colt I rode that night was—Torch Bearer."

Blister drew in his breath with a whistling sound.

"Torch Bearer!" he gasped. "Did you own Torch Bearer?"

"I did, suh," came the quiet answer. "I bred him and raised him. His blood flows in the veins of many—er—goats, I believe you call them."

"Man, oh, man!" said Blister, and became speechless.

I too was silent of necessity. There was something wrong with my throat.

And now Judge Dillon spoke, and it was apparent that he was afflicted like myself. Once more the big hand covered the thin knee.

"Mr. Sanford," I heard, "you can do me a favor if you will."

"My deah suh, name it!"

"Go to Lexington. Look over the colts at Thistle Ridge. If you find one good enough for the purple and white—bring him back here. . . . He's yours!"

I went along. Oh, yes: I went along. I should miss two days of racing; but I would have missed more than that quite willingly. I was to see Old Man Sanford pick out one from a hundred colts— and all "Bred clear to the clouds," as Blister explained to us on the train. I wondered whether any one of them would have that look—"the birthright of eagles,"—and I hoped, I almost prayed, that we should find it.

That the colt was to be a purchase, not a gift, had made our journey possible. Five hundred dollars cash and "my note, suh, for a like amount."

Judge Dillon had broken the deadlock by accepting; then offered his car for the trip to Lexington.

"I thank you, suh, foh yoh generosity," apologized Mr. Sanford. "It gives me the deepest pleasuh, the deepest gratification, suh; but, if you will pahdon me, I shall feel moah at home on the train."

We spent the night at the hotel and drove to Thistle Ridge early next morning behind a plodding pair. Even in Kentucky, livery horses are—livery horses.

A letter from Judge Dillon opened the big gates wide and placed us in charge of one Wesley Washington—as I live by bread, that was his name—suspicious by nature and black as a buzzard. I reminded him of my previous visit to Thistle Ridge. He acknowledged it with no sign of enthusiasm.

"What kind a colt you want?" he asked Blister.

"A good one!" answered Blister briefly.

Wesley rolled the whites of his eyes at him and sniffed.

"You ain' said nothin'," he stated. "Dat's all we got."

"You're lucky," Blister told him. "Well, trot 'em out."

Then Wesley waved his wand—it chanced to be a black paw with a pinkish palm—and they were trotted out; or, rather, they came rearing through the doorway of the biggest of the big stables. Bays, browns, blacks, sorrels, chestnuts, roans—they bubbled out

at us in an endless stream. Attached precariously to each of them
—this was especially true when they reared—was a colored boy.
These Wesley addressed in sparkling and figurative speech. His
remarks, as a rule, were prefaced by the word "Niggah."

At last Blister shouted through the dust.

"Say," he said, "this ain't gettin' us nowhere. Holy fright! How
many you got?"

"Dat ain't half," said Wesley ominously.

"Cut it out!" directed Blister. "You'll have me pop-eyed in a
minute. We'll go through the stalls 'n' pick out the live ones. This
stuff's too young anyway. We want a two-year-old broke to the
barrier. Have you got any?"

I turned to Mr. Sanford. He was standing hat in hand, as was
his custom, his face ablaze.

"The grandest spectacle I have witnessed in thirty yeahs, suh!"
he informed me.

"Has we got a two-year-old broke to de barrieh?" I heard
Wesley. "Hush! just ambulate oveh disaway."

He led us to a smaller stable. It contained two rows of box stalls
with a wide alley down the middle. Through the iron gratings in
each stall I could see a snakelike head. The door at the opposite
end of the stable looked out on the tawny oval of the farm track,
and suddenly something flashed across the doorway so quickly that
I only guessed it to be a thoroughbred with a boy crouching along
his neck.

Wesley's eye swept up and down the two lines of box stalls. He
looked at Blister with a prideful gleam.

"All two-yeah-olds," he said, "'n' ready to race."

If this statement made any impression it was concealed. Blister
yawned and sauntered to the first stall on the right.

"Well, there might be a plater among 'em," he said. "This all
you got?"

"Ain' dat enough?" inquired Wesley with a snort.

"Not if they're the culls," said Blister. "You read that letter,
didn't you? We're to see 'em all. Don't forget that."

"Hyar dey is," said Wesley. "Jus' use yoh eyes an' yoh han's."

"All right," said Blister as he opened the stall door—"but
don't hold nothin' out on us. Mr. Sanford here is an old friend
of the Judge."

Wesley rolled an inspecting eye over Mr. Sanford.

"I ain' neveh seen him roun' hyah," and honors were easy.

The battle was on in earnest a moment later. The colt in the first stall was haltered and led out into the runway. He was jet black with one white star, and wonderful to see.

"Nothin' finah on fo' laigs," said Wesley, and I mentally agreed with him; but Blister walked once round that glorious creature and waved him back into his stall.

"Yep," he said; "he's right good on four legs, but he'll be on three when that curb begins to talk to him."

"Shuh!" said Wesley in deep disgust, "you ain' goin' to call dat little fullness in de tendon a curb, is you? He'll die of ole aige an' neveh know he's got it."

"He dies of old age before I own him," said Blister, and walked to the second stall.

And so it went for an hour. Mr. Sanford was strangely silent. When he ventured an opinion at all it was to agree with Wesley, and I was disappointed. I had hoped for delightful dissertations, for superhuman judgments. I had expected to see a master at work with his chosen medium. Instead, he seemed a child in the hands of the skillful Wesley; and I felt that Blister was our only hope.

This opinion had become settled when the unexpected happened. After a more than careful inspection of a chestnut colt, Blister turned to Wesley.

"What's this colt done?" he asked.

"Half in fifty," Wesley stated. "Jus' play foh him."

"Put a boy on him 'n' let's see him move," said Blister.

Then Mr. Sanford spoke.

"It will be unnecessary," he said quietly. "I do not like him."

A puzzled expression spread itself over Blister's face.

"All right," he said with a shade of annoyance in his voice. "You're the doctor."

And then I noticed Wesley—Wesley, the adroit—and a look of amazement, almost terror, was in his eyes as he stared at Mr. Sanford.

"Yessuh," he said with a gulp. "Yessuh." Then he pulled himself together.

"Put him up, black boy," he directed magnificently, and moved to the next stall.

I stayed behind and displayed a quarter cautiously.

"Do you like this colt?" I asked, looking the boy straight in the face.

For a moment he hesitated. Then:

"No, suh," he whispered.

"Why not?" I inquired.

There was a flicker of contempt in the white eyeballs.

"He's a houn'," I barely heard as the quarter changed owners.

"It was a well spent quarter; it had purchased knowledge. I knew now that among our party was a pair of eyes that could look deep into the heart of things. Old they were and faded, those eyes; but I felt assured that a glistening flank could not deceive them.

We worked down one side of the stable and up the other. We had seen twenty colts when we arrived at the last stall. It contained a long-legged sorrel and Blister damned him with a grunt when he was led out.

"If he ever gets tangled up," was his comment, "you don't get his legs untied that year. This all you got?"

Wesley assured him it was. We seemed to have reached an *impasse*. Then, as Blister frowned absently at the sorrel colt, a voice began singing just outside the stable. It was a rich treble and it chanted in a minor key. I saw the absent look wiped slowly from Blister's face. It was supplanted by a dawning alertness as he listened intently.

Suddenly he disappeared through the doorway and there came to me a regular scuff-scuff on the gravel outside, in time to the words of the song, which were these:

> "Bay colt wock in fo'ty-eight,
>   Goin' to de races—goin' to de races;
> Bay colt wock on fo'ty-eight,
>   Goin' to de races now."

I felt my jaw begin to drop, for Blister's voice had joined the unknown singer's.

> "Bay colt wock in fo'ty-eight,"

sang the voice; and then a bellow from Blister:

"Goin' to the races—goin' to de races."

The voice repeated:

"Bay colt wock in fo'ty-eight,"

and resigned to Blister's:

"Goin' to de races now!"

I went hastily through that doorway and arrived at the following phenomena:

Exhibit A—One chocolate-colored boy, not more than three feet high. His shoes—I mention them first because they constituted one-half of the whole exhibit—were—— But words are feeble—prodigious, Gargantuan, are only mildly suggestive of those shoes. His stockings—and now I cross my heart and hope to die—were of the variety described commercially as ladies' hose, and they were pink and they were silk. Somewhere beneath their many folds two licorice sticks performed the miracle of moving those unbelievable shoes through an intricate clog dance.

Exhibit B—One Blister Jones, patting with feet and hands an accompaniment to the wonders being performed by the marvelous shoes.

Both exhibits were entirely in earnest and completely absorbed. As has been already told, they were joined in song.

As I assured myself that the phenomena were real and not imaginary, the words of the song changed.

"Bay colt wock in fo'ty-eight."

came steadfastly from the smaller singer; but Blister instead of "Goin' to the races," sang

"Where's he at? Where's he at?"

"Bay colt wock in fo'ty-eight,"

insisted Exhibit A; and Exhibit B sang:

"Where's that bay colt now?"

They learn early, in Kentucky, that track and farm secrets are sacred. A suspicion of all outsiders, though dulled by the excitement of white folks' appreciation, still flickered somewhere in the kinky dome of Exhibit A. The song was twice repeated without variation, and the "Where's he at?" became tragic in its pleading tone.

At last Exhibit A must have decided that his partner in song was a kindred spirit and worthy of trust. At any rate

"Oveh in de coolin' shed—oveh in de coolin' shed,"

I heard; and Blister brought the duet to a triumphant close with:

"Over in the coolin' shed now!"

He swung round and grinned at Wesley, who was standing stupefied in the doorway.

"Why, Wes!" he said reproachfully, "I'm surprised at you!"

Wesley glowered at Exhibit A.

"You ramble!" he said, and the marvelous shoes bore their owner swiftly from our sight.

So, through song, was the wily Wesley brought to confusion. We found four two-year-olds in the long, squatty cooling shed, and Wesley admitted, under pressure, that they were the pick of their year, kept for special training.

Three of them stood in straw to their knees, confined in three tremendous box stalls. One was being led under blankets up and down the runway. His sides lifted their covering regularly. His clean-cut velvet nostrils widened and contracted as he took his breath. His eyes were blazing jewels. To him went Blister, like iron filings to a magnet.

"Peel him fur a minute," he said, and the still dazed and somewhat chastened Wesley nodded his permission.

Then appeared the most perfect living creature I had ever seen.

He was a rich bay—now dark mahogany because of a recent bath—and the sheer beauty of him produced in me a feeling of awe, almost of worship. I was moved as though I listened to the Seventh Symphony or viewed the Winged Victory; and this was fit and proper, for my eyes were drinking in a piece by the greatest of all masters.

Blister was cursing softly, reverently, as though he were at prayer.

"If he's only half as good as he looks!" he sighed at last. "How about *him,* Mr. Sanford?"

I had forgotten Old Man Sanford. I now discovered him standing before a stall and gazing raptly at what was within. At Blister's words he turned and surveyed the bay colt.

"The most superb piece of hawse-flesh," he said, "I have eveh had the pleasuh of observing. I could not fault him with a microscope. He is nothing shawt of perfection, suh—nothing shawt of perfection." His eyes lingered for an instant on the wet flanks of the uncovered colt. "He's too wahm to be without his clothing," he suggested, and turned again to the stall before him.

Blister covered the colt with one dextrous swing. He glanced at the name embroidered on the blankets.

"Postman," he read aloud. "He'll be by Messenger, won't he?" The boy at the colt's head nodded. "Worked in forty-eight just now, eh?" said Blister to no one in particular. Again the boy nodded. "Well," decided Blister, "we'll take a chance on him. Train fur Looeyville at four o'clock—ain't they, Wes?"

Wesley gave a moan of anguish.

"My Gawd!" he said.

"What's bitin' you?" demanded Blister. "We're payin' fur him, ain't we?"

"Lemme have dat letter one moh time," said Wesley. He absorbed the letter's contents as though it were poison, and came at last to the fatal "John C. Dillon" at the end. This he read aloud slowly and shook his head. "He's los' his min'," he stated, and glared at Mr. Sanford. "What you payin' fo' dis hyar colt?" he demanded.

Mr. Sanford glanced in our direction. His eyes had a far-away look.

"Were you addressing me?" he asked.

"Yessuh," replied Wesley. "I was inquirin' de price you aim to pay foh dis colt."

"That is a matteh," said Old Man Sanford, "that concerns only yoh mas—employeh and myself. Howeveh, I am not going to pu'chase the colt to which you refeh." He glanced dreamily into the stall before which he seemed rooted. "I have taken a fancy to my little friend in hyar. . . . Could you oblige me with a piece of sugah?"

As one man, Blister and I made a rush for that stall. We peered through the bars for a moment and our amazed eyes met. In Blister's an angry despair was dawning. He turned savagely on Mr. Sanford.

"You going to buy that shrimp?" he demanded.

"Yes, suh," said Old Man Sanford mildly. "I expect to pu'chase him. . . . Ah, here's the sugah!" He took some lumps of sugar from the now beaming Wesley and opened the stall door.

Blister stepped inside the stall and devoted some moments to vain pleadings. Mr. Sanford was unmoved by them.

Then the storm broke. Blister became a madman who raved. He cursed not only the small black two-year-old, standing knee-deep in golden straw, but the small, white-haired old gentleman who was placidly feeding him sugar. The storm raged on, but Mr. Sanford gave no sign.

At last I saw a hand that was extended to the colt's muzzle begin to tremble, and I took Blister by the arm and drew him forcefully away.

"Stop!" I said in an undertone. "You're doing no good and he's an old man."

Blister tore his arm from mine.

"He's an old fool!" he cried. "He's chuckin' away the chance of a lifetime." Then his eyes fell on the bay colt and his voice became a wail. "Ain't it hell," he inquired of high heaven. "Ain't it just hell."

At this point Wesley saw fit to emit a loud guffaw. Blister advanced on him like a tiger.

"Laugh, you black boob!" he shot out, and Wesley's joyous expression vanished.

I saw that I was doing no good and joined Mr. Sanford in the stall.

"Rather small, isn't he?" I suggested.

"He could be a little larger," Mr. Sanford admitted. "He could stand half a han' and fifty pounds moh at his aige; but then, he'll grow. He'll make a hawse some day."

And now came Blister, rather sheepish, and stood beside us.

"I got sore, Mr. Sanford," he said. "I oughta be kicked!"

Old Man Sanford proffered a lump of sugar to the slim black muzzle. It was knocked from the extended hand. Mr. Sanford pointed a reproving finger at the colt.

"Not quite so fast, young man!" he exclaimed. Then he turned to Blister with a gentle smile. "Youth is hasty," he said, "and sometimes—mistaken."

I returned to Cincinnati and work that night, filled with speculations about a small black colt and his new owner. The latter, I felt, had reached a stubborn dotage. Two months rolled by. Those were full days but I found time somehow for a daily glance at the racing news. One morning I read the following:

"Postman, a bay colt, bred and owned by John C. Dillon, captured the two-year-old event without apparent effort. It was the winner's first appearance under colors. He is a big, rangy youngster, as handsome as a picture. He appears to be a very high-class colt and should be heard from."

"Poor Blister!" I thought; and later, as I read again and again of smashing victories by a great and still greater Postman, I became quite venomous when I thought of Old Man Sanford. I referred to him mentally as "That old fool!" and imagined Blister in horrid depths of despair.

Then the bugle called for the last time that year at Lexington, and the thoroughbreds came to my very door to listen for it.

For days thereafter, as luck would have it, I was forced to pound my typewriter viciously, everlastingly, and was too tired when night came to do more than stagger to bed. At last there came a lull, and I fled incontinently to Latonia and the world of horse.

I approached Blister's stalls as one draws near a sepulcher. I felt that my voice, when I addressed him, should be pitched as though in the presence of a casket. I was shocked, therefore, at his lightness of mein.

"Hello, Four Eyes!" he said cheerfully. "How's the ole scout?"

I assured him that my scouting days were not yet over. And then:

"I've been reading about Postman," I said.

"Some colt!" said Blister. "He's bowed 'em home five times now. They've made him favorite fur the Hammond against all them Eastern babies."

There was genuine enthusiasm in his voice and I was filled with admiration for a spirit that could take a blow so jauntily. His attitude was undoubtedly the correct one, but I could not accomplish it. I thought of the five thousand dollars that went, with the floral horseshoe, to the winner of the Hammond stake. I thought of a gentle, fine, threadbare old man who needed that five thousand—oh, so desperately—and I was filled with bitter regrets, with malice and bad words.

"Of course he'll win it?" I burst out spitefully.

"Why, I dunno," drawled Blister, and added: "I thought Judge Dillon was a friend of yours."

"Oh damn!" I said.

"Why, Four Eyes!" said Blister. " 'N' Chick listenin' to you too!"

Chick grinned appreciatively.

"Don't let him kid ya," he advised. "He wasn't so gay hisself till—"

"Take a shot of grape juice," interrupted Blister, " 'n' hire a hall."

Chick's voice trailed off into unintelligible mutterings as he turned away.

"How about Mr. Sanford's colt?" I asked. "Have you still got him?"

To my astonishment Blister broke into one of his rare fits of laughter. He all but doubled up with unaccountable mirth.

"Say, Chick," he called when he could control his voice, "he wants to know if we still got the Sanford colt!"

Chick had turned a rather glum face our way; but at the words his expression became instantly joyous.

"Oh, say!" he said.

Then began a series of hilarious exchanges, entirely without meaning to me.

"He's hangin' round somewhere, ain't he, Chick?"

"Why, maybe he is," said Chick.

"You still throw a little rough feed into him occasionally, don't you, Chick?"

"When I got time," said Chick: and the two imbeciles roared with laughter.

At last Blister began beating me between the shoulder blades.

"We got him, Four Eyes," he told me between thumps. "Yep —we got him."

"Stop!" I shouted. "What the devil's the matter with you?"

Blister became serious.

"Come here!" He threw back the upper door and a shaft of sunlight streamed into the stall's interior, bathing a slim black head and neck until they glistened like a vein of coal.

"Know him?" asked Blister.

"Yes," I said. "He's bigger though."

"Look at him good!" ordered Blister.

I peered at the relaxed inmate of the stall, who blinked sleepily at me through the shaft of sunlight. Blister pulled me back, closed the stall door, and tightened his grip on my arm.

"Now listen!" he said. "You just looked at the best two-year-old God ever put breath in!"

I took in this incredible information slowly. I exulted in it for a moment, and then came doubts.

"How do you know?" I demanded.

"How do I know!" exclaimed Blister. "It'ud take me a week to tell you. Man, he can fly! He makes his first start tomorrow—in the Hammond. Old Man Sanford'll get in tonight. Come out 'n' see a real colt run."

My brain was whirling.

"In the Hammond?" I gasped. "Does Mr. Sanford know all this?"

Blister gave me a slow, a thoughtful look.

"It sounds nutty," he said; "but I can't figger it no other way. As sure as you 'n' me are standin' here—he knowed it from the very first."

Until I closed my eyes that night I wondered whether Blister's words were true. If so, what sort of judgment, instinct, intuition, had been used that day at Thistle Ridge? I gave it up at last and slept, to dream of a colt that suddenly grew raven wings and soared over the grand stand while I nodded wisely and said, "Of course—the birthright of eagles!"

I got to Blister's stalls at one o'clock next day, and found Mr. Sanford clothed in a new dignity hard to describe. Perhaps he had donned it with the remarkable flowered waistcoat he wore—or was it due to his flowing double-breasted coat, a sprightly blue in color and suggesting inevitably a leather trunk, dusty, attic-bound, which had yawned and spat it forth?

"Welcome, suh; thrice welcome!" he said to me. "I take the liberty of presuming that the pu'ple and white is honored with yoh best wishes today."

I assured him that from the bottom of my heart this was so. He wrung my hand again and took out a gold watch the size of a bun.

"Three hours moh," he said, "before our hopes are realized or shattered."

"You think the colt will win?" I inquired.

Mr. Sanford turned to the southwest. I followed his eyes and saw a bank of evil-looking clouds creeping slowly up the sky.

"I like our chances, suh," he told me; "but it will depend on those clouds yondeh. We want a fast track foh the little chap. He is a swallow. Mud would break his heart."

"She's fast enough now," said Blister, who had joined us; and Mr. Sanford nodded.

So for three hours I watched the sky prayerfully and saw it become more and more ominous. When the bugle called for the Hammond at last, Latonia was shut off from the rest of the world by an inverted inky cup, its sides shot now and then with lightning flashes. We seemed to be in a great vacuum. I found my lungs snatching for each breath, while my racing card grew limp as I clutched it spasmodically in a sweating hand.

I had seen fit to take a vital interest in the next few moments; but I glanced at the faces all about me in the grand stand and found them strained and unnatural. Perhaps in the gloom they seemed whiter than they really were; perhaps my own nerves pricked my imagination until this packed humanity became one beating heart.

I do not think that this was so. The dramatic moment goes straight to the soul of a crowd, and this crowd was to see the Ham-

mond staged in a breathless dark, with the lightning's flicker for an uncertain spotlight.

No rain would spoil our chances that day, for now, across the center field at the half-mile post, a mass of colors boiled at the barrier. The purple and white was somewhere in the shifting, surging line, borne by a swallow, so I had been told. Well, even so, the blue and gold was there likewise—and carried by what? Perhaps an eagle!

Suddenly a sigh—not the customary roar, but a deep intaking of the grand stand's breath—told me they were on the wing. I strained my eyes at the blurred mass of them, which seemed to move slowly in the distance as it reached the far turn of the back stretch. Then a flash of lightning came and my heart skipped a beat and sank.

They were divided into two unequal parts. One was a crowded, indistinguishable mass. The other, far ahead in unassailable isolation, was a single spot of bay with a splash of color clinging above.

A roar of "Postman!" shattered the quiet like a bombshell, for that splash of color was blue and gold. The favorite was making a runaway race of it. He was coming home to twenty thousand joyful backers, who screamed and screamed his name.

Until that moment I had been the victim of a dream. I had come to believe that the little old man, standing silent at my side, possessed an insight more than human. Now I had wakened. He was an old fool in a preposterous coat and waistcoat, and I looked at him and laughed a mirthless laugh. He was squinting slightly as he peered with his washed-out eyes into the distance. His face was placid; and as I noticed this I told myself that he was positively witless. Then he spoke.

"The bay colt is better than I thought," he said.

"True," I agreed bitterly, and noted, as the lightning flashed again, that the blue and gold was an amazing distance ahead of those struggling mediocre others.

"A pretty race," muttered Old Man Sanford; and now I thought him more than doddering—he was insane.

Some seconds passed in darkness while the grand stand gave off a contented mumur. Then suddenly the murmur rose to a new note. It held fear and consternation in it. My eyes leaped up the track. The bay colt had rounded the curve into the stretch. He was coming down the straight like a bullet; but—miracle of miracles!—it was plain that he was not alone. . . .

In a flash it came to me: stride for stride, on the far side of him, one other had maintained a flight equal to his own. And then I went mad; for this other, unsuspected in the darkness until now, commenced to creep slowly, surely, into the lead. Above his stretching neck his colors nestled proudly. He was bringing the purple and white safe home to gold and glory.

Nearer and nearer he came, this small demon whose coat matched the heavens, and so shot past us, with the great Postman—under the whip—two lengths behind him!

I remember executing a sort of bear dance, with Mr. Sanford enfolded in my embrace. I desisted when a smothered voice informed me that my conduct was "unseemly, suh—most unseemly!"

A rush to the track followed, where we found Blister, quite pale, waiting with a blanket. Suddenly the grand stand, which had groaned once and become silent, broke into a roar that grew and grew.

"What is it?" I asked.

Blister whirled and stared at the figures on the timing board. I saw a look of awe come into his face.

"What is it?" I repeated. "Why are they cheering? Is it the time?"

"Oh, no!" said Blister with scornful sarcasm and a look of pity at my ignorance. "It ain't the time!" He nodded at the figures. "That's only the world's record fur the age 'n' distance."

And now there came mincing back to us on slender, nervous legs, something wet and black and wonderful. It pawed and danced wildly in a growing ring of curious eyes.

Then, just above the grand stand, the inky cup of the sky was broken and there appeared the light of an unseen sun. It turned the piled white clouds in the break to marvels of rose and gold. They seemed like the ramparts of heaven, set there to guard from earthly eyes the abode of the immortals.

"Whoa, man! Whoa, hon!" said Blister, and covered the heaving sides.

As he heard Blister's voice and felt the touch of the blanket the colt grew quiet. His eyes became less fiery wild. He raised his head, with its dilated blood-red nostrils, and stared—not at the mortals standing reverently about him, but far beyond our gaze—through the lurid gap in the sky, straight into Valhalla.

I felt a hand on my arm.

"The look of eagles, suh!" said Old Man Sanford.

Skipper

By SEWELL FORD

AT THE age of six Skipper went on the force. Clean of limb and sound of wind he was, with not a blemish from the tip of his black tail to the end of his crinkly forelock. He had been broken to saddle by a Green Mountain boy who knew more of horse nature than of the trashy things writ in books. He gave Skipper kind words and an occasional friendly pat on the flank. So Skipper's disposition was sweet and his nature a trusting one.

This was why Skipper learned so soon the ways of the city. The first time he saw one of those little wheeled houses, all windows and full of people, come rushing down the street with a fearful whirr and clank of bell, he wanted to bolt. But the man on his back spoke in an easy, calm voice, saying "So-o-o! There, me b'y. Aisy wid ye. So-o-o!" which was excellent advice, for the queer contrivance whizzed by and did him no harm. In a week he could watch one without even pricking up his ears.

It was strange work Skipper had been brought to the city to do. As a colt he had seen horses dragging ploughs, pulling big loads of hay, and hitched to many kinds of vehicles. He himself had drawn a light buggy and thought it good fun, though you did have to keep your heels down and trot instead of canter. He had liked best to lope off with the boy on his back, down to the Corners, where the store was.

But here there were no ploughs, nor hay-carts, nor mowing-machines. There were many heavy wagons, it was true, but these were all drawn by stock Percherons and big Western grays or stout Canada blacks who seemed fully equal to the task.

Also there were carriages—my, what shiny carriages! And what smart, sleek-looking horses drew them! And how high they did hold their heads and how they did throw their feet about—just as if they were dancing on eggs.

"Proud, stuck-up things," thought Skipper.

It was clear that none of this work was for him. Early on the first morning of his service men in brass-buttoned blue coats came to the stable to feed and rub down the horses. Skipper's man had two names. One was Officer Martin; at least that was the one to which he answered when the man with the cap called the roll before they rode out for duty. The other name was "Reddy." That was what the rest of the men in blue coats called him. Skipper noticed that he had red hair and concluded that "Reddy" must be his real name.

As for Skipper's name, it was written on the tag tied to the halter which he wore when he came to the city. Skipper heard him read it. The boy on the farm had done that, and Skipper was glad, for he liked the name.

There was much to learn in those first few weeks, and Skipper learned it quickly. He came to know that at inspection, which began the day, you must stand with your nose just on a line with that of the horse on either side. If you didn't you felt the bit or the spurs. He mastered the meaning of "right dress," "left dress," "forward," "fours right," and a lot of other things. Some of them were very strange.

Now on the farm they had said, "Whoa, boy," and "Gid a-a-ap." Here they said "Halt!" and "Forward!" But "Reddy" used none of these terms. He pressed with his knees on your withers, loosened the reins, and made a queer little chirrup when he wanted you to gallop. He let you know when he wanted you to stop, by the lightest pressure on the bit.

It was lazy work, though. Sometimes when Skipper was just aching for a brisk canter he had to pace soberly through the park driveways—for Skipper, I don't believe I mentioned it before, was part and parcel of the mounted police force. But there, you could know that by the coat of arms in yellow brass on his saddle blanket.

For half an hour at a time he would stand, just on the edge of the roadway and at an exact right angle with it, motionless as the horse ridden by the bronze soldier up near the Mall. "Reddy" would sit as still in the saddle, too. It was hard for Skipper to stand there and see those mincing cobs go by, their pad-housings all a-glitter, crests on their blinders, jingling their pole-chains and switching their absurd little stubs of tails. But it was still more tantalizing to watch the saddle horses canter past on the soft bridle path on the other side of the roadway. But then, when you are on the force you must do your duty.

One afternoon as Skipper was standing post like this he caught a new note that rose above the hum of the park traffic. It was the quick, nervous beat of hoofs which rang sharply on the hard macadam. There were screams, too. It was a runaway. Skipper knew this even before he saw the bell-like nostrils, the straining eyes, and the foam-flecked lips of the horse, or the scared man in the carriage behind. It was a case of broken rein.

How the sight made Skipper's blood tingle! Wouldn't he just like to show that crazy roan what real running was! But what was

Reddy going to do? He felt him gather up the reins. He felt his knees tighten. What! Yes, it must be so. Reddy was actually going to try a brush with the runaway. What fun!

Skipper pranced out into the roadway and gathered himself for the sport. Before he could get into full swing, however, the roan had shot past with a snort of challenge which could not be misunderstood.

"Oho! You will, eh?" thought Skipper. "Well now, we'll see about that."

Ah, a free rein! That is—almost free. And a touch of the spurs! No need for that, Reddy. How the carriages scatter! Skipper caught hasty glimpses of smart hackneys drawn up trembling by the roadside, of women who tumbled from bicycles into the bushes, and of men who ran and shouted and waved their hats.

"Just as though that little roan wasn't scared enough already," thought Skipper.

But she did run well; Skipper had to admit that. And had a lead of fifty yards before he could strike his best gait. Then for a few moments he could not seem to gain an inch. But the mare was blowing herself and Skipper was taking it coolly. He was putting the pent-up energy of weeks into his strides. Once he saw he was overhauling her he steadied to the work.

Just as Skipper was about to forge ahead, Reddy did a queer thing. With his right hand he grabbed the roan with a nose-pinch grip, and with the left he pulled in on the reins. It was a great disappointment to Skipper for he had counted on showing the roan his heels. Skipper knew, after two or three experiences of this kind, that this was the usual thing.

Those were glorious runs, though. Skipper wished they would come more often. Sometimes there would be two and even three in a day. Then a fortnight or so would pass without a single runaway on Skipper's beat. But duty is duty.

During the early morning hours, when there were few people in the park, Skipper's education progressed. He learned to pace around in a circle, lifting each forefoot with a sway of the body and a pawing movement which was quite rhythmical. He learned to box with his nose. He learned to walk sedately behind Reddy and to pick up a glove dropped apparently by accident. There was always a sugar-plum or a sweet cracker when Reddy stopped and Skipper, poking his nose over his shoulder, let the glove fall into his hands.

As he became more accomplished, he noticed that Reddy took more pains with his toilet. Every morning Skipper's coat was brushed until it shone almost as if it had been varnished. His fetlocks were carefully trimmed, a ribbon braided into his forelock, and his hoofs polished as brightly as Reddy's boots. Then there were apples and carrots and other delicacies which Reddy brought him.

So it happened that one morning Skipper heard the Sergeant tell Reddy that he had been detailed for the Horse Show squad. Reddy had saluted and said nothing at the time, but when they were once out on post he told Skipper all about it.

"Sure an' it's app'arin' before all the swells in town you'll be, me b'y. Phat do ye think of that, eh? And mebbe ye'll be gettin' a blue ribbon, Skipper, me lad; an' mebbe Mr. Patrick Martin will have a roundsman's berth and chevrons on his sleeves afore the year's out."

The Horse Show was all that Reddy had promised, and more. The light almost dazzled Skipper. The sounds and the smells confused him. But he felt Reddy on his back, heard him chirrup softly, and soon felt at ease on the tanbark.

Then there was a great crash of noise and Skipper, with some fifty of his friends on the force, began to move around the circle. First it was fours abreast, then by twos, and then a rush to troop front, when, in a long line, they swept around as if they had been harnessed to a beam by traces of equal length.

After some more evolutions a half-dozen were picked out and put through their paces. Skipper was one of these. Then three of the six were sent to join the rest of the squad. Only Skipper and two others remained in the center of the ring. Men in queer clothes, wearing tall black hats, showing much white shirt-front and carrying long whips, came and looked them over carefully.

Skipper showed these men how he could waltz in time to the music, and the people who banked the circle as far up as Skipper could see shouted and clapped their hands until it seemed as if a thunderstorm had broken loose. At last one of the men in tall hats tied a blue ribbon on Skipper's bridle.

When Reddy got him into the stable, he fed him four big red apples one after the other. Next day Skipper knew that he was a famous horse. Reddy showed him their pictures in the paper.

For a whole year Skipper was the pride of the force. He was shown to visitors at the stables. He was patted on the nose by the Mayor. The Chief, who was a bigger man than the Mayor, came up especially to look at him. In the park Skipper did his tricks every day for ladies in fine dress who exclaimed, "How perfectly wonderful!" as well as for pretty nursemaids who giggled and said, "Now did you ever see the likes o' that, Norah?"

And then came the spavin. Ah but that was the beginning of the end! Were you ever spavined? If so, you know all about it. If you weren't, there's no use of my trying to tell you. Rheumatism? Well, that may be bad; but spavin is worse. For three weeks Reddy rubbed the hump on the hock with stuff from a brown bottle, and hid it from the inspector. Then, one black morning it was discovered. That day Skipper did not go out on post. Reddy came into the stall, put his arm around his neck and said "Goodby" in a voice that Skipper had never heard him use before. Something had made it thick and husky. Very sadly Skipper saw him saddle one of the newcomers and go out for duty.

Before Reddy came back Skipper was led away. He was taken to a big building where there were horses of every kind—except the right kind. Each one had his own peculiar "out" although you couldn't always tell what it was at a first glance.

But Skipper did not stay here long. He was led out before a lot of men in a big ring. A man on a box shouted out a number and began to talk very fast. Skipper gathered that he was talking about him. Skipper learned that he was still only six years old, and that he had been owned as a saddle horse by a lady who was about to sail for Europe and was closing out her stable. This was news to Skipper. He wished Reddy could hear it.

The man talked very nicely about Skipper. He said he was kind, gentle, sound in wind and limb, and was not only trained to the saddle but would work either single or double. The man wanted to know how much the gentlemen were willing to pay for a bay gelding of this description.

Someone on the outer edge of the crowd said "Ten dollars."

At this the man on the box grew quite indignant. He asked if

the other man wouldn't like a silver-mounted harness and a lap-robe thrown in.

"Fifteen," said another man.

Somebody else said "Twenty." Then there was a hitch. The man on the box began to talk very fast indeed.

"Thutty-thutty-thutty-thutty—do I hear five? Thutty-thutty-thutty-thutty—will you make it five?"

"Thirty-five," said a red-faced man who had pushed his way to the front and was looking Skipper over sharply.

The man on the box said "Thutty-five" a good many times and asked if he "heard forty." Evidently he did not, for he stopped and said very slowly and distinctly, looking expectantly around, "Are you all done? Thirty-five—once. Thirty-five—twice. Third and last call—sold, for thirty-five dollars!"

When Skipper heard this he hung his head. When you have been a $250 blue-ribboner and the pride of the force it is sad to be "knocked down" for thirty-five.

The next year of Skipper's life was a dark one. We will not linger over it. The red-faced man who led him away was a grocer. He put Skipper in the shafts of a heavy wagon very early every morning and drove him a long way through the city to a big down-town market where men in long frocks shouted and handled boxes and barrels. When the wagon was heavily loaded the red-faced man drove him back to the store. Then a tow-haired boy who jerked viciously on the lines and was fond of using the whip, drove him recklessly about the streets and avenues.

But one day the tow-haired boy pulled the near rein too hard while rounding a corner and a wheel was smashed against a lamp-post. The tow-haired boy was sent head first into an ash-barrel, and Skipper, rather startled at the occurrence, took a little run down the avenue, strewing the pavement with eggs, sugar, canned corn, celery and other assorted groceries.

Perhaps this was why the grocer sold him. Skipper pulled a cart through the flat-house district for a while after that. On the seat of the cart sat a leather-lunged man who roared, "A-a-a-a-puls! Nice a-a-a-a-puls! A who-o-ole lot fer a quarter!"

Skipper felt this disgrace keenly. Even the cab-horses, on whom he used to look with disdain, eyed him scornfully. Skipper stood it as long as possible and then one day, while the apple fakir was standing on the back step of the cart shouting things at a woman who was leaning halfway out of a fourth-story window, he bolted. He distributed that load of apples over four blocks, much to the profit of the street children, and he wrecked the wagon on a hydrant. For this the fakir beat him with a piece of the wreckage until a blue-coated officer threatened to arrest him. Next day Skipper was sold again.

Skipper looked over his new owner without joy. The man was evil of face. His long whiskers and hair were unkempt and sun-bleached like the tip end of a pastured cow's tail. His clothes were greasy. His voice was like the grunt of a pig. Skipper wondered to what use this man would put him. He feared the worst.

Far up through the city the man took him and out on a broad avenue where there were many open spaces, most of them fenced in by huge bill-boards. Behind one of these sign-plastered barriers Skipper found his new home. The bottom of the lot was more than twenty feet below the street level. In the center of a waste of rocks, ash heaps, and dead weeds tottered a group of shanties, strangely made of odds and ends. The walls were partly of mud-chinked rocks and partly of wood. The roofs were patched with strips of rusty tin held in place by stones.

Into one of these shanties just tall enough for Skipper to enter and no more, the horse that had been the pride of the mounted park police was driven with a kick as a greeting. Skipper noted first that there was no feed-box and no hay-rick. Then he saw, or rather felt—for the only light came through cracks in the walls—that there was no floor. His nostrils told him that the drainage was bad. Skipper sighed as he thought of the clean, sweet straw which Reddy used to change in his stall every night.

But when you have a lump on your leg—a lump that throbs, throbs with pain, whether you stand still or lie down—you do not think much on other things.

Supper was late in coming to Skipper that night. He was almost starved when it was served. And such a supper! What do you think? Hay? Yes, but marsh hay; the dry, tasteless stuff they use for bedding in cheap stables. A ton of it wouldn't make a pound of good flesh. Oats? Not a sign of an oat! But with the hay there were a few potato peelings. Skipper nosed them out and nibbled the marsh hay. The rest he pawed back under him, for the whole had been thrown at his feet. Then he dropped on the ill-smelling ground and went to sleep to dream that he had been turned into a forty-acre field of clover, while a dozen brass bands played a waltz and multitudes of people looked on and cheered.

In the morning more salt hay was thrown to him and water was brought in a dirty pail. Then, without a stroke of brush or curry-comb he was led out. When he saw the wagon to which he was to be hitched Skipper hung his head. He had reached the bottom. It was unpainted and rickety as to body and frame, the wheels were unmated and dished, while the shafts were spliced and wound with wire.

But worst of all was the string of bells suspended from two uprights above the seat. When Skipper saw these he knew he had fallen low indeed. He had become the horse of a wandering junk-man. The next step in his career, as he well knew, would be the glue factory and the bone-yard. Now when a horse has lived for twenty years or so, it is sad enough to face these things. But at eight years to see the glue factory close at hand is enough to make a horse wish he had never been foaled.

For many weary months Skipper pulled that crazy cart, with its hateful jangle of bells, about the city streets and suburban roads while the man with the faded hair roared through his matted beard; "Buy o-o-o-o-olt ra-a-a-a-a-ags! Buy o-o-o-o-olt ra-a-a-a-a-ags! Olt boddles! Olt copper! Olt iron! Vaste baber!"

The lump on Skipper's hock kept growing bigger and bigger. It seemed as if the darts of pain shot from hoof to flank with every step. Big hollows came over his eyes. You could see his ribs as plainly as the hoops on a pork-barrel. Yet six days in the week he went on long trips and brought back heavy loads of junk. On Sunday he hauled the junkman and his family about the city.

Once the junkman tried to drive Skipper into one of the Park entrances. Then for the first time in his life Skipper balked. The junkman pounded and used such language as you might expect from a junkman, but all to no use. Skipper took the beating with lowered head, but go through the gate he would not. So the junkman gave it up, although he seemed very anxious to join the line of gay carriages which were rolling in.

Soon after this there came a break in the daily routine. One morning Skipper was not led out as usual. In fact, no one came

Paul Brown

near him, and he could hear no voices in the near-by shanty. Skipper decided that he would take a day off himself. By backing against the door he readily pushed it open, for the staple was insecure.

Once at liberty, he climbed the roadway that led out of the lot. It was late in the fall but there was still short sweet winter grass to be found along the gutters. For a while he nibbled at this hungrily. Then a queer idea came to Skipper. Perhaps the padding of a smartly groomed saddle horse was responsible.

At any rate, Skipper left off nibbling grass. He hobbled out to the edge of the road, turned so as to face the opposite side, and held up his head. There he stood just as he used to stand when he was the pride of the mounted squad. He was on post once more.

Few people were passing and none of them seemed to notice him. Yet he was an odd figure. His coat was shaggy and weather stained. It looked patched and faded. The spavined hock caused one hind quarter to sag somewhat, but aside from that his pose was strictly according to the regulations.

Skipper had been playing at standing post for a half-hour, when a trotting dandy who sported ankle-boots and toe-weights, pulled up before him. He was drawing a light, bicycle-wheeled road-wagon in which were two men.

"Queer?" one of the men was saying. "Can't say I see anything queer about it, Captain. Some old plug that's got away from a squatter; that's all I see in it."

"Well, let's have a look," said the other. He stared hard at Skipper for a moment and then, in a loud sharp tone said:

" 'Ten-shun! Right dress!"

Skipper pricked up his ears, raised his head and side-stepped stiffly. The trotting dandy turned and looked curiously at him.

"Forward!" said the man in the wagon. Skipper hobbled out into the road.

"Right wheel! Halt. I thought so," said the man as Skipper obeyed the orders. "That fellow has been on the force. He was standing post. Looks mighty familiar too—white stockings on two forelegs, white star on forehead. Now I wonder if that can be— here hold the reins a minute."

Going up to Skipper the man patted his nose once or twice, and

then pushed his muzzle to one side. Skipper ducked and countered. He had not forgotten his boxing trick. The man turned his back and began to pace down the road. Skipper followed and picked up a riding-glove which the man dropped.

"Doyle," said the man, as he walked back to the wagon, "two years ago that was the finest horse on the force—took the blue ribbon at the Garden. Alderman Martin would give a thousand dollars for him as he stands. He has hunted the State for him. You remember Martin—Reddy Martin—who used to be on the mounted squad! Didn't you hear? An old uncle who made a fortune as a building contractor died about a year ago and left the whole pile to Reddy. He's got a fine country place up in Westchester and is in the city government. Just elected this fall. But he isn't happy because he can't find his old horse—and here's the horse."

Next day an astonished junkman stood before an empty shanty which served as a stable and feasted his eyes on a $50 bank note.

If you are ever up in Westchester County be sure to visit the stables of Alderman P. Sarsfield Martin. Ask to see that oak-panelled box-stall with the stained glass windows and the porcelain feed-box. You will notice a polished brass name-plate on the door bearing this inscription:

SKIPPER

You may meet the Alderman himself, wearing an English-made riding suit, loping comfortably along on a sleek bay gelding with two white forelegs and a white star on his forehead. Yes, high-priced veterinaries can cure spavin—Alderman Martin says so.

It Happened at Aintree

By PAUL BROWN

THE Grand National, which, until the outbreak of the present war, was run annually for more than a hundred years at Aintree near Liverpool, was, and every horse lover hopes it will be again, the greatest racing spectacle in the world. On the course at Aintree great horses made history and attracted thousands of fans whose pulses leaped at the sight of the beautifully made and trained animals although they may not have known the power and capacity of the "chasers" who made the race.

The old timer who could get there early felt his scalp begin to tingle as he watched the preparations, especially the grooming and manicuring of the fences, huge barriers of growing thorn hedge built up with fir and gorse. These were works of art and so solid that a man could walk across them.

On the actual day of the race he surveyed with practiced eye the vast and detailed preparations for every emergency, details that escape the eye of the casual visitor. The field telephones are run about the field and tested. Piles of blankets, flags, medical supplies, and stretchers with their ties loosened are placed at each fence for the use of the bobbies or the men of the first aid corps who are stationed there. The flags are of two colors, yellow and red. The yellow one is waved when a man is hurt and summons one of the many doctors spaced around the course, the red one summons a veterinarian when a horse is hurt.

The fire extinguishers at each obstacle are not put there to furnish amusement for the crowd. Although you may wonder why there should be danger of fire, there actually is. The management has to guard against the possibility that a fanatic who opposes racing may attempt to focus attention on his cause by setting fire to one of the fences, or a political devotee may choose this means of gaining publicity. They do not forget the suffragette who threw herself in front of the King's horse at the Derby, killed herself and brought down the horse near Tottenham Corner.

After all of these preparations are complete, comes the slow procession of black ambulances for humans and heavy rumbling ones for horses pulled by towering draft animals, ready to carry off injured chasers. Stationed with these around the two and a fourth mile circuit are the knackers' carts, those ominous two-wheeled wagons for the removal of horses that are killed or must be destroyed.

There you have the setting for the Grand National, everything ready for the fans, the two hundred and fifty to three hundred thousand souls who watch with an intensity that charges the atmosphere with suspense. Now what of the horses who will run this four miles, eight hundred and fifty-six yards, and negotiate thirty fences carrying an average of a hundred and fifty-four pounds? The favorite totes a weight of a hundred and seventy-five.

Many people are surprised that these chasers are not four or five-year-olds, but are for the most part at least six years old, often twelve or fourteen. It took the British over ninety years to bar five-year-olds from the event. While it is true they may win, they

are not mature enough to stand the gruelling gallop and are never worth anything afterward.

The clip at which these horses gallop is astonishing. According to Dave Monroe, another student of Aintree, these horses go four miles, eight hundred and fifty-six yards with the heavy imposts, they pick up their burdens and negotiate the fences, endure the bumping, confusion and turns of the course in an average of *twenty-four seconds more per mile* than the time of the Derby horse who is running a mile and a half carrying a hundred and twenty-six pounds.

This observation illustrates the power and endurance of these mature Aintree entries. Take, for instance, the matter of fences. Their measurement in height is taken from a point ten feet before a fence and ten feet beyond it because at this distance horses usually take off and land (the measurements taken beyond the fences are to show the degree of drop, in some cases ten to fifteen inches, which many people believe causes horses to turn over).

The fences are from two feet, six inches, to over three feet in thickness. This measurement, plus the ten feet on each side, would indicate that the average leap is about twenty-three feet.

But a leap of twenty-three feet is mere child's play for these horses. Remember most of them are striding twenty feet, so to leap twenty-three is little more than a big stride. Leaps of over thirty feet occur in every race. They are spectacular when they approach that of Chandler who leaped over thirty-nine out of fetlock-deep mud while running in a downpour that had turned a course into an oozy quagmire.

I saw little Tootenhill go over thirty-one at Becher's without an effort. Billy Barton, the American timber horse, did over thirty-three while schooling over post and rails, and Heatherbloom— they say more hunters have changed hands on these figures than for any other horsey reason—leaped thirty-seven while clearing eight feet three plus, for an unofficial high jump record.

Manifesto, the greatest of all National horses, won twice in two starts, was third the next three times he ran and, when sixteen years old, finished seventh, carrying a hundred and sixty-nine pounds.

Something just over two thousand horses have started on this great racing field of Aintree. They ran from twelve to sixty-six

These pictures, drawn to scale, show the famous Bechers Brook and the comparison of a 16-hand-2-inch horse to a 30-foot leap.

The way horses "bank" Bechers. (1) The chaser seems to be in a normal leaping position. He is, however, in this case making a quick collection of his hindquarters so that (2) he can plant them in the top of the fence and (3) kick back hard so as to thrust himself farther into the next field.

in a field, and in each field about twenty per cent finished, forty fell, and the balance refused, pulled up or lost riders.

Unfortunately (and remember this if you want horses to run well and safely) most of the horses that have been killed or destroyed at Aintree have lost their lives because of man-made mistakes. They have been killed because the fences were not properly shaped on the take-off side. The general belief that the destruction of horses on this course, and the numerous falls, is due to the height and solidity of the fences, is absolutely unfounded. Facts gathered by studying the tracks in the turf, the holes in the fences and by questioning the men on duty at the obstacles during the running of races year after year, show that the trouble lies in the vertical faces of the fences on the approach side. They are so designed that horses can not "measure" them

P.B

and so take off properly. They get in unbelievably close, check and lose momentum, try to rise, hook the fences with their knees and come pitching head first to untimely ends. Make your fences slant away with the leap and you will get safe chasing or jumping over obstacles that you'd never think a horse could take.

Will du Pont's Fair Hill course bears out this theory. The fences there are so big that you could hide the average Aintree horse-killer in one of them and never find it again, but Mr. du Pont has never had a horse killed or even a bad fall over any of the big jumps on the outside course.

Aintree, however, is a law unto itself. In spite of the hazards, it is the mecca of all who follow steeplechasing. Where else would a man fill his horse's hoofs with butter to enable him to win? And he did! Or where else would a horse fall four times in one race and finish fourth? Only at Aintree would a horse fall and break his neck and run in the same steeplechase a year later.

Strider: The Story of a Horse

By LEO TOLSTOI

HIGHER and higher receded the sky, wider and wider spread the streak of dawn, whiter grew the pallid silver of the dew, more lifeless the sickle of the moon, and more vocal the forest. People began to get up, and in the owner's stable-yard the sounds of snorting, the rustling of litter, and even the shrill angry neighing of horses crowded together and at variance about something, grew more and more frequent.

'Hold on! Plenty of time! Hungry?' said the old huntsman, quickly opening the creaking gate. 'Where are you going?' he shouted, threateningly raising his arm at a mare that was pushing through the gate.

The keeper, Nester, wore a short Cossack coat with an ornamental leather girdle, had a whip slung over his shoulder, and a hunk of bread wrapped in a cloth stuck in his girdle. He carried a saddle and bridle in his arms.

The horses were not at all frightened or offended at the horseman's sarcastic tone: they pretended that it was all the same to them and moved leisurely away from the gate; only one old brown mare, with a thick mane, laid back an ear and quickly turned her back on him. A small filly standing behind her and not at all concerned in the matter took this opportunity to whinny and kick out at a horse that happened to be near.

'Now then!' shouted the keeper still louder and more sternly, and he went to the opposite corner of the yard.

Of all the horses in the enclosure (there were about a hundred of them) a piebald gelding, standing by himself in a corner under the penthouse and licking an oak post with half-closed eyes, displayed least impatience.

It is impossible to say what flavour the piebald gelding found

P.B.

in the post, but his expression was serious and thoughtful while he licked.

'Stop that!' shouted the groom, drawing nearer to him and putting the saddle and a glossy saddle-cloth on the manure heap beside him.

The piebald gelding stopped licking, and without moving gave Nester a long look. The gelding did not laugh, nor grow angry, nor frown, but his whole belly heaved with a profound sigh and he turned away. The horseman put his arm round the gelding's neck and placed the bridle on him.

'What are you sighing for?' said Nester.

The gelding switched his tail as if to say, 'Nothing in particular, Nester!' Nester put the saddle-cloth and saddle on him, and this caused the gelding to lay back his ears, probably to express dissatisfaction, but he was only called a 'good-for-nothing' for it and his saddle-girth were tightened.

At this the gelding blew himself out, but a finger was thrust into his mouth and a knee hit him in the stomach, so that he had to let out his breath. In spite of this, when the saddle-cloth was being buckled on he again laid back his ears and even looked round. Though he knew it would do no good he considered it necessary to show that it was disagreeable to him and that he would always express his dissatisfaction with it. When he was saddled he thrust forward his swollen off foot and began champing his bit, this too for some reason of his own, for he ought to have known by that time that a bit cannot have any flavour at all.

Nester mounted the gelding by the short stirrup, unwound his long whip, straightened his coat out from under his knee, seated himself in the manner peculiar to coachmen, huntsmen, and horsemen, and jerked the reins. The gelding lifted his head to show his readiness to go where ordered, but did not move. He knew that before starting there would be much shouting, and that Nester, from the seat on his back, would give many orders to Váska, the other groom, and to the horses. And Nester did shout: 'Váska! Hullo, Váska. Have you let out the brood mares? Where are you going, you devil? Now then! Are you asleep . . . Open the gate! Let the brood mares get out first!'—and so on.

The gate creaked. Váska, cross and sleepy, stood at the gate-

post holding his horse by the bridle and letting the other horses
pass out. The horses followed one another and stepped carefully
over the straw, smelling at it: fillies, yearling colts with their
manes and tails cut, suckling foals, and mares in foal carrying
their burden heedfully, passed one by one through the gateway.
The fillies sometimes crowded together in twos and threes, throwing their heads across one another's backs and hitting their hoofs
against the gate, for which they received a rebuke from the
grooms every time. The foals sometimes darted under the legs
of the wrong mares and neighed loudly in response to the short
whinny of their own mothers.

A playful filly, directly she had got out at the gate, bent her
head sideways, kicked up her hind legs, and squealed, but all
the same she did not dare to run ahead of old dappled Zhuldýba
who at a slow and heavy pace, swinging her belly from side to
side, marched as usual ahead of all the other horses.

In a few minutes the enclosure that had been so animated became deserted, the posts stood gloomily under the empty penthouse, and only trampled straw mixed with manure was to be
seen. Used as he was to that desolate sight it probably depressed
the piebald gelding. As if making a bow he slowly lowered his
head and raised it again, sighed as deeply as the tightly drawn
girth would allow, and hobbling along on his stiff and crooked
legs shambled after the herd, bearing old Nester on his bony
back.

'I know that as soon as we get out on the road he will begin
to strike a light and smoke his wooden pipe with its brass mount-
ings and little chain,' thought the gelding. 'I am glad of it because early in the morning when it is dewy I like that smell, it
reminds me of much that was pleasant; but it's annoying that
when his pipe is between his teeth the old man always begins
to swagger and thinks himself somebody and sits sideways, always
sideways—and that side hurts. However, it can't be helped! Suffering for the pleasure of others is nothing new to me. I have
even begun to find a certain equine pleasure in it. Let him swagger, poor fellow! Of course he can only do that when he is alone
and no one sees him—let him sit sideways!' thought the gelding,
and stepping carefully on his crooked legs he went along the
middle of the road.

Having driven the horses to the riverside where they were to graze, Nester dismounted and unsaddled. Meanwhile the herd had begun gradually to spread over the untrampled meadow, covered with dew and by the mist that rose from it and the encircling river.

When he had taken the bridle off the piebald gelding, Nester scratched him under the neck, in response to which the gelding expressed his gratitude and satisfaction by closing his eyes. 'He likes it, the old dog!' muttered Nester. The gelding however did not really care for the scratching at all, and pretended that it was agreeable merely out of courtesy. He nodded his head in assent to Nester's words; but suddenly Nester quite unexpectedly and without any reason, perhaps imagining that too much familiarity might give the gelding a wrong idea of his importance, pushed the gelding's head away from himself without any warning and, swinging the bridle, struck him painfully with the buckle on his lean leg, and then without saying a word went up the hillock to a tree-stump beside which he generally seated himself.

Though this action grieved the piebald gelding he gave no indication of it, but leisurely switching his scanty tail, sniffed at something and, biting off some wisps of grass merely to divert his mind, walked to the river. He took no notice whatever of the antics of the young mares, colts, and foals around him, who were filled with the joy of the morning; and knowing that, especially at his age, it is healthier to have a good drink on an empty stomach and to eat afterwards, he chose a spot where the bank was widest and least steep, and wetting his hoofs and fetlocks, dipped his muzzle in the water and began to suck it up through his torn lips, to expand his filling sides, and from pleasure to switch his scanty tail with its half bald stump.

An aggressive chestnut filly, who always teased the old fellow and did all kinds of unpleasant things to him, now came up to him in the water as if attending to some business of her own, but in reality merely to foul the water before his nose. But the piebald gelding, who had already had his fill, as though not noticing the filly's intention quietly drew one foot after the other out of the mud in which they had sunk, jerked his head, and stepping aside from the youthful crowd started grazing. Sprawling his feet apart in different ways and not trampling the grass needlessly, he went on eating without unbending himself for exactly three hours. Having eaten till his belly hung down from his steep skinny ribs like a sack, he balanced himself equally on his four sore legs so as to have as little pain as possible, especially in his off foreleg which was the weakest, and fell asleep.

Old age is sometimes majestic, sometimes ugly, and sometimes pathetic. But old age can be both ugly and majestic, and the gelding's old age was just of that kind.

He was tall, rather over fifteen hands high. His spots were black, or rather they had been black, but had now turned a dirty brown. He had three spots, one on his head, starting from a crooked bald patch on the side of his nose and reaching half-way down his neck. His long mane, filled with burrs, was white in some places and brownish in others. Another spot extended down his off side to the middle of his belly, the third, on his croup, touched part of his tail and went half-way down his quarters. The rest of the tail was whitish and speckled. The big bony head, with deep hollows over the eyes and a black hanging lip that had been torn at some time, hung low and heavily on his neck, which was so lean that it looked as though it were carved of wood. The pendant lip revealed a blackish, bitten tongue and the yellow stumps of the worn lower teeth. The ears, one of which was slit, hung low on either side, and only occasionally moved lazily to drive away the pestering flies. Of the forelock, one tuft which was still long hung back behind an ear; the uncovered forehead was dented and rough, and the skin hung down like bags on his broad jawbones. The veins of his neck had grown knotty, and twitched and shuddered at every touch of a fly. The expression of his face was one of stern patience, thoughtfulness, and suffering.

His forelegs were crooked to a bow at the knees, there were swellings over both hoofs, and on one leg, on which the piebald spot reached half-way down, there was a swelling at the knee as big as a fist. The hind legs were in better condition, but apparently long ago his haunches had been so rubbed that in places the hair would not grow again. The leanness of his body made all four legs look disproportionately long. The ribs, though straight, were so exposed and the skin so tightly drawn over them, that it seemed to have dried fast to the spaces between. His back and

withers were covered with marks of old lashings, and there was
a fresh sore behind, still swollen and festering; the black dock of
his tail, which showed the vertebrae, hung down long and almost
bare. On his dark-brown croup—near the tail—was a scar, as
though of a bite, the size of a man's hand and covered with
white hair. Another scarred sore was visible on one of his shoulders. His tail and hocks were dirty because of chronic bowel
troubles. The hair on the whole body, though short, stood out
straight. Yet in spite of the hideous old age of this horse one involuntarily paused to reflect when one saw him, and an expert
would have said at once that he had been a remarkably fine horse
in his day. The expert would even have said that there was only
one breed in Russia that could furnish such breadth of bone,
such immense knees, such hoofs, such slender cannons, such a
well-shaped neck, and above all such a skull, such eyes—large,
black, and clear—and such a thoroughbred network of veins on
head and neck, and such delicate skin and hair.

There was really something majestic in that horse's figure and
in the terrible union in him of repulsive indications of decrepi-
tude, emphasized by the motley colour of his hair, and his manner which expressed the self-confidence and calm assurance that
go with beauty and strength. Like a living ruin he stood alone in
the midst of the dewy meadow, while not far from him could be
heard the tramping, snorting and youthful neighing and whinnying of the scattered herd.

The sun had risen above the forest and now shone brightly on
the grass and the winding river. The dew was drying up and con-
densing into drops, the last of the morning mist was dispersing
like tiny smoke-clouds. The cloudlets were becoming curly but
there was as yet no wind. Beyond the river the verdant rye stood
bristling, its ears curling into little horns, and there was an odour
of fresh verdure and blossom. A cuckoo called rather hoarsely
from the forest, and Nester, lying on his back in the grass, was
counting the calls to ascertain how many years he still had to
live. The larks were rising over the rye and the meadow. A belated hare, finding himself among the horses, leaped into the
open, sat down by a bush, and pricked his ears to listen. Váska
fell asleep with his head in the grass, the fillies, making a still
wider circle about him, scattered over the field below. The old

mares went about snorting, and made a shining track across the dewy grass, always choosing a place where no one would disturb them. They no longer grazed, but only nibbled at choice tufts of grass. The whole herd was moving imperceptibly in one direction.

And again it was old Zhuldýba who, stepping sedately in front of the others, showed the possibility of going farther. Black Múshka, a young mare who had foaled for the first time, with uplifted tail kept whinnying and snorting at her bluish foal; the young filly Satin, sleek and brilliant, bending her head till her black silky forelock hid her forehead and eyes, played with the grass, nipping off a little and tossing it and stamping her leg with its shaggy fetlock all wet with dew. One of the older foals, probably imagining he was playing some kind of game, with his curly tail raised like a plume, ran for the twenty-sixth time round his mother, who quietly went on grazing, having grown accustomed to her son's ways, and only occasionally glanced askance at him with one of her large black eyes.

One of the very youngest foals, black, with a big head, a tuft sticking up in astonishment between his ears, and a little tail still twisted to one side as it had been in his mother's womb, stood motionless, his ears pricked and his dull eyes fixed, gazing at the frisking and prancing foal—whether admiring or condemning him it is hard to say. Some of the foals were sucking and butting with their noses, some—heaven knows why—despite their mothers' calls were running at an awkward little trot in quite the opposite direction as if searching for something, and then, for no apparent reason, stopping and neighing with desperate shrillness. Some lay on their sides in a row, some were learning to eat grass, some again were scratching themselves behind their ears with their hind legs. Two mares still in foal were walking apart from the rest, and while slowly moving their legs continued to graze. The others evidently respected their condition, and none of the young ones ventured to come near to disturb them. If any saucy youngsters thought of approaching them, the mere movement of an ear or tail sufficed to show them all how improper such behaviour was.

That morning the chestnut filly was in a specially playful mood. She was seized with a joyous fit, just as human beings sometimes are. Already at the riverside she had played a trick on the old gelding, and after that she ran along through the water pretending to be frightened by something, gave a hoarse squeal, and raced full speed into the field so that Váska had to gallop after her and the others who followed her. Then after grazing a little she began rolling, then teasing the old mares by dashing in front of them, then she drove away a small foal from its dam and chased it as if meaning to bite it. Its mother was frightened and stopped grazing, while the little foal cried in a piteous tone, but the mischievous one did not touch him at all, she only wanted to frighten him and give a performance for the benefit of her companions, who watched her escapade approvingly. Then she set out to turn the head of a little roan horse with which a peasant was ploughing in a rye-field far beyond the river. She stopped, proudly lifted her head somewhat to one side, shook herself, and neighed in a sweet, tender, long-drawn voice. Mischief, feeling, and a certain sadness, were expressed in that call. There was in it the desire for and the promise of love, and a pining for it.

'There in the thick reeds is a corn-crake running backwards and forwards and calling passionately to his mate; there is the cuckoo, and the quails are singing of love, and the flowers are sending their fragrant dust to each other by the wind. And I too am young and beautiful and strong,' the mischievous one's voice said, 'but it has not yet been allowed me to know the sweetness of that feeling, and not only to experience it, but no lover—not a single one—has ever seen me!'

And this neighing, sad and youthful and fraught with feeling, was borne over the lowland and the field to the roan horse far away. He pricked up his ears and stopped. The peasant kicked him with his bast shoe, but the little horse was so enchanted by the silvery sound of the distant neighing that he neighed too. The peasant grew angry, pulled at the reins, and kicked the little roan so painfully in the stomach with his bast shoes that he could not finish his neigh and walked on. But the little roan felt a sense of sweetness and sadness, and for a long time the sounds of unfinished and passionate neighing, and of the peasant's angry voice, were carried from the distant rye-field over to the herd.

If the sound of her voice alone so overpowered the little roan that he forgot his duty, what would have happened had he seen the naughty beauty as she stood pricking her ears, breathing in the air with dilated nostrils, ready to run, trembling with her whole beautiful body, and calling to him?

But the mischievous one did not brood long over her impressions. When the neighing of the roan died away she gave another scornful neigh, lowered her head and began pawing the ground, and then she went to wake and to tease the piebald gelding. The piebald gelding was the constant martyr and butt of those happy youngsters. He suffered more from them than at the hands of men. He did no harm to either. People needed him, but why should these young horses torment him?

He was old, they were young; he was lean, they were sleek; he was miserable, they were gay; and so he was quite alien to them, an outsider, an utterly different creature whom it was impossible for them to pity. Horses only have pity on themselves, and very occasionally on those in whose skins they can easily imagine themselves to be. But was it the old gelding's fault that he was old, poor and ugly? . . .

The gelding felt so offended that he went up himself to Nester when the old man was getting ready to drive the horses home, and felt happier and quieter when he was saddled and the old man had mounted him.

That evening, as Nester drove the horses past the huts of the domestic serfs, he noticed a peasant horse and cart tethered to his porch: some friends had come to see him. When driving the horses in he was in such a hurry that he let the gelding in without unsaddling him and, shouting to Váska to do it, shut the gate and went to his friends. Whether because of the affront to the white-spotted filly—Creamy's great-grand-daughter—by that 'mangy trash' bought at the horse fair, who did not know his father or mother, and the consequent outrage to the aristocratic sentiment of the whole herd, or because the gelding with his high saddle and without a rider presented a strangely fantastic spectacle to the horses, at any rate something quite unusual occurred that night in the paddock. All the horses, young and old, ran after the gelding, showing their teeth and driving him all round the yard; one heard the sound of hoofs striking against his bare ribs, and his deep groaning. He could no longer endure this, nor could he avoid the blows. He stopped in the middle of the paddock, his face expressing first the repulsive weak malevolence of helpless old age, and then despair: he dropped his ears, and then something happened that caused all the horses to quiet down. The oldest of the mares, Vyazapúrikha, went up to the gelding, sniffed at him and sighed. The gelding sighed too . . .

In the middle of the moonlit paddock stood the tall gaunt figure of the gelding, still wearing the high saddle with its prominent peak at the bow. The horses stood motionless and in deep silence around him as if they were learning something new and unexpected. And they had learnt something new and unexpected.

This is what they learnt from him . . .

FIRST NIGHT

Yes, I am the son of Affable I and of Bába. My pedigree name is Muzhík, and I was nicknamed Strider by the crowd because of my long and sweeping strides, the like of which was nowhere to be found in all Russia. There is no more thoroughbred horse in the world. I should never have told you this. What good would it have done? You would never have recognized me: even Vyazapúrikha, who was with me in Khrénovo, did not recognize me till now. You would not have believed me if Vyazapúrikha were not here to be my witness, and I should never have told you this. I don't need equine sympathy. But you wished it. Yes, I am that Strider whom connoisseurs are looking for and cannot find—that Strider whom the count himself knew and got rid of from his stud because I outran Swan, his favourite.

When I was born I did not know what *piebald* meant—I thought I was just a horse. I remember that the first remark we heard about my colour struck my mother and me deeply.

I suppose I was born in the night; by the morning, having been licked over by my mother, I already stood on my feet. I remember I kept wanting something and that everything seemed very surprising and yet very simple. Our stalls opened into a long warm passage and had latticed doors through which everything could be seen.

My mother offered me her teats but I was still so innocent that I poked my nose now between her forelegs and now under her udder. Suddenly she glanced at the latticed door and lifting her

leg over me stepped aside. The groom on duty was looking into our stall through the lattice.

'Why, Bába has foaled!' he said, and began to draw the bolt. He came in over the fresh bedding and put his arms round me. 'Just look, Tarás!' he shouted, 'what a piebald he is—a regular magpie!'

I darted away from him and fell on my knees.

'Look at him—the little devil!'

My mother became disquieted, but did not take my part, she only stepped a little to one side with a very deep sigh. Other grooms came to look at me, and one of them ran to tell the stud groom.

Everybody laughed when they looked at my spots, and they gave me all kinds of strange names, but neither I nor my mother understood those words. Till then there had been no piebalds among all my relatives. We did not think there was anything bad in it. Everybody even then praised my strength and my form.

'See what a frisky fellow!' said the groom. 'There's no holding him.'

Before long the stud groom came and began to express astonishment at my colour; he even seemed aggrieved.

'And who does the little monster take after?' he said. 'The general won't keep him in the stud. Oh, Bába, you have played me a trick!' he addressed my mother. 'You might at least have dropped one with just a star—but this one is all piebald!'

My mother did not reply, but as usual on such occasions drew a sigh.

'And what devil does he take after—he's just like a peasant-horse!' he continued. 'He can't be left in the stud—he'd shame us. But he's well built—very well!' said he, and so did everyone who saw me.

A few days later the general himself came and looked at me, and again everyone seemed horrified at something, and abused me and my mother for the colour of my hair. 'But he's a fine colt—very fine!' said all who saw me.

Until spring we all lived separately in the brood mares' stable, each with our mother, and only occasionally when the snow on the stable roofs began to melt in the sun were we let out with our mothers into the large paddock strewn with fresh straw. There I first came to know all my near and my distant relations. Here I saw all the famous mares of the day coming out from different doors with their little foals. There was the old mare Dutch, Fly (Creamy's daughter), Ruddy the riding-horse, Wellwisher—all celebrities at that time. They all gathered together with their foals, walking about in the sunshine, rolling on the fresh straw and sniffing at one another like ordinary horses. I have never forgotten the sight of that paddock full of the beauties of that day. It seems strange to you to think, and hard to believe, that I was ever young and frisky, but it was so. This same Vyazapúrikha was then a yearling filly whose mane had just been cut; a dear, merry, lively little thing, but—and I do not say it to offend her—although among you she is now considered a remarkable thoroughbred she was then among the poorest horses in the stud. She will herself confirm this.

My mottled appearance, which men so disliked, was very attractive to all the horses; they all came round me, admired me, and frisked about with me. I began to forget what men said about my mottled appearance, and felt happy. But I soon experienced the first sorrow of my life and the cause of it was my mother. When the thaw had set in, the sparrows twittered under the eaves, spring was felt more strongly in the air, and my mother's treatment of me changed.

Her whole disposition changed: she would frisk about without any reason and run round the yard, which did not at all accord with her dignified age; then she would consider and begin to neigh, and would bite and kick her sister mares, and then begin to sniff at me and snort discontentedly; then on going out into the sun she would lay her head across the shoulder of her cousin, Lady Merchant, dreamily rub her back, and push me away from her teats.

One day the stud groom came and had a halter put on her and she was led out of the stall. She neighed and I answered and rushed after her, but she did not even look back at me. The strapper, Tarás, seized me in his arms while they were closing the door after my mother had been led out.

I bolted and upset the strapper on the straw, but the door was shut and I could only hear the receding sound of my mother's neighing; and that neigh did not sound like a call to me but had another expression. Her voice was answered from afar by a powerful voice—that of Dóbry I, as I learned later, who was being led by two grooms, one on each side, to meet my mother.

I don't remember how Tarás got out of my stall: I felt too sad, for I knew that I had lost my mother's love for ever. 'And it's all because I am piebald!' I thought, remembering what people said about my colour, and such passionate anger overcame me that I began to beat my head and knees against the walls of the stall and continued till I was sweating all over and quite exhausted.

The gelding heaved a deep sigh and walked away from the other horses.

The dawn had broken long before. The gates creaked. Nester came in, and the horses separated. The keeper straightened the saddle on the gelding's back and drove the horses out.

SECOND NIGHT

As soon as the horses had been driven in they again gathered round the piebald, who continued:

In August they separated me from my mother and I did not feel particularly grieved. I saw that she was again heavy (with my brother, the famous Usán) and that I could no longer be to her what I had been. I was not jealous, but felt that I had become indifferent to her. Besides I knew that having left my mother I should be put in the general division of foals, where we were kept two or three together and were every day let out in a crowd into the open. I was in the same stall with Darling. Darling was a saddle-horse, who was subsequently ridden by the Emperor and portrayed in pictures and sculpture. At that time he was a mere foal, with soft glossy coat, a swanlike neck, and straight slender legs taut as the strings of an instrument. He was always lively, good-tempered and amiable, always ready to gambol, exchange licks, and play tricks on horse or man. Living together as we did we involuntarily made friends, and our friendship lasted the whole of our youth. He was merry and giddy. Even then he began to make love, courted the fillies, and laughed at my guilelessness. To my misfortune vanity led me to imitate him, and I was soon carried away and fell in love. And this early tendency of mine was the cause of the greatest change in my fate. It happened that I was carried away . . . Vyazapúrikha was a year older than I, and we were special friends, but towards the autumn I noticed that she began to be shy with me . . .

But I will not speak of that unfortunate period of my first love; she herself remembers my mad passion, which ended for me in the most important change of my life.

The strappers rushed to drive her away and to beat me. That evening I was shut up in a special stall where I neighed all night as if foreseeing what was to happen next.

In the morning the general, the stud groom, the stableman and the strappers came into the passage where my stall was, and there was a terrible hubbub. The general shouted at the stud groom, who tried to justify himself by saying that he had not told them to let me out but that the grooms had done it of their own accord. The general said that he would have everybody flogged, and that it would not do to keep young stallions. The stud groom promised that he would have everything attended to. They grew quiet and went away. I did not understand anything, but could see that they were planning something concerning me.

The day after that I ceased neighing for ever. I became what I am now. The whole world was changed in my eyes. Nothing mattered any more; I became self-absorbed and began to brood. At first everything seemed repulsive to me. I even ceased to eat, drink, or walk, and there was no idea of playing. Now and then it occurred to me to give a kick, to gallop, or to start neighing, but immediately came the question: Why? What for? and all my energy died away.

One evening I was being exercised just when the horses were driven back from pasture. I saw in the distance a cloud of dust enveloping the indistinct but familiar outlines of all our brood mares. I heard their cheerful snorting and the trampling of their feet. I stopped, though the cord of the halter by which the groom was leading me cut the nape of my neck, and I gazed at the approaching drove as one gazes at a happiness that is lost for ever and cannot return. They approached, and I could distinguish one after another all the familiar, beautiful, stately, healthy, sleek figures. Some of them also turned to look at me. I was un-

conscious of the pain the groom's jerking at my halter inflicted.
I forgot myself and from old habit involuntarily neighed and began to trot, but my neighing sounded sad, ridiculous and mean-
ingless. No one in the drove made sport of me, but I noticed that
out of decorum many of them turned away from me. They evidently felt it repugnant, pitiable, indelicate, and above all ridiculous, to look at my thin expressionless neck, my large head (I had
grown lean in the meantime), my long, awkward legs, and the
silly awkward gait with which by force of habit I trotted round
the groom. No one answered my neighing—they all looked away.
Suddenly I understood it all, understood how far I was for ever
removed from them, and I do not remember how I got home
with the groom.

It was in winter at holiday time. I had not been fed or watered
all day. As I learnt later this happened because the lad who fed
us was drunk. That day the stud groom came in, saw that I had
no food, began to use bad language about the missing lad, and
then went away.

Next day the lad came into our stable with another groom to
give us hay. I noticed that he was particularly pale and sad and
that in the expression of his long back especially there was something significant which evoked compassion.

He threw the hay angrily over the grating. I made a move to
put my head over his shoulder, but he struck me such a painful
blow on the nose with his fist that I started back. Then he kicked
me in the belly with his boot.

'If it hadn't been for this scurvy beast,' he said, 'nothing would
have happened!'

'How's that?' inquired the other groom.

'You see, he doesn't go to look after the count's horses, but
visits his own twice a day.'

'What, have they given him the piebald?' asked the other.

'Given it, or sold it—the devil only knows! The count's horses
might all starve—he wouldn't care—but just dare to leave *his*
colt without food! "Lie down!" he says, and they begin wallop-
ing me! No Christianity in it. He has more pity on a beast than
on a man. He must be an infidel—he counted the strokes himself,
the barbarian! The general never flogged like that! My whole
back is covered with wales. There's no Christian soul in him!'

What they said about flogging and Christianity I understood well enough, but I was quite in the dark as to what they meant by the words '*his* colt', from which I perceived that people considered that there was some connexion between me and the head groom. What that connexion was I could not at all understand then. Only much later when they separated me from the other horses did I learn what it meant. At that time I could not at all understand what they meant by speaking of *me* as being a man's property. The words '*my* horse' applied to me, a live horse, seemed to me as strange as to say 'my land', 'my air', or 'my water'.

It was this right to speak of me as *my horse* that the stud groom had obtained, and that was why he had the stable lad flogged. I was kept apart from the other horses, was better fed, oftener taken out on the line, and was broken in at an earlier age. I was first harnessed in my third year. I remember how the stud groom, who imagined I was his, himself began to harness me with a crowd of other grooms, expecting me to prove unruly or to resist. They put ropes round me to lead me into the shafts; put a cross of broad straps on my back and fastened it to the shafts so that I could not kick, while I was only awaiting an opportunity to show my readiness and love of work.

They were surprised that I started like an old horse. They began to brake me and I began to practise trotting. Every day I made greater and greater progress, so that after three months the general himself and many others approved of my pace. But strange to say, just because they considered me not as their own, but as belonging to the head groom, they regarded my paces quite differently.

The stallions who were my brothers were raced, their records were kept, people went to look at them, drove them in gilt sulkies, and expensive horse-cloths were thrown over them. I was driven in a common sulky to Chesménka and other farms on the head groom's business. All this was the result of my being piebald, and especially of my being in their opinion not the count's, but the head groom's property.

To-morrow, if we are alive, I will tell you the chief consequence for me of this right of property the head groom considered himself to have.

All that day the horses treated Strider respectfully, but Nester's treatment of him was as rough as ever. The peasant's little roan horse neighed again on coming up to the herd, and the chestnut filly again coquettishly replied to him.

THIRD NIGHT

The new moon had risen and its narrow crescent lit up Strider's figure as he once again stood in the middle of the stable yard. The other horses crowded round him.

The gelding continued:

For me the most surprising consequence of my not being the count's, nor God's, but the head groom's, was that the very thing that constitutes our chief merit—a fast pace—was the cause of my banishment. They were driving Swan round the track, and the head groom, returning from Chesménka, drove me up and stopped there. Swan went past. He went well, but all the same he was showing off and had not the exactitude I had developed in myself—so that directly one foot touched the ground another instantaneously lifted and not the slightest effort was lost but every atom of exertion carried me forward. Swan went by us. I pulled towards the ring and the head groom did not check me. 'Here, shall I try my piebald?' he shouted, and when next Swan came abreast of us he let me go. Swan was already going fast, and so I was left behind during the first round, but in the second I began to gain on him, drew near to his sulky, drew level—and passed him. They tried us again—it was the same thing. I was the faster. And this dismayed everybody. The general asked that I should be sold at once to some distant place, so that nothing more should be heard of me: 'Or else the count will get to know of it and there will be trouble!' So they sold me to a horse-dealer as a shaft-horse. I did not remain with him long. An hussar who came to buy remounts bought me. All this was so unfair, so cruel, that I was glad when they took me away from Khrénovo and parted me for ever from all that had been familiar and dear to me. It was too painful for me among them. They had love, hon-our, freedom, before them; I had labour, humiliation; humiliation, labour, to the end of my life. And why? Because I was pie-bald, and because of that had to become somebody's horse. . . .

FOURTH NIGHT

In the evening when the gate was closed and all had quieted down, the piebald continued:

The happiest years of my life I spent with the officer of hussars.

Though he was the cause of my ruin, and though he never loved anything or anyone, I loved and still love him for that very reason.

What I liked about him was that he was handsome, happy, rich, and therefore never loved anybody.

You understand that lofty equine feeling of ours. His coldness and my dependence on him gave special strength to my love for him. 'Kill me, drive me till my wind is broken!' I used to think in our good days, 'and I shall be all the happier.'

He bought me from an agent to whom the head groom had sold me for eight hundred rubles, and he did so just because no one else had piebald horses. That was my best time. He had a mistress. I knew this because I took him to her every day and sometimes took them both out.

His mistress was a handsome woman, and he was handsome, and his coachman was handsome, and I loved them all because they were. Life was worth living then. This was how our time was spent: in the morning the groom came to rub me down—not the coachman himself but the groom. The groom was a lad from among the peasants. He would open the door, let out the steam from the horses, throw out the droppings, take off our rugs, and begin to fidget over our bodies with a brush, and lay whitish streaks of dandruff from a curry-comb on the boards of the floor that was dented by our rough horseshoes. I would playfully nip his sleeve and paw the ground. Then we were led out one after another to the trough filled with cold water, and the lad would admire the smoothness of my spotted coat which he had polished, my foot with its broad hoof, my legs straight as an arrow, my glossy quarters, and my back wide enough to sleep on. Hay was piled onto the high racks, and the oak cribs were filled with oats. Then Feofán, the head coachman, would come in.

Master and coachman resembled one another. Neither of them was afraid of anything or cared for anyone but himself, and for that reason everybody liked them. Feofán wore a red shirt, black velveteen knickerbockers, and a sleeveless coat. I liked it on a holiday when he would come into the stable, his hair pomaded, and wearing his sleeveless coat, and would shout:

'Now then, beastie, have you forgotten?' and push me with the handle of the stable fork, never so as to hurt me but just as a joke. I immediately knew that it was a joke, and laid back an ear, making my teeth click.

We had a black stallion, who drove in a pair. At night they used to put me in harness with him. That Polkán, as he was called, did not understand a joke but was simply vicious as the devil. I was in the stall next to his and sometimes we bit one another seriously. Feofán was not afraid of him. He would come up and give a shout: it looked as if Polkán would kill him, but no, he'd miss, and Feofán would put the harness on him.

Once he and I bolted down Smiths Bridge Street. Neither my master nor the coachman was frightened; they laughed, shouted at the people, checked us, and turned so that no one was run over.

In their service I lost my best qualities and half my life. They ruined me by watering me wrongly, and they foundered me. . . . Still for all that it was the best time of my life. At twelve o'clock they would come to harness me, black my hoofs, moisten my forelock and mane, and put me in the shafts.

The sledge was of plaited cane upholstered with velvet; the reins were of silk, the harness had silver buckles, sometimes there was a cover of silken flynet, and altogether it was such that when all the traces and straps were fastened it was difficult to say where the harness ended and the horse began. We were harnessed at ease in the stable. Feofán would come, broader at his hips than at the shoulders, his red belt up under his arms: he would examine the harness, take his seat, wrap his coat round him, put his foot into the sledge stirrup, let off some joke, and for appearance sake always hang a whip over his arm though he hardly ever hit me, and would say, 'Let go!', and playfully stepping from foot to foot I would move out of the gate, and the cook who had come out to empty the slops would stop on the threshold and the peasant who had brought wood into the yard would open his eyes wide. We

STRIDER: THE STORY OF A HORSE

would come out, go a little way, and stop. Footmen would come
out and other coachmen, and a chatter would begin. Everybody
would wait: sometimes we had to stand for three hours at the entrance, moving a little way, turning back, and standing again. .

At last there would be a stir in the hall: old Tíkhon with his
paunch would rush out in his dress coat and cry, 'Drive up!' (In
those days there was not that stupid way of saying, 'Forward!' as
if one did not know that we moved forward and not back.. Feofán would cluck, drive up, and the prince would hurry out carelessly, as though there were nothing remarkable about the sledge,
or the horse, or Feofán—who bent his back and stretched out his
arms so that it seemed it would be impossible for him to keep them
long in that position. The prince would have a shako on his head
and wear a fur coat with a grey beaver collar hiding his rosy,
black-browed, handsome face, that should never have been concealed. He would come out clattering his sabre, his spurs, and the
brass backs of the heels of his overshoes, stepping over the carpet
as if in a hurry and taking no notice of me or Feofán whom everybody but he looked at and admired. Feofán would cluck, I would
tug at the reins, and respectably, at a foot pace, we would draw
up to the entrance and stop. I would turn my eyes on the prince
and jerk my thoroughbred head with its delicate forelock. . . .
The prince would be in good spirits and would sometimes jest
with Feofán. Feofán would reply, half turning his handsome head,
and without lowering his arms would make a scarcely perceptible
movement with the reins which I understood: and then one, two,
three . . . with ever wider and wider strides, every muscle quivering, and sending the muddy snow against the front of the sledge,
I would go. In those days, too, there was none of the present-day
stupid habit of crying, 'Oh!' as if the coachman were in pain, instead of the sensible, 'Be off! Take care!' Feofán would shout 'Be
off! Look out there!' and the people would step aside and stand
craning their necks to see the handsome gelding, the handsome
coachman, and the handsome gentleman . . .

I was particularly fond of passing a trotter. When Feofán and
I saw at a distance a turn-out worthy of the effort, we would fly
like a whirlwind and gradually gain on it. Now, throwing the dirt
right to the back of the sledge, I would draw level with the occu-
pant of the vehicle and snort above his head: then I would reach

the horse's harness and the arch of his troyka, and then would no longer see it but only hear its sounds in the distance behind. And the prince, Feofán, and I, would all be silent, and pretend to be merely going on our own business and not even to notice those with slow horses whom we happened to meet on our way. I liked to pass another horse, but also liked to meet a good trotter. An instant, a sound, a glance, and we had passed each other and were flying in opposite directions.

The gate creaked and the voices of Nester and Váska were heard.

FIFTH NIGHT

The weather began to break up. It had been dull since morning and there was no dew, but it was warm and the mosquitoes were troublesome. As soon as the horses were driven in they collected round the piebald, and he finished his story as follows:

The happy period of my life was soon over. I lived in that way only two years. Towards the end of the second winter the happiest event of my life occurred, and following it came my greatest misfortune. It was during carnival week. I took the prince to the races. Glossy and Bull were running. I don't know what people were doing in the pavilion, but I know the prince came out and ordered Feofán to drive onto the track. I remember how they took me in and placed me beside Glossy. He was harnessed to a racing sulky and I, just as I was, to a town sledge. I outstripped him at the turn. Roars of laughter and howls of delight greeted me.

When I was led in, a crowd followed me and five or six people offered the prince thousands for me. He only laughed, showing his white teeth.

'No,' he said, 'this isn't a horse, but a friend. I wouldn't sell him for mountains of gold. *Au revoir*, gentlemen!'

He unfastened the sledge apron and got in.

'To Ostózhenka Street!'

That was where his mistress lived, and off we flew . . .

That was our last happy day. We reached her home. He spoke of her as *his*, but she loved someone else and had run away with

Paul Brown
'45

him. The prince learnt this at her lodgings. It was five o'clock, and without unharnessing me he started in pursuit of her. They did what had never been done to me before, struck me with the whip and made me gallop. For the first time I fell out of step and felt ashamed and wished to correct it, but suddenly I heard the prince shout in an unnatural voice: 'Get on!' The whip whistled through the air and cut me, and I galloped, striking my foot against the iron front of the sledge. We overtook her after going sixteen miles. I got him there, but trembled all night long and could not eat anything. In the morning they gave me water. I drank it and after that was never again the horse that I had been. I was ill, and they tormented me and maimed me—doctoring me, as people call it. My hoofs came off, I had swellings and my legs grew bent; my chest sank in and I became altogether limp and weak. I was sold to a horse-dealer who fed me on carrots and something else and made something of me quite unlike myself, though good enough to deceive one who did not know. My strength and my pace were gone.

When purchasers came the dealer also tormented me by coming into my stall and beating me with a heavy whip to frighten and madden me. Then he would rub down the stripes on my coat and lead me out.

An old woman bought me of him. She always drove to the Church of St. Nicholas the Wonder Worker, and she used to have her coachman flogged. He used to weep in my stall and I learnt that tears have a pleasant, salty taste. Then the old woman died. Her steward took me to the country and sold me to a hawker. Then I overate myself with wheat and grew still worse. They sold me to a peasant. There I ploughed, had hardly anything to eat, my foot got cut by a ploughshare and I again became ill. Then a gipsy took me in exchange for something. He tormented me terribly and finally sold me to the steward here. And here I am.

All were silent. A sprinkling of rain began to fall.

THE EVENING AFTER

As the herd returned home the following evening they encountered their master with a visitor. Zhuldýba when nearing the house looked askance at the two male figures: one was the young master in his straw hat, the other a tall, stout, bloated military man. The old mare gave the man a side-glance and, swerving, went near him; the others, the young ones, were flustered and hesitated, especially when the master and his visitor purposely stepped among them, pointing something out to one another and talking.

'That one, the dapple grey, I bought of Voékov,' said the master.

'And where did you get that young black mare with the white legs? She's a fine one!' said the visitor. They looked over many of the horses, going forward and stopping them. They noticed the chestnut filly too.

'That is one I kept of Khrénov's saddle-horse breed,' said the master.

They could not see all the horses as they walked past, and the master called to Nester, and the old man, tapping the sides of the piebald with his heels, trotted forward. The piebald limped on one leg but moved in a way that showed that as long as his strength lasted he would not murmur on any account, even if they wanted him to run in that way to the end of the world. He was even ready to gallop, and tried to do so with his right leg.

'There, I can say for certain that there is no better horse in Russia than this one,' said the master, pointing to one of the mares.

So they went past all the horses till there were no more to show. Then they were silent.

'Well, shall we go now?'

'Yes, let's go.'

They went through the gate. The visitor was glad the exhibition was over and that he could now go to the house where they could eat and drink and smoke, and he grew perceptibly brighter. As he went past Nester, who sat on the piebald waiting for orders, the visitor slapped the piebald's crupper with his big fat hand.

'What an ornamented one!' he said. 'I once had a piebald like him; do you remember my telling you of him?'

The master, finding that it was not his horse that was being spoken about, paid no attention but kept looking round at his own herd.

Suddenly above his ear he heard a dull, weak, senile neigh. It was the piebald that had begun to neigh and had broken off as if ashamed.

Neither the visitor nor the master paid any attention to this neighing, but went into the house.

In the flabby old man Strider had recognized his beloved master, the once brilliant, handsome, and wealthy Serpukhovskóy.

It kept on drizzling. In the stable yard it was gloomy, but in the master's house it was very different. The table was laid in a luxurious drawing-room for a luxurious evening tea, and at it sat the host, the hostess, and their guest. They were silent awhile.

'Yes, you were saying you bought him of Voékov,' remarked Serpukhovskóy with assumed carelessness.

'Oh yes, that was of Atlásny, you know. I always meant to buy some mares of Dubovítzki, but he had nothing but rubbish left.'

'He has failed . . .' said Serpukhovskóy, and suddenly stopped and glanced round. He remembered that he owed that bankrupt twenty thousand rubles, and if it came to talking of being bankrupt it was certainly said that he was one. He laughed.

Both again sat silent for a long time. The host considered what he could brag about to his guest. Serpukhovskóy was thinking what he could say to show that he did not consider himself bankrupt. But the minds of both worked with difficulty, in spite of efforts to brace themselves up with cigars. 'When are we going to have a drink?' thought Serpukhovskóy. 'I must certainly have a drink or I shall die of ennui with this fellow,' thought the host.

'I wanted to tell you that in my stud . . .' he began, but Serpukhovskóy interrupted him.

'I may say that there was a time,' Serpukhovskóy began, 'when I liked to live well and knew how to do it. Now you talk about trotting— You know I told you I had a driving-horse, a piebald with just the same kind of spots as the one your keeper was riding. Oh, what a horse that was! You can't possibly know: it was in 1842, when I had just come to Moscow; I went to a horse-dealer and there I saw a well-bred piebald gelding. I liked him. The price? One thousand rubles. I liked him, so I took him and began to drive with him. I never had, and you have not and never will have, such a horse. I never knew one like him for speed and

w. Brown
45

for strength. You were a boy then and couldn't have known, but you may have heard of him. All Moscow was talking about him.'

'Yes, I heard of him,' the host unwillingly replied. 'But what I wished to say about mine . . .'

'Ah, then you did hear! I bought him just as he was, without his pedigree and without a certificate; it was only afterwards that I got to know Voékov and found out. He was a colt by Affable I. Strider—because of his long strides. On account of his piebald spots he was removed from the Khrénov stud and given to the head keeper, who had him castrated and sold him to a horse-dealer. There are no such horses now, my dear chap. Ah, those were days! Ah, vanishd youth!'—and he sang the words of the gipsy song. He was getting tipsy.—'Ah, those were good times. I was twenty-five and had eighty thousand rubles a year, not a single grey hair, and all my teeth like pearls. . . . Whatever I touched succeeded, and now it is all ended . . .'

'But there was not the same mettlesomeness then,' said the host, availing himself of the pause. 'Let me tell you that my first horses began to trot without . . .'

'Your horses! But they used to be more mettlesome . . .'

'How—more mettlesome?'

'Yes, more mettlesome! I remember as if it were to-day how I drove him once to the trotting races in Moscow. No horse of mine was running. I did not care for trotters, mine were thoroughbreds: General Chaulet, Mahomet. I drove up with my piebald. My driver was a fine fellow, I was fond of him, but he also took to drink. . . . Well, so I got there.

' "Serpukhovskóy," I was asked, "when are you going to keep trotters?" "The devil take your lubbers!" I replied. "I have a pie-bald hack that can outpace all your trotters!" "Oh no, he won't!" "I'll bet a thousand rubles!" Agreed, and they started. He came in five seconds ahead and I won the thousand rubles. But what of it? I did a hundred versts[1] in three hours with a troyka of thoroughbreds. All Moscow knows it.'

And Serpukhovskóy began to brag so glibly and continuously that his host could not get a single word in and sat opposite him with a dejected countenance, filling up his own and his guest's glass every now and then by way of distraction.

[1] A little over sixty-six miles.

The dawn was breaking and still they sat there. It became intolerably dull for the host. He got up.

'If we are to go to bed, let's go!' said Serpukhovskóy rising, and reeling and puffing he went to the room prepared for him.

The host was lying beside his mistress.

'No, he is unendurable,' he said. 'He gets drunk and swaggers incessantly.'

'And makes up to me.'

'I'm afraid he'll be asking for money.'

Serpukhovskóy was lying on the bed in his clothes, breathing heavily.

'I must have been lying a lot,' he thought. 'Well, no matter! The wine was good, but he is an awful swine. There's something cheap about him. And I'm an awful swine,' he said to himself and laughed aloud. 'First I used to keep women, and now I'm kept. Yes, the Winkler girl will support me. I take money of her. Serves him right. Still, I must undress. Can't get my boots off. Hullo! Hullo!' he called out, but the man who had been told off to wait on him had long since gone to bed.

He sat down, took off his coat and waistcoat and somehow managed to kick off his trousers, but for a long time could not get his boots off—his soft stomach being in the way. He got one off at last, and struggled for a long time with the other, panting and becoming exhausted. And so with his foot in the boot-top he rolled over and began to snore, filling the room with a smell of tobacco, wine, and disagreeable old age.

If Strider recalled anything that night, he was distracted by Váska, who threw a rug over him, galloped off on him, and kept him standing till morning at the door of a tavern, near a peasant horse. They licked one another. In the morning when Strider returned to the herd he kept rubbing himself.

'Something itches dreadfully,' he thought.

Five days passed. They called in a veterinary, who said cheerfully:

'It's the itch, let me sell him to the gipsies.'

'What's the use? Cut his throat, and get it done to-day.'

The morning was calm and clear. The herd went to pasture,

but Strider was left behind. A strange man came—thin, dark, and dirty, in a coat splashed with something black. It was the knacker. Without looking at Strider he took him by the halter they had put on him and led him away. Strider went quietly without looking round, dragging along as usual and catching his hind feet in the straw.

When they were out of the gate he strained towards the well, but the knacker jerked his halter, saying: 'Not worth while.'

The knacker and Váska, who followed behind, went to a hollow behind the brick barn and stopped as if there were something peculiar about this very ordinary place. The knacker, handing the halter to Váska, took off his coat, rolled up his sleeves, and produced a knife and a whetstone from his boot-leg. The gelding stretched towards the halter meaning to chew it a little from dullness, but he could not reach it. He sighed and closed his eyes. His nether lip hung down, disclosing his worn yellow teeth, and he began to drowse to the sound of the sharpening of the knife. Only his swollen, aching, outstretched leg kept jerking. Suddenly he felt himself being taken by the lower jaw and his head lifted. He opened his eyes. There were two dogs in front of him; one was sniffing at the knacker, the other was siting and watching the gelding as if expecting something from him. The gelding looked at them and began to rub his jaw against the arm that was holding him.

'Want to doctor me probably—well, let them!' he thought.

And in fact he felt that something had been done to his throat. It hurt, and he shuddered and gave a kick with one foot, but restrained himself and waited for what would follow. . . . Then he felt something liquid streaming down his neck and chest. He heaved a profound sigh and felt much better.

The whole burden of his life was eased.

He closed his eyes and began to droop his head. No one was holding it. Then his legs quivered and his whole body swayed. He was not so much frightened as surprised.

Everything was so new to him. He was surprised, and started forward and upward, but instead of this, in moving from the spot his legs got entangled, he began to fall sideways, and trying to take a step fell forward and down on his left side.

The knacker waited till the convulsions had ceased; drove away the dogs that had crept nearer, took the gelding by the legs, turned him on his back, told Váska to hold a leg, and began to skin the horse.

'It was a horse, too,' remarked Váska.

'If he had been better fed the skin would have been fine,' said the knacker.

The herd returned down hill in the evening, and those on the left saw down below something red, round which dogs were busy and above which hawks and crows were flying. One of the dogs, pressing his paws against the carcass and swinging his head, with a crackling sound tore off what it had seized hold of. The chestnut filly stopped, stretched out her head and neck, and sniffed the air for a long time. They could hardly drive her away.

At dawn, in a ravine of the old forest, down in an overgrown glade, big-headed wolf cubs were howling joyfully. There were five of them: four almost alike and one little one with a head bigger than his body. A lean old wolf who was shedding her coat, dragging her full belly with its hanging dugs along the ground, came out of the bushes and sat down in front of the cubs. The cubs came and stood round her in a semi-circle. She went up to the smallest, and bending her knee and holding her muzzle down, made some convulsive movements, and opening her large sharp-tooth jaws disgorged a large piece of horseflesh. The bigger cubs rushed towards her, but she moved threateningly at them and let the little one have it all. The little one, growling as if in anger, pulled the horseflesh under him and began to gorge. In the same way the mother wolf coughed up a piece for the second, the third, and all five of them, and then lay down in front of them to rest.

A week later only a large skull and two shoulder-blades lay behind the barn, the rest had all been taken away. In summer a peasant, collecting bones, carried away these shoulder-blades and skull and put them to use.

The dead body of Serpukhovskóy, which had walked about the earth eating and drinking, was put under ground much later. Neither his skin, nor his flesh, nor his bones, were of any use.

Just as for the last twenty years his body that had walked the earth had been a great burden to everybody, so the putting away of that body was again an additional trouble to people. He had not been wanted by anybody for a long time and had only been a burden, yet the dead who bury their dead found it necessary to clothe that swollen body, which at once began to decompose, in a good uniform and good boots and put it into a new and expensive coffin with new tassels at its four corners, and then to place that coffin in another coffin of lead, to take it to Moscow and there dig up some long buried human bones, and to hide in that particular spot this decomposing maggotty body in its new uniform and polished boots, and cover it all up with earth.